13

ALGEBRAIC CURVES

By ROBERT J. WALKER

DOVER PUBLICATIONS, INC.
NEW YORK

Published in the United Kingdom by Constable and Company Limited, 10 Orange Street, London W.C.2.

This new Dover edition, first published in 1962, is an unabridged and corrected republication of the work first published by Princeton University Press in 1950.

Manufactured in the United States of America

Dover Publications, Inc.
180 Varick Street
New York 14, N.Y.

Preface

This book was written to furnish a starting point for the study of algebraic geometry. The topics presented and methods of presenting them were chosen with the following ideas in mind; to keep the treatment as elementary as possible, to introduce some of the recently developed algebraic methods of handling problems of algebraic geometry, to show how these methods are related to the older analytic and geometric methods, and to apply the general methods to specific geometric problems. These criteria led to a selection of topics from the theory of curves, centering around birational transformations and linear series.

Experience in teaching the material showed the need of an introduction to the underlying algebra and projective geometry, so this is supplied in the first two chapters. The inclusion of this material makes the book almost entirely self-contained.

Methods of presentation, proof of theorems, and problems, have been adapted from various sources. We should mention, in particular, Severi-Löffler, *Vorlesungen über Algebraische Geometrie*, van der Waerden, *Algebraische Geometrie* and *Moderne Algebra*, and lecture notes of S. Lefschetz and O. Zariski. We also wish to thank Mr. R. L. Beinert and Prof. G. L. Walker for suggestions and assistance with the proof, and particularly Prof. Saunders MacLane for a very careful examination and criticism of an early version of the work.

R. J. WALKER

Cornell University
December 1, 1949

v

Contents

CHAPTER III. PLANE ALGEBRAIC CURVES

CHAPTER IV. FORMAL POWER SERIES

CHAPTER V. TRANSFORMATIONS OF A CURVE

CHAPTER VI. LINEAR SERIES

ALGEBRAIC CURVES

Notation and Symbols

References are to pages where symbol is defined or first appears. A relation is negated by putting a slanting bar through its symbol.

$a \in S$, a is a member of S, 3

$A \supset B$, $B \subset A$, A contains B, 3

$a \sim b$, a is equivalent to b, 5

∞, value of a parameter, 46

∞, order of a power series, 89

$a|b$, a is a factor of b, 14

$a \nmid b$, a is not a factor of b, 15

$|a_j^i|$, determinant, 10

$|A|$, complete series determined by A, 168

$D[x_1, \cdots, x_r]$, polynomial domain over D, 12

$D[x]'$, domain of power series of non-negative order, 87

$D[x]^*$, domain of fractional power series of non-negative order, 97

$K(x_1, \cdots, x_r)$, field of rational functions over K, 12

$K(x)'$, field of power series, 88

$K(x)^*$, field of fractional power series, 97

$K(\theta_1, \cdots, \theta_r)$, field generated by $\theta_1, \cdots, \theta_r$, 127

$f'(x)$, derivative, 21, 92

f_x, f_1, partial derivative, 22

F_n, homogeneous polynomial of degree n, 27

$\bar{a}$, $\bar{x}$, etc., elements of $K(t)$ or $K(t)^*$, 93

ξ, θ,, etc., elements of Σ, 132

Φ, Θ, adjoints, 180

A_n, n-dimensional affine space, 45

$d\theta$, differential, 177

g_n^r, linear series of order n and dimension r, 164

K, ground field, 32

K, canonical series, 178

$O(f)$, order of power series, 89, 97

$O_P(f)$, order of polynomial at a place, 108

$O_P(\theta)$, order of rational function at a place, 133

S_n, SK_n, n-dimensional projective space over K, 34

Σ, field of rational functions on a curve, 131

Theorems, numbered equations, and subsections are numbered consecutively in each section. Reference to "Theorem 3.5" is to the fifth theorem in §3 of the same chapter; to "Theorem IV–3.5," to the fifth theorem in §3 of Chapter IV.

I. Algebraic Preliminaries

As might be gathered from the name of the subject, the study of algebraic geometry has always involved a considerable use of algebra. As time went on, the algebraic technique became more and more important, until now a large part of algebraic geometry has become essentially a chapter in algebra. It is obvious, then, that one cannot hope to make a systematic study of this topic without a good algebraic background. The material in this chapter is presented with a view to supplying this background. We make no attempt to present any complete algebraic theory, being content merely to provide the tools with which we shall work. A more complete exposition of the concepts discussed here can be found in any of the following works:

A. A. Albert, *Modern Higher Algebra*, University of Chicago, 1937.

G. Birkhoff and S. MacLane, *A Survey of Modern Algebra*, Macmillan, New York, 1941.

C. C. MacDuffee, *Introduction to Abstract Algebra*, Wiley, New York, 1940.

B. L. van der Waerden, *Moderne Algebra*, 2 volumes, Springer, Berlin, 1937 and 1940.

§1. SET THEORY

1.1. Sets. In any mathematical discussion we are interested in the properties of certain classes of objects. Thus in elementary algebra we are mainly concerned with real numbers, in plane geometry with the points of a plane. In general we shall refer to any class of objects as a *set*, and the objects themselves as *elements* of the set. If we indicate a set by S and an object by a, the symbol $a \in S$ will mean that a is an element of S, and $a \notin S$ that a is not an element of S.

A set S is said to be a *subset* of a set S' if every element of S is an element of S'. We write $S \subset S'$, or $S' \supset S$. For example, if S_1 is the set of all real numbers, S_2 the set of all integers, and S_3 the set consisting of the single number 3, we have $S_1 \supset S_2 \supset S_3$.

By our definition, any set is a subset of itself. In fact, a necessary and sufficient condition that two sets are the same, that is that they consist of the same elements, is that each is a subset of the other. If we wish to specify that S is a subset of S' but is not the same as S' we say that S is a *proper* subset of S'.

A rather peculiar set, but one that is convenient to use at times, is the *empty* set, the set containing no elements at all. This set is evidently a subset of every set.

1.2. Single valued transformations. By a *single valued transformation* of a set S into a set S' we mean a rule which associates with each element a of S a unique element a' of S'. Such a transformation is sometimes called a *mapping* of S into S', and a' is called the *map* or the *image* of a. A mapping of S into S' is said to be a *one-to-one* correspondence if each element a' of S' corresponds to exactly one element a of S. We then also have a mapping of S' into S.

Familiar examples of mappings occur in analytic geometry. Let S be the set of all pairs (a,b) of real numbers and S' the set of points of the euclidean plane. Cartesian and polar coordinate systems are then seen to be mappings of S into S'. The cartesian coordinate system is a one-to-one mapping, while the polar coordinate system is not. The mapping associated with a projective coordinate system will be discussed in Chapter II.

In each of the various types of sets that we shall have occasion to consider there will be certain relations between the elements or the subsets. With regard to a given system of such relations a mapping will be called a *homomorphism*, or said to be *homomorphic*, if it preserves these relations; that is, if the images of the elements satisfy the same relations as the elements themselves. A one-to-one correspondence which is homomorphic in both directions is called an *isomorphism*. If S and S' have a common subset S_0, and if in a homomorphism of S into S' every element of S_0 corresponds to itself, then the homomorphism is said to be *over* S_0. As an example, let S be the set of all complex numbers and S' the set of all real numbers. Then the transformation taking $a + bi$ into a is a homomorphism over S' of S into S' which preserves the additive relations among the elements.

If two sets are isomorphic with respect to certain relations, then as far as these relations are concerned the sets have identical properties. As long as we are interested only in these particular relations it is frequently useless to distinguish between the two sets. Hence we shall usually regard isomorphic sets as being actually identical.

1.3. Equivalence classes. If we say that two elements a and b of some set S are equal, $a = b$, we mean that the two letters a and b stand for the same element of S. This relationship of equality between elements, or more precisely between symbols for elements, has the following properties:

   (i)   Reflexivity, $a = a$;

  (ii)   Symmetry, $a = b$ implies $b = a$;

 (iii)   Transitivity, $a = b$ and $b = c$ imply $a = c$.

Now it often happens that one considers other relations which have these properties. Such a relation is usually called an *equivalence*. As an example, let S be the set of positive integers and define two elements of S to be equivalent if their difference is even. Properties (i), (ii), and (iii) are easily verified.

Let $\sim$ indicate an equivalence relation between the elements of S. For any $a \in S$ we denote by S_a the set of all elements of S equivalent to a. By (i), $a \in S_a$. We note first that for any a and b either $S_a = S_b$ or S_a and S_b have no elements in common. For if S_a and S_b have a common element c, then $c \sim a$ and $c \sim b$, and hence $a \sim b$. Now if $d \in S_a$, then $d \sim a$, from which follows $d \sim b$ and hence $d \in S_b$. Therefore $S_a \subset S_b$, and as we can prove similarly that $S_b \subset S_a$, we must have $S_a = S_b$. S is therefore divided into mutually exclusive subsets. These subsets are commonly called *equivalence classes*.

Now $S_a = S_b$ if and only if $a \sim b$. For if $a \sim b$ then $a \in S_b$, and since also $a \in S_a$ we must have $S_a = S_b$. Conversely, if $S_a = S_b$, then $a \in S_b$, and so $a \sim b$. Hence the relation of equivalence between elements of S can be replaced by the relation of equality between certain subsets of S. This is a very useful process, as it relieves us of the necessity of carrying several kinds of equivalence throughout our entire work.

§2. INTEGRAL DOMAINS AND FIELDS

2.1. Algebraic systems. In elementary algebra the objects in which we are mainly interested are the real numbers. It is noticeable, however, that we pay no attention to the *nature* of these numbers, but only to their *properties*, that is, to the ways in which they are combined and related. A general algebraic system, then, will consist of the elements of a set S together with certain rules, or *axioms*, relating these elements to one another. The following set of axioms define an important type of algebraic system known as a *field*.

A_1.   To every ordered pair a, b of elements of S there corresponds a unique element of S called the *sum* of a and b and designated by $a + b$.

A_2. $a + b = b + a$.

A_3. $(a + b) + c = a + (b + c)$.

A_4.   There is an element 0 of S such that $a + 0 = 0 + a = a$ for every $a \in S$. 0 is called *zero*.

A_5.   Corresponding to any element a of S there is an element $-a$ such that $a + (-a) = -a + a = 0$. $-a$ is called the *negative* of a.

A_6.   To every ordered pair a, b of elements of S there corresponds a unique element of S called the *product* of a and b and designated by ab, or $a \cdot b$.

A_7. $ab = ba$.

A_8. $(ab)c = a(bc)$.

A_9.   There is an element $u \neq 0$ of S such that $au = ua = a$ for every $a \in S$. u is called *unity*.

A_{10}.   Corresponding to any element $a \neq 0$ of S there is an element a^{-1} such that $aa^{-1} = a^{-1}a = u$. a^{-1} is called the *inverse* of a.

A_{11}. $a(b + c) = ab + ac$; $(b + c)a = ba + ca$.

A_{12}.   If $ab = 0$ and $a \neq 0$ then $b = 0$.

Since the set of all real numbers satisfies all these axioms, this set is a field. Similarly the complex numbers and the rational numbers form fields. The set of integers is not a field, for A_{10} is not satisfied. However, all the other axioms are satisfied by the integers. In general, a set satisfying $A_1, \cdots, A_9$, A_{11}, A_{12} is called an *integral domain*. Weakening the conditions still further, a *ring* is a set satisfying $A_1, \cdots, A_6$, A_8, A_{11}; the ring is *commutative* if it satisfies A_7. Finally, a *group* need only satisfy A_1, A_3, A_4, A_5.

Examples. 1. Let S consist of the two elements 0, u, with the following rules for addition and multiplication:

$$0 + 0 = u + u = 0, \quad 0 + u = u + 0 = u,$$

$$00 = 0u = u0 = 0, \quad uu = u.$$

S is then a field.

2. Taking S as above, we define

$$0 + 0 = u + u = 0, \quad 0 + u = u + 0 = u,$$

$$00 = 0u = u0 = uu = 0.$$

S is a commutative ring which is neither a field nor an integral domain.

3. The set of square matrices of a given order $n > 1$ is a non-commutative ring.

4. The set of continuous functions of a real variable defined on $-\infty < x < \infty$ is a commutative ring. Is it an integral domain?

2.2. Integral domains. The sets of most interest in algebraic geometry are the fields and the integral domains. For brevity we shall refer to an integral domain merely as a domain. The following properties of a domain D follow very quickly from the axioms, and their proofs are omitted.

D_1. 0 and u are unique, and $-a$ and a^{-1} are uniquely determined by a.

D_2.   Any finite set $a_1, a_2, \cdots, a_n$ of elements of D has a unique sum $\Sigma_{i=1}^n a_i$ (or $\Sigma_i a_i$, or Σa_i, if there is no ambiguity), obtained by combining them by A_1 in any order. Similarly it has a unique product $\Pi_{i=1}^n a_i$.

D_3. If $a_1 = a_2 = \cdots = a_n = a$ we write $\Sigma a_i = na = an$. We then have $n(ma) = (nm)a$, $(na)(mb) = (nm)(ab)$, $n(a + b) = na + nb$, $(n + m)a = na + ma$. Now each of these relations remains true if n and m are replaced by nu and mu respectively. Hence whenever a positive integer n appears as a factor it may be assumed to be the element nu of D, and we shall use 1 instead of u. By thinking of $(-n)a$ as $n(-a)$ the same process may be applied to negative integers.

D_4. If $a_1 = a_2 = \cdots = a_n = a$ we write $\Pi a_i = a^n$; the usual laws of positive exponents are then seen to hold.

D_5. $(\Sigma a_i)(\Sigma b_j) \cdots (\Sigma e_k) = \Sigma a_i b_j \cdots e_k$, the last summation being over all products of the indicated type. As a special case we have the binomial theorem,

$$(a + b)^n = \Sigma_{i=0}^{n} \binom{n}{i} a^{n-i} b^i,$$

where

$$\binom{n}{i} = \frac{n!}{i! \, (n - i)!}, \; 0! = 1, \; n! = 1 \cdot 2 \cdot \cdots \cdot n.$$

D_6. We write $a - b$ for $a + (-b)$. Then $a(-b) = -(ab)$, $(-a)(-b) = ab$, $a(b - c) = ab - ac$, etc.

D_7. $a0 = 0a = 0$ for every a. This is the reason for excepting 0 in A_{10}.

D_8. If $ab = ac$ and $a \neq 0$ then $b = c$.

D_9. If $a = bc$, a is said to be divisible by b, and we write $c = a/b$. If $a \neq 0$, c is unique, if it exists at all.

D_{10}. If for a given element $a \neq 0$ of D there is a positive integer n such that $na = 0$, then $nb = 0$ for every $b \in D$. The smallest such integer n is called the *characteristic* of D. If no such integer exists, D is said to have characteristic zero.

2.3. Fields. Fields have the following additional properties.

F_1. a/b exists and equals ab^{-1} if $b \neq 0$. The familiar properties of fractions hold for elements of a field.

F_2. If we define $a^{-n} = (a^{-1})^n$, $a^0 = 1$, then the usual laws hold for integral exponents.

F_3. If a field is of characteristic zero then $nu \neq 0$ if $n \neq 0$, and we can define a/n to be a/nu.

2.4. Homomorphisms of domains. A mapping of a domain D into a domain D' will be called homomorphic if it preserves addition and multiplication. That is, if a, b map into a', b' respectively we must have $a + b$ and ab map into $a' + b'$ and $a'b'$. It follows from this that $a - b$, a/b, na, etc. will map into $a' - b'$, a'/b', na', etc. For example, to see that $a - b$ maps into $a' - b'$ let $c = a - b$. Then $a = b + c$, and so $a' = b' + c'$; that is $c' = a' - b'$.

2.5. Exercises. 1. The characteristic of a domain is either zero or a prime number.

2. (a) Every field of characteristic zero contains a subfield isomorphic to the field of rational numbers.

(b) Every field of characteristic two contains a subfield isomorphic to the field of §2.1, Example 1.

3. Let S be the domain of integers and S' the field of §2.1, Example 1. We define a mapping of S into S' by

$$a \rightarrow 0 \text{ if } a \text{ is even,}$$

$$a \rightarrow u \text{ if } a \text{ is odd.}$$

Show that this mapping is a homomorphism.

4. Let K be a field and let S be the set of all ordered n-tuples $(a_1, \cdots, a_n)$ of elements of K. We define addition and multiplication in S by

$$(a_1, \cdots, a_n) + (b_1, \cdots, b_n) = (a_1 + b_1, \cdots, a_n + b_n),$$

$$(a_1, \cdots, a_n)(b_1, \cdots, b_n) = (c_1, \cdots, c_n),$$

where $c_i = \Sigma_{j,k}\gamma_{ijk}a_jb_k$, the γ's being fixed elements of K. S is called a hypercomplex number system, or an *algebra*, over K. Show that an algebra satisfies $A_1, \cdots, A_6$, A_{11}; that it is commutative (satisfies A_7) if $\gamma_{ijk} = \gamma_{ikj}$; that it is associative (satisfies A_8) if

$$\Sigma_s\gamma_{ijs}\gamma_{skl} = \Sigma_s\gamma_{isl}\gamma_{sjk}.$$

5. Show that the complex numbers are an algebra of degree 2 ($n = 2$) over the real field, and determine the values of the γ's.

6. If $S \rightarrow S'$ is a homomorphism of a field S into any ring S' then either every element of S maps into the zero of S' or the mapping is an isomorphism between S and a subset S_0 of S'.

7. Show that axiom A_{12} is a consequence of axioms $A_1, \cdots, A_{11}$.

8. Show that axioms A_1, A_3, A_4, A_5 are equivalent to

A'_1. Same as A_1.

A'_3. Same as A_3.

A'_4. There is at least one element 0 of S such that $a + 0 = a$ for every $a \in S$.

A'_5. Corresponding to any element a of S there is at least one element $-a$ of S such that $a + (-a) = 0$.

[Prove first that $-(-a) = a$.]

§3. QUOTIENT FIELDS

One of the ways of defining the real number system is to build it up from the positive integers by a series of enlargements. One of these enlargements consists in passing from integers to rational numbers by considering each rational number as an ordered pair of integers. The same process can be used to enlarge any domain to a field.

THEOREM 3.1. *Corresponding to any domain D there is a unique* field K, called the quotient field of D, such that*

(i) $K \supset D$,

(ii) *Any element of K is the quotient of two elements of D.*

PROOF. K will be built up by an application of the process described in §1.3. Let S be the set of all pairs (a,b) of elements of D for which $b \neq 0$. We write $(a,b) \sim (c,d)$ if and only if there exist non-zero elements ρ, σ of D such that $\rho a = \sigma c$, $\rho b = \sigma d$. It is evident that this relationship is reflexive, symmetric, and transitive, and so is an equivalence. Designate by $S(a,b)$ the equivalence class containing (a,b). We define addition and multiplication of these classes by

$$S(a,b) + S(c,d) = S(ad + bc, bd),$$

$$S(a,b)S(c,d) = S(ac, bd),$$

and shall now show that the set K of all such classes is a field of the required type.

In the first place, the sum and the product of two elements of K are uniquely defined, for if

$$S(a_1, b_1) = S(a_2, b_2), \; S(c_1, d_1) = S(c_2, d_2),$$

we must have

$$\rho_1 a_1 = \rho_2 a_2, \quad \rho_1 b_1 = \rho_2 b_2,$$

$$\sigma_1 c_1 = \sigma_2 c_2, \quad \sigma_1 d_1 = \sigma_2 d_2,$$

Hence

$$\rho_1 \sigma_1 (a_1 d_1 + b_1 c_1) = \rho_2 \sigma_2 (a_2 d_2 + b_2 c_2),$$

$$\rho_1 \sigma_1 a_1 c_1 = \rho_2 \sigma_2 a_2 c_2,$$

$$\rho_1 \sigma_1 b_1 d_1 = \rho_2 \sigma_2 b_2 d_2;$$

so that

---

* In accordance with the convention mentioned in §1.2 this is to mean that any two such fields are isomorphic.

$$S(a_1,b_1) + S(c_1,d_1) = S(a_2,b_2) + S(c_2,d_2),$$

$$S(a_1,b_1)S(c_1,d_1) = S(a_2,b_2)S(c_2,d_2).$$

It is now a straightforward matter to check the axioms of a field; we find that $S(0,b)$ and $S(a,a)$ are the zero and unity elements, and that $S(-a,b)$ and $S(b,a)$ are the negative and the inverse of $S(a,b)$. Finally the mapping $a \rightarrow S(a,1)$ is an isomorphism of D with a subset of K. We can, therefore, identify $S(a,1)$ with a and consider D to be a subset of K. Then $S(a,b) = a/b$, and so (ii) is satisfied. The uniqueness of K is an immediate consequence of (i) and (ii). For if L is any field satisfying (i) and (ii) then any element of L is a quotient of two elements of D and so is contained in K, since K, containing D, contains the quotients of elements of D. Hence $K \supset L$, and similarly $L \supset K$, so that $L = K$.

Since fields are easier to work with than domains, this theorem often enables one to simplify one's work by passing from a given domain to its quotient field. We shall see an example of this in §6.

§4. LINEAR DEPENDENCE AND LINEAR EQUATIONS

4.1. Linear dependence. Since fields admit the operations of addition, subtraction, multiplication, and division, with their customary properties, any algebraic theory that involves only these processes applies to a general field. Such a theory is that of linear dependence. As the usual proofs* can be applied to the case of a general field we shall give here only a summary of the definitions and results of this theory.

The m ordered n-tuples†

$$(a_1^\alpha, \cdots, a_n^\alpha), \ \alpha = 1, \cdots, m,$$

of elements of a field K are said to be *linearly dependent* (or simply *dependent*) if there exist elements b_α of K, not all zero, such that

$$\Sigma_\alpha b_\alpha a_i^\alpha = 0, \quad i = 1, \cdots, n.$$

$(a_1, \cdots, a_n)$ is said to be *dependent* on, or to be a *combination* of, the $(a_1^\alpha, \cdots, a_n^\alpha)$ if there exist b_α such that

$$a_i = \Sigma_\alpha b_\alpha a_i^\alpha, \quad i = 1, \cdots, n.$$

The principal theorem concerning linear dependence is

THEOREM 4.1. *The n-tuples*

$$(a_1^\alpha, \cdots, a_n^\alpha), \quad \alpha = 1, \cdots, m,$$

are dependent if and only if the matrix $||a_i^\alpha||$ is of rank less than m.

* See Bôcher, *Introduction to Higher Algebra*, Macmillan, New York, 1929, Chaps. III and IV.

† In this section the superscripts are merely indices, not exponents.

From this result we obtain

THEOREM 4.2. (i)   *m n-tuples are dependent if $m > n$.*

(ii)   *Given m independent n-tuples, $m \leqslant n$, there exist n-m other n-tuples such that the entire set of n n-tuples are independent.*

4.2. Linear equations. Closely related to the theory of linear dependence is the theory of the solutions of linear equations. We shall have occasion to use the following properties of these solutions.

THEOREM 4.3. *Let r be the rank of the matrix $\|a_\alpha^i\|$. Then the set of homogeneous equations*

$$(4.1) \qquad \Sigma_{i=1}^n a_\alpha^i x_i = 0, \quad \alpha = 1, \cdots, m,$$

has n-r independent solutions

$$x_i = \zeta_i^\beta, \quad \beta = 1, \cdots, n - r,$$

and every solution of (4.1) is a combination of these.

THEOREM 4.4. *The equations*

$$\Sigma_{j=1}^n a_i^j x_j = b_i, \quad i = 1, \cdots, n,$$

have a unique solution if the determinant $|a_i^j| = a \neq 0$.

This solution is given by

$$x_j = \Sigma_i A_j^i b_i,$$

where A_j^i is a^{-1} times the cofactor of a_i^j in $|a_i^j|$.

§5. POLYNOMIALS

5.1. Polynomial domains. In elementary algebra and calculus we think of an expression of the type $x^2 - 2x - 3$ as a "function," and the symbol x as a "variable" which can assume certain numerical values. However, the formal processes of addition, multiplication, and differentiation of such polynomials are carried out without any use of the functional concept. It should therefore be possible to develop an algebraic theory of polynomials on a purely formal basis. This is what we shall now do.

Let D be an arbitrary domain. We shall refer to the elements of D as *constants*. Corresponding to any ordered finite set $a_0, a_1, \cdots, a_n$ of constants we form the expression $a_0 x^0 + a_1 x^1 + \cdots + a_n x^n$, and call it a *polynomial in x over D*. The symbol x is called an *indeterminate* or a *variable;* it is introduced merely to facilitate computation, and is not to be thought of as an element of D. The set of all polynomials in x over D is denoted by $D[x]$.

The two polynomials $a_0 x^0 + \cdots + a_n x^n$, $b_0 x^0 + \cdots + b_m x^m$, $m \geqslant n$, will be considered to be equal if $a_i = b_i$, $i = 0,\cdots,n$, and $b_i = 0$, $i = n + 1,\cdots,m$. In writing polynomials we shall often find it convenient to omit terms with zero coefficients, and to write x^i instead of $1x^i$. The polynomial with all $a_i = 0$ may be indicated by $0x^0$. For brevity we may designate a polynomial by a single letter, or, if it is advisable to indicate the indeterminate, by the functional notation $f(x)$.

Polynomials are added and multiplied under the rules

$$(a_0x^0 + a_1x^1 + \cdots + a_nx^n) + (b_0x^0 + b_1x^1 + \cdots + b_nx^n)$$
$$= (a_0 + b_0)x^0 + (a_1 + b_1)x^1 + \cdots + (a_n + b_n)x^n.$$

(Since zero coefficients can be introduced at will we may suppose that the two polynomials have the same number of terms.)

$$(a_0x^0 + a_1x^1 + \cdots + a_nx^n)(b_0x^0 + b_1x^1 + \cdots + b_mx^m)$$
$$= a_0b_0x^0 + (a_0b_1 + a_1b_0)x^1 + (a_0b_2 + a_1b_1 + a_2b_0)x^2 + \cdots + a_nb_mx^{n+m}.$$

It is then easy to show that $D[x]$ is a domain with $0x^0$ and x^0 as the zero and unity elements. Furthermore $D[x] \supset D$, for the set of all polynomials of the form ax^0 constitutes a domain isomorphic to D. It will cause no trouble, therefore, if we replace x^0 by the unity element of D; we shall also write x instead of x^1. Then x is an element of $D[x]$, and the polynomials may be considered as actual, and not merely formal, algebraic expressions in x.

In the same way, the elements of $D[x,y] = D[x][y]$ may be regarded as obtained from the two elements x and y by multiplication and addition. From this point of view $D[x,y]$ is the same as $D[y,x]$, and by induction

$$D[x_1,\cdots,x_r] = D[x_1,\cdots,x_{r-1}][x_r]$$

is independent of the order of the x's. We shall find that most properties of $D[x_1,\cdots,x_r]$ for $r > 1$ can be obtained inductively by considering this domain as $D'[x_r]$, where $D' = D[x_1,\cdots,x_{r-1}]$.

The quotient field of $D[x_1,\cdots,x_r]$ is denoted by $D(x_1,\cdots,x_r)$ and is called the field of *rational functions* of $x_1,\cdots,x_r$ over D.

5.2. The division transformation. If $a_n \neq 0$, the polynomial $a_0 + \cdots + a_nx^n$ is said to be of *degree n*. The polynomial 0 is not regarded as having a degree. We shall denote the degree of a polynomial f by $\deg f$.

Obviously,

$$\deg (f_1 + f_2) \leqslant \max (\deg f_1, \deg f_2),$$
$$\deg (f_1 f_2) = \deg f_1 + \deg f_2.$$

Many properties of polynomials are based on the fact that a process which reduces the degree of a polynomial cannot be repeated more than a finite number of times. In the next theorem we establish the existence of such a process, known as the *division transformation*.

THEOREM 5.1. *If f and g are polynomials, $g \neq 0$, there exist a non-zero constant a and two polynomials q and r, with either $r = 0$ or $\deg r < \deg g$, such that $af = qg + r$.*

PROOF. If $\deg f < \deg g$, or if $f = 0$, we take $a = 1$, $q = 0$, $r = f$. If g is a constant we take $a = g$, $q = f$, $r = 0$. Hence we may assume that $\deg g > 0$, and, using induction, that the theorem is true if f is replaced by a polynomial of smaller degree or by 0. Let

$$f = a_0 + \cdots + a_n x^n, \ g = b_0 + \cdots + b_m x^m,$$

with $n \geqslant m$, $a_n b_m \neq 0$. Then either

$$b_m f - a_n x^{n-m} g = 0,$$

or

$$\deg(b_m f - a_n x^{n-m} g) < \deg f,$$

and so we have

$$a'(b_m f - a_n x^{n-m} g) = q'g + r,$$

with either $r = 0$ or $\deg r < \deg g$. Hence

$$a'b_m f = (a'a_n x^{n-m} + q')g + r,$$

which proves the theorem.

In describing this process we say that g has been divided into af to give the *quotient* q and the *remainder* r.

A slight variation in the proof of Theorem 5.1 will show that if b_m has an inverse, a may be taken to be unity. In particular this can always be done if D is a field.

5.3. Exercise. 1. Prove the existence of a division transformation in the domain of integers, in the following form:

If f and g are integers, $g \neq 0$, there exist integers q and r, with either $r = 0$ or $|r| < |g|$, such that $f = qg + r$.

§6. FACTORIZATION IN POLYNOMIAL DOMAINS

6.1. Factorization in domains. One of the important parts of the theory of any domain is that concerned with the possibility of factoring elements of the domain, that is, of expressing an element as the product of two or more elements. In this section, we shall prove the well-known factorization properties of polynomials.

We first give some definitions. Let D be a given domain. If $a,b \in D$ we say that a is a *factor* of b, or that b is *divisible* by a, written $a \mid b$, if there exists $c \in D$ such that $b = ac$. We see at once that

(i) $a \mid b$, $b \mid c$ imply $a \mid c$,

(ii) $a \mid b$, $a \mid c$ imply $a \mid (\alpha b + \beta c)$ for any $\alpha, \beta \in D$,

(iii) $a \mid 0$ for any a,

(iv)   If $b = ac$, $b \neq 0$, then c is uniquely determined by a and b.

An element e of D which has an inverse e^{-1} is called a *unit;* if e is a unit, ea is said to be an *associate* of a.

(v)   The units of D form a commutative group with respect to multiplication.

(vi)   Any element of D is divisible by its associates and by units.

An element is called *irreducible* if it is divisible only by its associates and by units.

The most useful domains are those in which there is a certain uniqueness in the process of factoring. We characterize them as follows. D is said to have *unique factorization* if

(A)   For every element $a \neq 0$ of D there exists a finite set of irreducible elements $a_1, \cdots, a_r$ whose product is a.

(B)   If $a_1 a_2 \cdots a_r = b_1 b_2 \cdots b_s$, the a_i, b_i being irreducible non-units, then $s = r$ and the factors can be arranged so that a_i is associate to b_i.

Condition (A) implies that every element has an irreducible factorization, and (B) says that such a factorization is unique to within associates.

The best known example of a domain with unique factorization is the set of integers. That domains exist which do not have unique factorization is seen by the following example. Let D consist of all complex numbers of the form $a + b\sqrt{-3}$, a and b being integers. Then

$$2 \cdot 2 = (1 + \sqrt{-3})(1 - \sqrt{-3}).$$

It is easy to show that 2 is irreducible, and since the only units are 1 and -1, condition (B) is violated. In Exercise 7 below an example is given of a domain in which (A) is not true.

6.2. Unique factorization of polynomials. The property of domains with unique factorization with which we shall be mainly concerned is contained in the following theorem.

THEOREM 6.1. *If D has unique factorization so has $D[x]$.*

From this follows by induction

THEOREM 6.2. *If D has unique factorization so has $D[x_1, \cdots, x_r]$.*

The proof of Theorem 6.1 is rather complicated and will be broken up into a series of theorems. We assume throughout the rest of this section that D has unique factorization.

THEOREM 6.3. *If a constant a is a factor of a polynomial f, a is a factor of each coefficient of f.*

PROOF. If $f = b_0 + b_1x + \cdots + b_nx^n$ and $a \mid f$ then there is a $g = c_0 + c_1x + \cdots + c_nx^n$ such that $ag = f$. This implies that $ac_i = b_i$, $i = 0, \cdots, n$, and so a is a factor of each b_i.

THEOREM 6.4. *If a,b,c are constants, and a is irreducible and $a \mid bc$, then $a \mid b$ or $a \mid c$.*

PROOF. If $a \mid bc$ there is a constant d such that $ad = bc$. Expressing b,c,d in terms of their irreducible factors, we have

$$ad_1 \cdots d_r = b_1 \cdots b_s c_1 \cdots c_t.$$

Hence either a is a unit or a is associate to some b_i or c_i; that is, $a \mid b$ or $a \mid c$.

THEOREM 6.5. *If a is an irreducible constant and $a \mid fg$, $f,g \in D[x]$, then $a \mid f$ or $a \mid g$.*

PROOF. Let

$$f = b_0 + b_1x + \cdots + b_nx^n, \quad g = c_0 + c_1x + \cdots + c_mx^m,$$

and suppose $a \nmid f$, $a \nmid g$. ($a \nmid f$ means that a is not a factor of f). Then there is at least one b_i such that $a \nmid b_i$; let p be the smallest i with this property, so that $a \nmid b_p$ but $a \mid b_i$ if $i < p$. Similarly, let $a \nmid c_q$ but $a \mid c_i$ if $i < q$. The coefficient of x^{p+q} in fg is

$$b_0c_{p+q} + b_1c_{p+q-1} + \cdots + b_pc_q + \cdots + b_{p+q}c_0,$$

where $b_i = c_j = 0$ if $i > n$, $j > m$. From the choice of p and q, and Theorem 6.4, b_pc_q is not divisible by a while every other term in this coefficient is. Hence the total sum is not divisible by a, and so $a \nmid fg$, by Theorem 6.3.

THEOREM 6.6. *Let K be the quotient field of D. If f is irreducible in $D[x]$ it is irreducible in $K[x]$.*

PROOF. If f is reducible in $K[x]$, then $f = g'h'$, $g',h' \in K[x]$, and neither g' nor $h' \in K$. Express the coefficients in g' as the ratios of elements of D and let a be a common multiple of the denominators. Then $ag' = g_1 \in D[x]$. Similarly let $bh' = h_1 \in D[x]$. Then $abf = g_1h_1$. If e is any irreducible factor of ab, then $e \mid g_1h_1$, and by Theorem 6.5, $e \mid g_1$ or $e \mid h_1$. Remove this factor and repeat the process. We eventually obtain $f = gh$, with $g,h \in D[x]$, and neither g nor h is a constant.

Theorem 6.6 essentially reduces our problem to that of proving that $K[x]$ has unique factorization. To do this we need the following important result.

THEOREM 6.7. *If $f,g \in K[x]$ there is an $h \in K[x]$ such that*
  (i) $h \mid f, h \mid g,$
  (ii) *If $k \mid f, k \mid g$, then $k \mid h$,*
  (iii) *There exist $A,B \in K[x]$ such that $h = Af + Bg$.*

PROOF. By successive application of the division transformation (Theorem 5.1) we obtain

$$f = q_1 g + r_1,$$
(6.1)
$$g = q_2 r_1 + r_2,$$
$$r_1 = q_3 r_2 + r_3,$$
$$\cdots$$

where $\deg g > \deg r_1 > \deg r_2 > \cdots$. Since the degree of a polynomial is a non-negative integer it cannot decrease indefinitely, and so for some p we must have $r_{p+1} = 0$. The sequence of equations (6.1) then ends with

$$r_{p-2} = q_p r_{p-1} + r_p,$$
$$r_{p-1} = q_{p+1} r_p.$$

We shall show that $h = r_p$ has the required properties.

(i)   From $r_{p-1} = q_{p+1} h$, we have $h \mid r_{p-1}$. From $r_{p-2} = q_p r_{p-1} + h$, we have $h \mid r_{p-2}$. Continuing in this way we see that $h \mid g, h \mid f$.

(ii) Let $k \mid f, k \mid g$. Then from $r_1 = f - q_1 g$ we have $k \mid r_1$. From $r_2 = g - q_2 r_1$ we have $k \mid r_2$. Continuing in this way we obtain $k \mid h$.

(iii) Starting with the next-to-last of equations (6.1) and working upwards, we have

$$h = r_{p-2} - q_p r_{p-1}$$
$$= r_{p-2} - q_p(r_{p-3} - q_{p-1} r_{p-2})$$
$$= -q_p r_{p-3} + (1 + q_p q_{p-1})r_{p-2}$$
$$\cdots$$
$$= Af + Bg.$$

An element h satisfying (i) and (ii) is called a *highest common factor* of f and g. It is evident from (i) and (ii) that h is unique to within associates. The successive application of the division transformation used in proving this theorem is known as the Euclidean Algorithm.

THEOREM 6.8. *If $f,g,h \in K[x]$, and if f is irreducible and $f \mid gh$, then $f \mid g$ or $f \mid h$.*

PROOF. Suppose $f \mid gh$ but $f \nmid g$. Then f and g have no common factors except elements of K, and by Theorem 6.7 there exist $A, B \in K[x]$ such that $1 = Af + Bg$. Hence $h = Afh + Bgh$. But $f \mid gh$, and so $f \mid Afh + Bgh$; that is, $f \mid h$.

THEOREM 6.9. *If $f, g, h \in D[x]$ and f is irreducible and $f \mid gh$, then $f \mid g$ or $f \mid h$.*

PROOF. The case $f \in D$ is covered by Theorem 6.5, and so we can assume that f is not a constant. By Theorem 6.6, f is irreducible in $K[x]$, and so by Theorem 6.8, $f \mid g$ or $f \mid h$ in $K[x]$. Suppose $h = fk$, $k \in K[x]$. As in the proof of Theorem 6.6, there is an $a \in D$ such that $ak \in D[x]$. Then $ah = afk$. If e is an irreducible factor of a, say $a = ea_1$, then, by Theorem 6.5, $e \mid ak$, since f is irreducible and not a constant. Hence $a_1k \in D[x]$, and we have $a_1h = a_1fk$. Treating a_1 in the same fashion as we did a, we can continue to remove irreducible constant factors until we have $h = fk$ with $k \in D[x]$. This proves the theorem.

PROOF OF THEOREM 6.1. Let $f \in D[x]$. If f is reducible we have $f = f'_1 f'_2$, where $f'_1, f'_2 \in D[x]$ and neither is a unit. If either f'_1 or f'_2 is reducible it can be expressed as a product of non-units, and the process continued. At each step we either lower the degree of one of the factors or remove a constant factor from the coefficient of the term of highest degree. Since neither of these processes can be continued indefinitely condition (A) is satisfied. Now suppose $f = f_1 \cdots f_r = g_1 \cdots g_s$, where each f_i, g_i is irreducible. Then $g_1 \mid f_1 \cdots f_r$, and by an obvious extension of Theorem 6.9, $g_1 \mid f_i$ for some i. We may assume that $i = 1$. Since both g_1 and f_1 are irreducible they are associates, and we obtain $ef_2 \cdots f_r = g_2 \cdots g_s$, where e is a unit. Continuing this process we see that each g_i is associate to a corresponding f_i, so that condition (B) is satisfied.

6.3. Exercises. **1.** Using the division transformation of §5.3, Exercise 1, prove the existence of a highest common factor in the domain of integers.

2. Prove that the domain of integers has unique factorization.

3. For any finite set $f_1, \cdots, f_n$ of elements of $K[x]$ show the existence of a highest common factor h such that

    (i) $h \mid f_i$, $i = 1, \cdots, n$;

    (ii)   If $k \mid f_i$, $i = 1, \cdots, n$, then $k \mid h$.

Show also that

    (iii)   There exist $g_i \in K[x]$, $i = 1, \cdots, n$, such that $\Sigma g_i f_i = h$.

[Use induction on n.]

4. For any finite set $f_1, f_2, \cdots$ of elements of a domain D with unique factorization, there exists a finite set of irreducible elements $a_1, a_2, \cdots$ of D, no two a's being associate, such that $f_i = e_i \Pi_j a_j^{\alpha_{ij}}$ the α_{ij} being non-negative integers and the e_i units. If $\beta_j = \min\ (\alpha_{1j}, \alpha_{2j}, \cdots)$ then $\Pi_j a_j{}^{\beta_j}$ is a highest common factor of the f_i.

5. For any finite set $f_1, f_2, \cdots$ of elements of a domain D with unique factorization, there exists an element m of D, unique to within associates, such that

    (i) $f_i \mid m$ for all i;

    (ii) If $f_i \mid n$ for all i then $m \mid n$;

    (iii) If $\alpha_j = \max\ (\alpha_{1j}, \alpha_{2j}, \cdots)$ in the notation of Exercise 4, then $m = e\Pi_j a_j{}^{\alpha_j}$, e being a unit.

An element m satisfying (i) and (ii) is called a *least common multiple* of $f_1, f_2, \cdots$.

6. If h and m are a highest common factor and a least common multiple of two elements f and g of a domain with unique actorization, then $hm = efg$, e being a unit.

7. Let D consist of all expressions of the form

$$a_0 + \Sigma_{i=1}^{k}\ a_i\ x^{m_i/2^n},$$

where $a_0, \cdots, a_k$ are integers, $k, m_1, \cdots, m_k$ are positive integers, and n is a non-negative integer.

    (i)   Under obvious formal definitions of addition and multiplication, D is a domain.

    (ii) The only units in D are ± 1.

    (iii) Any element of D with $a_0 = 0$ is reducible.

    (iv) x cannot be expressed as the product of a finite number of irreducible elements.

§7. SUBSTITUTION

7.1. Substitution in polynomials. A familiar operation on a polynomial is the *substitution* of a constant for the indeterminate in the formal sum expressing the polynomial. If

$$f(x) = a_0 + a_1 x + \cdots + a_n x^n \in D[x],$$

we define $f(a)$ to be $a_0 + a_1 a + \cdots + a_n a^n$ for any $a \in D$. $f(a)$ is called the *value* of $f(x)$ for $x = a$. From the manner of adding and multiplying polynomials it follows that if $f(x) + g(x) = h(x)$ and $f(x)g(x) = k(x)$, then $f(a) + g(a) = h(a)$ and $f(a)g(a) = k(a)$. That is, the correspondence between $f(x)$ and $f(a)$ is a homomorphism over D of $D[x]$ into D. This process can obviously be extended to polynomials in more than one variable.

If $f(x)$ is an element of the field $K(x)$, we have $f(x) = g(x)/h(x)$, where g and h are polynomials which we may assume have no common factor (besides units). Then $g(a)$ and $h(a)$ are defined for every $a \in K$, and we define $f(a) = g(a)/h(a)$ provided $h(a) \neq 0$. If $h(a) = 0$, $f(a)$ is not defined. This makes substitution somewhat harder to handle for rational functions than for polynomials, as one must always be on the lookout for exceptional cases. Note that $f(a) = 0$ implies $g(a) = 0$.

It is sometimes useful to extend the scope of the substitution process. Let D' be a domain containing D. Then $D'[x] \supset D[x]$, and if $f(x) \in D[x]$ we have $f(x) \in D'[x]$. Hence we may substitute for x any element α of D', and $f(\alpha)$ is an element of D'. For example, let $D' = D[x]$, and let $g(x)$ be an element of D'. Then $f(g(x))$ is defined and is an element of $D[x]$. This process can obviously be extended indefinitely.

7.2. Zeros of polynomials; the Remainder Theorem. A constant a is said to be a *zero* of a polynomial $f(x)$ if $f(a) = 0$. We also express this fact by saying that a is a *root* of the equation $f(x) = 0$. Note that such an "equation" does not express the equality of its two members, for $f(x)$ need not be the zero element of $D[x]$. In the terminology of elementary algebra, this is a "conditional equation," whereas we have so far restricted the use of the equality sign to "identities." Although we could avoid this ambiguity in the use of the equality sign by using the phrase "zero of a polynomial" instead of "root of an equation" it seems better to follow the customary wording, particularly when we come to speak of "the equation of an algebraic curve."

The fundamental properties of zeros of a polynomial follow from the familiar Remainder Theorem.

THEOREM 7.1. *If $f(x)$ is divided by $x - a$, the remainder is $f(a)$.*

PROOF. Let $f(x) = (x - a)q(x) + r$. r, being either zero or of degree less than deg $(x - a)$, is necessarily a constant. Substituting a for x, we obtain $r = f(a)$.

From the Remainder Theorem we obtain in the usual way the following theorems:

THEOREM 7.2. *a is a zero of $f(x)$ if and only if $x - a$ is a factor of $f(x)$.*

THEOREM 7.3. *A polynomial of degree n has at most n zeros.*

An extension of Theorem 7.3 to polynomials in several variables, which will be useful in the study of algebraic curves, is contained in the following theorem.

THEOREM 7.4. *If $f(x_1, \cdots, x_r) \in D[x_1, \cdots, x_r]$, and if $f(a_1, \cdots, a_r) = 0$ for all choices of $a_1, \cdots, a_r$ from any fixed infinite subset of D, then $f(x_1, \cdots, x_r) = 0$.*

PROOF. Theorem 7.3 implies the particular case of this theorem when $r = 1$. We may therefore proceed by induction, assuming the theorem true for polynomials in $r - 1$ variables. Let

$$f(x_1, \cdots, x_r) = f_0 + f_1 x_r + \cdots + f_n x_r^n, \quad n \geq 0,$$

where $f_i \in D[x_1,\cdots,x_{r-1}]$. If $f \neq 0$ we may assume that $f_n \neq 0$. Then by assumption $f_n(a_1,\cdots,a_{r-1}) \neq 0$ for some choice of the $a_1,\cdots,a_{r-1}$ from the given infinite subset. Hence there are at most n values of a_r for which $f(a_1,\cdots,a_{r-1},a_r) = 0$, contrary to assumption. Hence $f = 0$.

7.3. Algebraically closed domains. The theorems of §7.2 tell us, in a sense, that an equation cannot have too many roots. It is evident that in certain domains there are equations with no roots—for example, $2x - 1 = 0$ in the domain of integers, or $x^2 + 1 = 0$ in the domain of real numbers. An important class of domains consists of the ones in which every polynomial equation has a root. Such a domain is said to be *algebraically closed;* more explicitly, a domain D is algebraically closed if for every non-constant $f \in D[x]$ there is an element a of D such that $f(a) = 0$. An algebraically closed domain is necessarily a field, since $ax - 1 = 0$ has a root for any $a \neq 0$.

The so-called "fundamental theorem of algebra" states that the field of complex numbers is algebraically closed. This property of the complex field, together with the fact that it is of characteristic zero, accounts for most of its algebraic properties. In particular, we shall find that any field having these two properties can be used instead of the complex field throughout much of the theory of algebraic curves.

The following theorem follows in the usual way from Theorem 7.2.

THEOREM 7.5. *If D is algebraically closed and if $f \in D[x]$ is of degree n, then there exists a unique set of n constants $a_1,\cdots,a_n$, not necessarily distinct, such that*

$$f(x) = a(x - a_1) \cdots (x - a_n), \ a \in D, \ a \neq 0.$$

7.4. Exercises. 1. A domain with a finite number of elements cannot be algebraically closed.

2. Show that the Vandermonde determinant

$$\begin{vmatrix} 1 & x_1 & x_1^2 & \cdots & x_1^{n-1} \\ 1 & x_2 & x_2^2 & \cdots & x_2^{n-1} \\ \cdots & \cdots & \cdots & \cdots & \cdots \\ 1 & x_n & x_n^2 & \cdots & x_n^{n-1} \end{vmatrix}$$

is divisible by $x_i - x_j$, $i \neq j$, and hence is equal to $\Pi_{i>j}(x_i - x_j)$.

3. Prove the following generalization of Theorem 7.4. Let $f(x_1,\cdots,x_r)$ be a polynomial over D of degree at most n_i in x_i. Let there be given the following subsets of D: S is any subset of D having more than n_1 elements; for each $a_1 \in S$ there is a subset S_{a_1} of D with more than n_2 elements; for each $a_2 \in S_{a_1}$ there is a subset S_{a_1,a_2} of D with more than n_3 elements; and so on. If $f(a_1,\cdots,a_r) = 0$ whenever $a_1 \in S$, $a_2 \in S_{a_1}$, etc., then $f(x_1,\cdots,x_r) = 0$.

§8. DERIVATIVES

8.1. Derivative of a polynomial. The derivative of a polynomial function, as of any function, is defined by limiting processes. The formula used for differentiating such functions, however, involves no such processes in any explicit fashion. We shall now see that a purely formal application of this formula will give us many of the properties of derivatives.

For any element

$$f = a_0 + a_1 x + \cdots + a_n x^n$$

of $D[x]$ we define the *derivative* of f with respect to x to be

$$f' = a_1 + 2a_2 x + \cdots + n a_n x^{n-1}.$$

The (partial) derivative of $f(x_1, \cdots, x_r)$ with respect to x_i may then be defined by regarding $f(x_1, \cdots, x_r)$ a polynomial over $D[x_1, \cdots, x_{i-1}, x_{i+1}, \cdots, x_r]$. The following properties of derivatives will be useful:

(i) $(f + g)' = f' + g'$.

(ii) If a is a constant, $a' = 0$ and $(af)' = af'$.

(iii) $(fg)' = f'g + fg'$; $(f^n)' = nf^{n-1} f'$.

(iv) $f(g_1(x), \cdots, g_r(x))' = \Sigma_i f_i (g_1(x), \cdots, g_r(x)) g'_i(x)$,

where $f_i(x_1, \cdots, x_r)$ is the derivative of f with respect to x_i, $i = 1, \cdots, r$.

(i) and (ii) follow at once from the definition, and the first part of (iii) can be easily checked; the last part of (iii) is obtained by repeated application of the first part. (iv) may be proved first in the case in which f consists of a single term, by use of (iii), and then in the general case by use of (i) and (ii).

Derivatives have certain undesirable properties for polynomials over a domain of characteristic $p \neq 0$. This is due to the fact that for such a domain any polynomial of the type $a_0 + a_1 x^p + a_2 x^{2p} + \cdots$ has zero for its derivative. Hence throughout the rest of this section we shall assume that D has characteristic zero. We also assume that D has unique factorization.

Our most important use of derivatives will be in the investigation of multiple factors of polynomials. A fundamental theorem in this connection is the following.

THEOREM 8.1. *If g is irreducible, and not a constant, $g^2 \mid f$ if and only if $g \mid f$ and $g \mid f'$.*

PROOF. If $g \mid f$ then $f = gh$, and so $f' = gh' + g'h$. If, also, $g \mid f'$, then $g \mid g'h$. Since $\deg g' < \deg g$, $g \nmid g'$, and so $g \mid h$, since g is irreducible. Therefore, $g^2 \mid f$. Conversely, if $f =_f g^2 k$ then $f' = 2gg'k + g^2 k'$, and so $g \mid f$ and $g \mid f'$.

As an important special case we obtain from Theorem 7.2,

THEOREM 8.2. $(x - a)^2 \mid f(x)$ *if and only if* $f(a) = f'(a) = 0$.

8.2. Taylor's Theorem. By induction, we define the nth derivative of $f(x)$ to be $f^{(n)}(x) = f^{(n-1)}(x)'$. Similarly, the higher partial derivatives can be defined. The partial derivative of $f(x_1, \cdots, x_n)$ with respect to x_i may be designated by $\partial f / \partial x_i$, f_{x_i}, or f_i, with obvious extensions to higher derivatives. The relation $f_{ij} = f_{ji}$ is easily verified, and from this it follows that all the higher partial derivatives are independent of the order of differentiation.

We shall now prove Taylor's Theorem.

THEOREM 8.3. *For any polynomial* $f(x)$ *of degree n and any constant a,*

$$f(x) = f(a) + f'(a)(x - a) + \frac{1}{2!} f''(a)(x - a)^2 +$$

$$\cdots + \frac{1}{n!} f^{(n)}(a)(x - a)^n.$$

PROOF. Let

$$(8.1) \qquad f(x + a) = a_0 + a_1 x + \cdots + a_n x^n.$$

Differentiating successively with respect to x, we obtain, using (iv),

$$f'(x + a) = a_1 + 2a_2 x + \cdots + na_n x^{n-1},$$

$$f''(x + a) = 2a_2 + 2 \cdot 3a_3 x + \cdots + n(n - 1)a_n x^{n-2},$$

$$\cdots\cdots\cdots\cdots\cdots\cdots\cdots\cdots\cdots\cdots\cdots\cdots\cdots\cdots\cdots$$

$$f^{(n)}(x + a) = n! \, a_n.$$

Putting $x = 0$ in each of these equations, we have

$$a_0 = f(a), \quad a_1 = f'(a), \quad a_2 = \frac{1}{2!} f''(a), \cdots, a_n = \frac{1}{n!} f^{(n)}(a).$$

Substituting in (8.1), and replacing x by $x - a$, we have the desired result.

This theorem is easily extended to polynomials in several variables.

THEOREM 8.4. *Let* $f(x_1 \cdots, x_r) \in D[x_1, \cdots, x_r]$, *let* $a_1, \cdots, a_r \in D$, *and designate by* $f_{ij} \ldots$ *the result of substituting* $a_1, \cdots, a_r$ *for* $x_1, \cdots, x_r$ *in the partial derivative of* f *with respect to* $x_i, x_j, \cdots$. *Then*

$$f(x_1, \cdots, x_r) = f(a_1, \cdots, a_r) + \Sigma_i f_i(x_i - a_i)$$

$$+ \frac{1}{2!} \Sigma_{i,j} f_{ij}(x_i - a_i)(x_j - a_j) + \cdots$$

PROOF. By the previous theorem expand

$F(t) = f(a_1 + (x_1 - a_1)t, \cdots, a_r + (x_r - a_r)t)$ in powers of t. Using (IV) we obtain

$$F(t) = f(a_1, \cdots, a_r) + \Sigma_i f_i(x_i - a_i)t$$

$$+ \frac{1}{2!} \Sigma_{i,j} f_{ij}(x_i - a_i)(x_j - a_j)t^2 + \cdots.$$

The desired result is obtained by putting $t = 1$.

8.3. Exercises. 1. Properties (i), $\cdots$, (iv) will hold for rational functions if and only if we define $(f/g)'$ to be $(f'g - fg')/g^2$.

2. Extend Theorems 8.1 and 8.2 from squares to nth powers.

3. Prove Theorem 8.2 and its generalization for domains of any characteristic.

§9. ELIMINATION

9.1. The resultant of two polynomials. The problem of elimination theory is to determine what conditions the coefficients in a set of polynomials must satisfy in order that the polynomials have a common (non-unit) factor. The general problem is quite complicated * and we shall consider only the case of two polynomials. In this case one answer to the question is given by Theorem 6.7. For we obviously have

THEOREM 9.1. *If K is a field and $f, g \in K[x]$, then f and g have a common factor if and only if the h of Theorem 6.7 is not a constant.*

That there is no loss of generality in considering polynomials over a field is assured by Theorem 6.6.

Theorem 9.1 could be used to decide in any given case whether or not two polynomials have a common factor. It has the advantage that it actually gives the factor if there is one, but the disadvantage that its application involves much tedious computation. To avoid this objection we shall develop another method.

Let

$$f = a_0 + a_1 x + \cdots + a_n x^n, \quad a_n \neq 0,$$

$$g = b_0 + b_1 x + \cdots + b_m x^m, \quad b_m \neq 0,$$

the coefficients being in a domain D with unique factorization. We shall assume that a method is available for factoring constants, so that common constant factors of f and g can be recognized. Hence we may assume that $n, m \geqslant 1$.

THEOREM 9.2. *f and g have a common non-constant factor if and only if there exist non-zero polynomials ϕ and ψ, of degrees less than n and m respectively, such that $\psi f = \phi g$.*

---

* See van der Waerden, *Moderne Algebra*, Vol. II, Chap. 11.

Proof. If f and g have a common non-constant factor h, then $f = h\phi$, $g = h\psi$ and $\psi f = \phi g$. Conversely, let $\psi f = \phi g$, and factor g into its irreducible factors. The non-constant factors, or their associates, must appear among the irreducible factors of ψf. They cannot all appear among the factors of ψ since deg $\psi <$ deg g. Hence one of them is a factor of f, and so f and g have a common non-constant factor.

Theorem 9.3. f and g have a common non-constant factor if and only if

$$R = \begin{vmatrix} a_0 & a_1 & \cdots & & & a_n & & \\ & a_0 & \cdots & & & a_{n-1} & a_n & \\ & & \cdots & \cdots & \cdots & & & \\ & & & a_0 & \cdots & \cdots & \cdots & a_n \\ b_0 & b_1 & \cdots & b_{m-1} & b_m & & & \\ & & \cdots & \cdots & \cdots & \cdots & & \\ & & b_0 & \cdots & \cdots & \cdots & b_m & \end{vmatrix} = 0,$$

there being m rows of a's and n rows of b's in the determinant, the rows being filled out with zeros.

Proof. We shall prove that the vanishing of R is a necessary and sufficient condition for the existence of the polynomials ϕ and ψ of Theorem 9.2. Suppose f and g have a common non-constant factor; then there exist ϕ and ψ such that $\psi f = \phi g$. Let

$$\phi = \alpha_1 + \alpha_2 x + \cdots + \alpha_n x^{n-1},$$
$$\psi = \beta_1 + \beta_2 x + \cdots + \beta_m x^{m-1},$$

where at least one $\alpha_i \neq 0$ and one $\beta_i \neq 0$. Then $\psi f = \phi g$ implies

$$a_0\beta_1 = b_0\alpha_1,$$
$$a_1\beta_1 + a_0\beta_2 = b_1\alpha_1 + b_0\alpha_2,$$
$$\cdots \cdots \cdots \cdots \cdots$$
$$a_n\beta_m = b_m\alpha_n.$$

Considering these as homogeneous equations in the $m + n$ variables $\beta_1, \cdots, \alpha_n$, we know that they have a non-trivial solution. Hence the determinant of the coefficients is zero, from which follows $R = 0$. Conversely, if $R = 0$ the equations have a non-trivial solution (Theorem 4.3) in the quotient field of D; multiplying by a common denominator gives a solution in D for which at least one α_i or one β_i is not zero. If one α_i, say, is not zero then $\phi \neq 0$, and we have $\psi f = \phi g$, with ϕ, and hence also ψ, different from zero.

R is called the *resultant*, or the *eliminant*, of f and g. The resultant of a polynomial and its derivative is called the *discriminant* of the polynomial. From Theorem 8.1 we obtain

THEOREM 9.4. *A polynomial over a domain of characteristic zero has a repeated non-constant factor if and only if its discriminant is zero.*

A useful consequence of Theorem 9.3 is

THEOREM 9.5. *Let $D' \supset D$ and let $f, g \in D[x]$. If f and g have a common factor which is in $D'[x]$ and not in D' then they have a common factor which is in $D[x]$ and not in D.*

PROOF. Thinking of f and g as elements of $D'[x]$, R, considered as an element of D', must vanish. Hence R, considered as an element of D, vanishes. Hence f and g have a common non-constant factor in $D[x]$.

An important way of expressing the resultant is given in the following theorem.

THEOREM 9.6. *There exist polynomials A and B, of degrees at most $m - 1$ and $n - 1$, such that $R = Af + Bg$.*

PROOF. We have

$$f = a_0 + a_1 x + \cdots + a_n x^n,$$
$$xf = \qquad a_0 x + \cdots + a_{n-1} x^n + a_n x^{n+1},$$
$$\cdots\cdots\cdots\cdots\cdots\cdots\cdots\cdots\cdots\cdots\cdots\cdots\cdots\cdots$$
$$x^{m-1} f = \qquad a_0 x^{m-1} + \cdots + a_n x^{m+n-1},$$
$$g = b_0 + b_1 x + \cdots + b_m x^m,$$
$$xg = \qquad b_0 x + \cdots + b_{m-1} x^m + b_m x^{m+1},$$
$$\cdots\cdots\cdots\cdots\cdots\cdots\cdots\cdots\cdots\cdots\cdots\cdots\cdots\cdots$$
$$x^{n-1} g = \qquad b_0 x^{n-1} + \cdots + b_m x^{m+n-1}.$$

Let $A_1, \cdots, A_{m+n}$ be the cofactors of the elements of the first column of R. If we multiply the ith equation above by A_i and add corresponding terms for $i = 1, \cdots, m + n$, we obtain

$$(A_0 + A_1 x + \cdots + A_m x^{m-1}) f + (A_{m+1} + A_{m+2} x + \cdots$$
$$+ A_{m+n} x^{n-1}) g = R,$$

which proves the theorem.

9.2. **Application to polynomials in several variables.** If $f, g \in D[x_1, \cdots, x_r]$ we can regard them as polynomials in x_r over $D[x_1, \cdots, x_{r-1}]$, that is,

$$f(x_1, \cdots, x_r) = a_0 + a_1 x_r + \cdots + a_n x_r^n,$$
$$g(x_1, \cdots, x_r) = b_0 + b_1 x_r + \cdots + b_m x_r^m,$$

where a_i, $b_i \in D[x_1, \cdots, x_{r-1}]$. Assuming $a_n b_m \neq 0$, and n, $m > 0$, the resultant of f and g with respect to x_r is a polynomial $R(x_1, \cdots, x_{r-1})$, which is zero if and only if f and g have a common factor involving x_r.

Now let $\alpha_1, \cdots, \alpha_{r-1} \in D$, and consider $R(\alpha_1, \cdots, \alpha_{r-1})$. From the definition of R, we see that $R(\alpha_1, \cdots, \alpha_{r-1})$ is the resultant of $f(\alpha_1, \cdots, \alpha_{r-1}, x_r)$ and $g(\alpha_1, \cdots, \alpha_{r-1}, x_r)$ provided $a_n(\alpha_1, \cdots, \alpha_{r-1}) b_m(\alpha_1, \cdots, \alpha_{r-1}) \neq 0$. We also see that if $a_n(\alpha_1, \cdots, \alpha_{r-1}) = b_m(\alpha_1, \cdots, \alpha_{r-1}) = 0$ then $R(\alpha_1, \cdots, \alpha_{r-1}) = 0$, even though $f(\alpha_1, \cdots, \alpha_{r-1}, x_r)$ and $g(\alpha_1, \cdots, \alpha_{r-1}, x_r)$ may have no common factor. We shall often have occasion to use these properties of the resultant.

The following consequence of Theorems 7.4 and 9.6 will be needed later.

THEOREM 9.7. *Let D be algebraically closed and let f, $g \in D[x_1, \cdots, x_r]$, f being irreducible. If $g(a_1, \cdots, a_r) = 0$ whenever $f(a_1, \cdots, a_r) = 0$, then $f \mid g$.*

PROOF. If $f \in D$ then either $f \neq 0$, in which case the desired conclusion follows from the fact that D is a field, or $f = 0$. In the latter case we must have $g(a) = 0$ for any choice of $a_1, \cdots, a_r$, and so by Theorem 7.4, $g = 0$ and $f \mid g$. Hence we may assume that

$$f = b_0 + b_1 x_r + \cdots + b_n x_r^n, \; b_i \in D[x_1, \cdots, x_{r-1}], \; b_n \neq 0, \; n > 0.$$

If $g = 0$ we have $f \mid g$, so let $g \neq 0$. Suppose that $g \in D[x_1, \cdots, x_{r-1}]$. Then by Theorem 7.4 there exist $a_1, \cdots, a_{r-1}$ such that $g(a_1, \cdots, a_{r-1}) \cdot b_n(a_1, \cdots, a_{r-1}) \neq 0$. Since D is algebraically closed the equation $f(a_1, \cdots, a_{r-1}, x_r) = 0$ has a root a_r. The set $a_1, \cdots, a_r$ then contradicts the hypothesis of the theorem, and so we cannot have $g \in D[x_1, \cdots, x_{r-1}]$. We can therefore form the resultant $R(x_1, \cdots, x_{r-1})$ of f and g with respect to x_r. By Theorem 9.6, $R = Af + Bg$, $A, B \in D[x_1, \cdots, x_{r-1}]$. But from this relation we conclude that $f(a) = 0$ implies $R(a) = 0$, and since we do have $R \in D[x_1, \cdots, x_{r-1}]$ we must have $R = 0$, by the above argument. Hence f and g have a common factor, and since f is irreducible this implies that $f \mid g$.

9.3. Exercises. 1. Show that the discriminants of $ax^2 + bx + c$ and $x^3 + px + q$ are respectively $-a(b^2 - 4ac)$ and $4p^3 + 27q^2$.

2. Prove that

$$\begin{vmatrix} a_0 & a_1 & a_2 & \cdots & a_{n-1} & a_n \\ -\lambda & 1 & 0 & \cdots & 0 & 0 \\ 0 & -\lambda & 1 & \cdots & 0 & 0 \\ \multicolumn{6}{c}{\dotfill} \\ 0 & 0 & 0 & \cdots & -\lambda & 1 \end{vmatrix} = a_0 + a_1 \lambda + \cdots + a_n \lambda^n.$$

3. Prove that if a polynomial with real coefficients has an imaginary number for a zero it also has the conjugate imaginary number for a zero. [Use Theorem 9.5 with D and D' as the real and the complex fields respectively.]

§10. HOMOGENEOUS POLYNOMIALS

10.1. Basic properties. By the degree of a term of a polynomial $f(x_1, \cdots, x_r)$ is meant the sum of the powers to which the variables appear in this term. The degree of f is the largest of the degrees of its terms. f is *homogeneous* if every one of its terms is of the same degree. In the following discussion we shall use capital letters to designate homogeneous polynomials, with a subscript to indicate, when convenient, the degree of the polynomial.

The following property of a homogeneous polynomial is often used as a definition.

THEOREM 10.1. $f(x_1, \cdots, x_r) \neq 0$ *is homogeneous of degree n if and only if the relation*

$$(10.1) \qquad f(tx_1, \cdots, tx_r) = t^n f(x_1, \cdots, x_r)$$

holds between these elements of $D[x_1, \cdots, x_r, t]$.

PROOF. The necessity of the condition is obvious. To prove the sufficiency, let

$$f = F_{n_1} + F_{n_2} + \cdots + F_{n_k}, \quad n_1 < n_2 < \cdots < n_k,$$

where F_{n_i} is homogeneous of degree n_i and is not zero. Then (10.1) becomes

$$t^{n_1} F_{n_1} + t^{n_2} F_{n_2} + \cdots = t^n F_{n_1} + t^n F_{n_2} + \cdots.$$

Hence we must have $t^{n_i} = t^n$ for each i. This implies that $k = 1$ and $n_1 = n$.

The following theorem is often called "Euler's Theorem."

THEOREM 10.2. *If $F(x_1, \cdots, x_r)$ is homogeneous of degree n, then*

$$\Sigma x_i \frac{\partial F}{\partial x_i} = nF.$$

PROOF. Substituting tx_i for x_i in F, we obtain

$$F(tx_1, \cdots, tx_r) = t^n F(x_1, \cdots, x_r).$$

Differentiate with respect to t;

$$\Sigma x_i \left(\frac{\partial F}{\partial x_i} \right)_0 = nt^{n-1} F(x_1, \cdots, x_r),$$

where $\left(\dfrac{\partial F}{\partial x_i}\right)_0$ is the result of substituting $tx_1,\cdots,tx_r$ for $x_1,\cdots,x_r$ in $\dfrac{\partial F}{\partial x_i}$. On putting $t = 1$ we obtain the desired result.

The following general result can be proved similarly:

THEOREM 10.3. *If $F(x_1,\cdots,x_r)$ is homogeneous of degree n, then*

$$\Sigma_{t_1,\cdots,t_s} x_{t_1}\cdots x_{t_s}\ \frac{\partial^s F}{\partial x_{t_1}\cdots\partial x_{t_s}} = n(n-1)\cdots(n-s+1)F.$$

10.2. Factorization. In many respects a homogeneous polynomial in $r + 1$ variables behaves like a non-homogeneous polynomial in r variables. We shall be greatly interested in this aspect of homogeneous polynomials.

Let $F_n \in D[x_0,\cdots,x_r]$. We single out one of the variables, say x_0, for special treatment. If $x_0 \nmid F_n$ the (possibly) non-homogeneous polynomial $f(x_1,\cdots,x_r) = F_n(1,x_1,\cdots,x_r)$ is also of degree n. f and F_n will be said to be *associated*. (This use of the word "associated" must not be confused with its use in connection with factoring. We shall no longer have occasion to use the word in its earlier meaning.) Conversely, given any polynomial $f(x_1,\cdots,x_r)$ of degree n we can obtain its associated homogeneous polynomial by introducing the proper powers of x_0 into those terms of f which are of degrees less than n.

THEOREM 10.4. *If F_n and f are associated, any factor of F_n is associated with a factor of f, and vice versa.*

This follows at once from

THEOREM 10.5. *Any factor of a homogeneous polynomial is homogeneous.*

PROOF. Let $F = fg$ and suppose that f is not homogeneous. Then we may write

$$f = F_i + F_{i+1} + \cdots + F_{i+j},$$

where $F_i \neq 0$, $F_{i+j} \neq 0$, and $j > 0$. Similarly,

$$g = G_k + G_{k+1} + \cdots + G_{k+l},$$

where $G_k \neq 0$, $G_{k+l} \neq 0$, and $l \geqslant 0$. Then

$$F = fg = F_iG_k + (F_{i+1}G_k + F_iG_{k+1}) + \cdots + F_{i+j}G_{k+l}.$$

Now $F_iG_k \neq 0$ and $F_{i+j}G_{k+l} \neq 0$, and

$$'\deg F_iG_k = i + k < i + j + k + l = \deg F_{i+j}G_{k+l}.$$

Hence F is not homogeneous, contrary to assumption.

As a corollary to Theorem 10.5 we have

THEOREM 10.6. *F is irreducible if and only if its associate is irreducible.*
Corresponding to Theorem 9.3 we have
THEOREM 10.7. *The homogeneous polynomials*

$$F = a_0 x_0^n + a_1 x_0^{n-1} x_1 + \cdots + a_n x_1^n,$$
$$G = b_0 x_0^m + b_1 x_0^{m-1} x_1 + \cdots + b_m x_1^m,$$

have a common non-constant factor if and only if their resultant R is zero

PROOF. If $a_n = b_m = 0$, then $R = 0$ and F and G have the common
factor x_0. If $a_n b_m \neq 0$ we can consider the associated polynomials and
apply Theorems 9.3 and 10.4. If $a_n = 0$, $b_m \neq 0$, let $F = x_0^r F^*$, $x_0 \nmid F^*$,
and apply Theorems 9.3 and 10.4 to F^* and G. It is easily seen from the
determinant forms of the resultants of F and G and of F^* and G that
these two resultants differ only by a factor $\pm b_m^r$. Hence the required
result follows as above. A similar procedure works when $a_n \neq 0$, $b_m = 0$.

Theorem 10.7 is in certain respects more satisfactory than Theorem
9.3, for in the homogeneous case no restrictions need be put on the
coefficients of the polynomials. This is generally true throughout
elimination theory.*

A similar extension of Theorem 7.5 is
THEOREM 10.8. *If D is algebraically closed and if $F_n \in D[x_0,x_1]$ then
there exist n pairs a_i, b_i of constants such that*

$$F_n(x_0,x_1) = a\Pi(a_i x_1 - b_i x_0), \ a \neq 0.$$

*Each pair a_i, b_i is unique to within multiplication by a common non-zero
constant.*

PROOF. Let $F_n = x_0^r F_{n-r}$, $0 \leqslant r \leqslant n$, where x_0 is not a factor of
F_{n-r}. Then $F_{n-r}(1,x_1)$ is of degree $n - r$ in x_1, and by Theorem 7.5

$$F_{n-r}(1,x_1) = a\Pi_{j=1}^{n-r}(x_1 - b_j).$$

Hence

$$F_{n-r}(x_0,x_1) = a\Pi(x_1 - b_j x_0),$$

and the required factorization of F_n follows at once. The uniqueness of
the pairs of constants follows from the uniqueness of factorization in
$D[x_0,x_1]$.

It is often convenient to say that the ratio $a:b$, where a,b are not
both zero, is a root of the homogeneous equation $F_n(x_0,x_1) = 0$ if
$F_n(a,b) = 0$. For any non-zero constant ρ, $\rho a:\rho b$ is regarded as being
the same ratio as $a:b$. Theorem 10.8 can then be stated in the form:
A homogeneous equation in two variables of degree n has a unique set
of n roots.

* See van der Waerden. *Moderne Algebra*, Vol. II, §80.

10.3. Resultants. The following result will be needed later.

THEOREM 10.9. *Let*

$$F_n = A_n + A_{n-1}x_r + \cdots + A_0 x_r^n,$$
$$G_m = B_m + B_{m-1}x_r + \cdots + B_0 x_r^m,$$

where A_i, B_i are homogeneous polynomials of degree i in $x_1, \cdots, x_{r-1}$, and $A_0 B_0 \neq 0$. If $R(x_1, \cdots, x_{r-1})$ is the resultant of F and G with respect to x_r, then either $R = 0$ or R is homogeneous of degree mn.

PROOF:

$$R(tx_1, \cdots, tx_{r-1}) = \begin{vmatrix} t^n A_n & t^{n-1}A_{n-1} \cdot & \cdots \cdot A_0 & & & \\ & t^n A_n & \cdots \cdots tA_1 & A_0 & & \\ & & \cdots \cdots \cdots \cdots & & & \\ & & & t^n A_n \cdots \cdots \cdots \cdots \cdot A_0 \\ t^m B_m & t^{m-1}B_{m-1} & \cdots tB_1 & B_0 & & \\ & & \cdots \cdots \cdots \cdots \cdots & & & \\ & & t^m B_m \cdots \cdots \cdots \cdots \cdot B_0 \end{vmatrix}.$$

Multiply the ith row of A's by t^{m-i+1} and the jth row of B's by t^{n-i+1}. We obtain

$$t^p R(tx_1, \cdots, tx_{r-1}) = \begin{vmatrix} t^{n+m}A_n & t^{n+m-1}A_{n-1} & \cdots \cdots t^m A_0 & & \\ & t^{n+m-1}A_n & \cdots \cdots t^m A_1 & t^{m-1}A_0 & \\ & & \cdots \cdots \cdots \cdots \cdots & & \\ & & & t^{n+1}A_n \cdots \cdots \cdots \cdot tA_0 \\ t^{n+m}B_m & t^{n+m-1}B_{m-1} & \cdots t^{n+1}B_1 & t^n B_0 & \\ & & \cdots \cdots \cdots \cdots \cdots & & \\ & & t^{m+1}B_m & \cdots \cdots \cdot tB_0 \end{vmatrix},$$

$$= t^q R(x_1, \cdots, x_{r-1}).$$

where $p = m(m+1)/2 + n(n+1)/2$, and $q = (m+n)(m+n+1)/2$. Hence

$$R(tx_1, \cdots, tx_{r-1}) = t^{mn} R(x_1, \cdots, x_{r-1}),$$

and the desired result follows from Theorem 10.1.

One consequence of this theorem is

THEOREM 10.10. *Let $R(y_1, \cdots, y_n, z_1, \cdots, z_m)$ be the resultant with respect to x of the polynomials*

$$\Pi_{i=1}^n (x - y_i), \quad \Pi_{j=1}^m (x - z_j).$$

Then

$$R = a\Pi_{i,j}(y_i - z_j), \quad a \neq 0, \quad a \in D.$$

PROOF. If we substitute z_1 for y_1 the polynomials have a common factor, and so R vanishes. Hence $y_1 - z_1$ is a factor of R, and similarly so is $y_i - z_j$ for every i,j. Therefore $\Pi_{i,j}(y_i - z_j) \mid R$. Now $\Pi(x - y_i)$ and $\Pi(x - z_j)$ are homogeneous of degrees n and m respectively, and so R is homogeneous of degree mn. But $\Pi(y_i - z_j)$ is also homogeneous of degree mn, and, therefore it can differ from R only by a constant factor a. Since R is obviously not identically zero, we have $a \neq 0$.

II. Projective Spaces

Geometry deals with properties of *spaces*, and in this chapter we shall develop the fundamental properties of the particular kinds of spaces with which we shall be concerned. As in the previous chapter we shall not attempt to give a complete discussion of these spaces, but shall consider only the aspects pertinent to our needs. The following books may be used as sources of additional material:

O. Veblen and J. W. Young, *Projective Geometry*, 2 volumes, Ginn, Boston, 1910 and 1918.

E. Bertini, *Einführung in die projektive Geometrie mehrdimensionaler Räume*, Seidel, Vienna, 1924.

W. V. D. Hodge and D. Pedoe, *Methods of Algebraic Geometry*, Cambridge, 1947.

§1. PROJECTIVE SPACES

1.1. Projective coordinate systems. The term "space" has various shades of meaning in mathematics, and we shall not attempt to give it a general definition. The particular type of space with which we are chiefly concerned is known as a *projective* space. Of the several ways of defining it we shall choose the one that leads most directly to the aspects that are of importance for algebraic geometry. This definition depends on the use of coordinate systems.

A projective space is associated with a set S, whose elements will be called *points*, and a field K, known as the *ground field*, whose elements will be called *constants* or *numbers*. An *n-dimensional projective coordinate system over K in S* is a correspondence between the points of S and ordered sets of $n + 1$ numbers $(a_0, a_1, \cdots, a_n)$ such that

(A) Each point corresponds to at least one set $(a_0, \cdots, a_n)$ with not all $a_i = 0$.

(B) Each set $(a_0, \cdots, a_n)$ with not all $a_i = 0$ corresponds to one and only one point.

(C) $(a_0, \cdots, a_n)$ and $(b_0, \cdots, b_n)$ correspond to the same point if and only if there is a number $\rho \neq 0$ such that $a_i = \rho b_i$, $i = 0, \cdots, n$.

The numbers $a_0, \cdots, a_n$ of any one of the $(n + 1)$-tuples associated with a point A are said to be *coordinates* of A in the given coordinate system. For the sake of brevity we shall usually write (a_i), or simply (a), instead of $(a_0, \cdots, a_n)$, and speak of "the point (a)" instead of "the point whose coordinates are $a_0, \cdots, a_n$."

To show the generality of the definition we shall give several examples of projective coordinate systems. In some of these the elements of S are taken to be points of the euclidean plane, and as it is convenient to use ordinary cartesian coordinates in discussing these points we shall enclose these coordinates in brackets to distinguish them from the projective coordinates.

Examples. 1. S consists of the points of the euclidean circle $x^2 + y^2 - y = 0$. If P is any point of the circle other than $A = [0,1]$ we take the projective coordinates of P to be $(\rho, \rho x)$, where x is the abscissa of the point in which the line AP intersects the x-axis, and ρ is any non-zero real number. As projective coordinates of A we take $(0, \rho)$, $\rho \neq 0$. It is easily verified that we actually have a 1-dimensional projective coordinate system in S over the field R of all real numbers.

2. Let S consist of all the points $[x,y]$ of the euclidean plane, plus some extra "ideal" points. These ideal points correspond to directions in the plane, and may be defined as equivalence classes of lines under the equivalence relation of parallelism. With the point $[x,y]$ we associate the projective coordinates $(\rho, \rho x, \rho y)$, ρ being a non-zero real number. With the ideal point corresponding to the set of parallel lines $ax + by + k = 0$ we associate the projective coordinates $(0, \rho b, \rho a)$. Here we have a 2-dimensional projective coordinate system over R.

3. Let S consist of all the lines through a fixed point in euclidean 3-space. As projective coordinates for a line we take its direction numbers, that is, any set of three numbers proportional to its direction cosines. We again obtain a 2-dimensional projective coordinate system.

4. Let the points of S consist of, first, the points inside the circle $x^2 + y^2 = 1$, and secondly, the pairs of points $[x,y]$, $[-x,-y]$ diametrically opposite on the circumference of this circle. If $[x,y]$ is a point in the circle, or one of a pair on the circumference, we take its projective coordinates to be $(\rho x, \rho y, \rho(1 - x^2 - y^2))$, with $\rho \neq 0$. Condition (A) is obviously satisfied, and we leave it to the reader to show that (B) and (C) also hold.

5. In each of the above examples K was the field of all real numbers. For an example with a different ground field, let K be the field of two elements defined in §I-2.1, Example 1, and let S be any set of seven objects. Any one-to-one correspondence between S and the set $(0,0,u)$, $(0,u,0)$, $(u,0,0)$, $(0,u,u)$, $(u,0,u)$, $(u,u,0)$, (u,u,u), is a 2-dimensional projective coordinate system in S over K.

6. A projective coordinate system of dimension zero can be constructed only in a set of points consisting of a single point. For if (a) and (b) are two sets of coordinates we always have $b = \rho a$ by taking $\rho = ba^{-1}$, which can be done since neither a nor b is zero.

Examples 2, 3, and 4 above can easily be generalized to give coordinate systems of more than two dimensions.

1.2. Equivalence of coordinate systems. A projective space is associated with coordinate systems, but not with any unique coordinate system. Before defining the space itself we must consider an equivalence relation between coordinate systems.

From a given n-dimensional projective coordinate system others may be obtained by the following process. Let* a_j^i, $i,j = 0,\cdots,n$, be numbers such that $| a_j^i | = a \neq 0$. Then from any coordinate system $\mathcal{S}$ a coordinate system $\mathcal{S}'$ is determined by associating with any point X the coordinates (y), where

$$(1.1) \qquad y_j = \Sigma_i a_j^i x_i,$$

the x_i being coordinates of X in the system $\mathcal{S}$. That this association satisfies conditions (A), (B), and (C) follows immediately from the properties of linear equations (Theorem I-4.4).

We now show that the relation between $\mathcal{S}$ and $\mathcal{S}'$ is an equivalence. In the first place, by taking a_j^i to be 1 if $i = j$ and 0 if $i \neq j$ we see that the relation is reflexive. Secondly, the transformation (1.1) has an inverse

$$(1.2) \qquad x_i = \Sigma_j A_i^j y_j,$$

by Theorem I-4.4. Here $| A_i^j | = a^{-1} \neq 0$, and so (1.2) tells us that the relation is symmetric. Finally, if $\mathcal{S}''$ is defined from $\mathcal{S}'$ by

$$z_k = \Sigma_j b_k^j y_j, \quad | b_k^j | = b \neq 0,$$

then

$$z_k = \Sigma_i c_k^i x_i,$$

where

$$c_k^i = \Sigma_j b_k^j a_j^i.$$

Here $| c_k^i | = ba \neq 0$, and so the relation is transitive.

We now define an *n-dimensional projective space over* K to be a set of points S together with an equivalence class of n-dimensional projective coordinate systems in S over K. Such a space will be designated by S_n, or by SK_n if we wish to emphasize the role of the field K. By a coordi-

* Throughout this chapter superscripts are used as indices, not exponents.

nate system in S_n we shall always mean a member of the equivalence class associated with S_n.

The significance of this definition can be made clearer by comparing the situation here with that in the euclidean plane E. Associated with E there are certain coordinate systems, namely the rectangular cartesian coordinate systems, and certain equations, those of translation and rotation, which relate these systems with one another. In discussing a geometric problem we merely use the coordinate systems as tools, choosing whichever one happens to be most convenient for the problem at hand.

However, the coordinate systems play another and more important role. When a space is defined in terms of coordinate systems, many properties of geometric figures in that space are defined, directly or indirectly, in terms of coordinates. We shall say that an algebraic condition connecting the coordinates of points of the space defines a *geometric* property of these points if the satisfaction of the condition in one coordinate system implies its satisfaction in all equivalent coordinate systems. Consider again the case of the euclidean plane. If (x_1, y_1) and (x_2, y_2) are the coordinates of two points the condition $x_2 - x_1 = 5$ does not define a geometric property of the points since it obviously does not hold simultaneously for all rectangular cartesian coordinate systems. But the condition $(x_2 - x_1)^2 + (y_2 - y_1)^2 = 25$ if true in one such system is true in all others, and defines a geometric property of the two points, namely that they are 5 units apart.

Those properties of figures in a space which can be defined without reference to coordinate systems, for example the points common to two figures, we shall also consider to be geometric properties. The *geometry* of a space will consist of the relationships between the geometric properties of figures in that space.*

Since we shall be interested in the geometry of S_n it will be important to notice which of our future definitions have this invariance with respect to changes of coordinates. This will be pointed out in certain cases, but often it is left to the reader to show that a newly introduced concept has a geometric significance.

As an example of a geometric property in a projective space consider the cross-ratio of four distinct points of an S_1. The cross-ratio is defined to be the expression

$$r = \frac{(x_0^1 \, x_1^3 - x_0^3 \, x_1^1)(x_0^2 \, x_1^4 - x_0^4 \, x_1^2)}{(x_0^1 \, x_1^4 - x_0^4 \, x_1^1)(x_0^2 \, x_1^3 - x_0^3 \, x_1^2)},$$

---

* This definition of a geometry is not that given by Felix Klein in his famous *Erlanger Programm*. (See Veblen and Young, *Projective Geometry*, Vol. II, Chap. 3.) However, it is equivalent to his definition in the case of projective, euclidean, and affine geometries, and it fits more naturally in our presentation.

where (x_0^i, x_1^i), $i = 1,2,3,4$, are the coordinates, in a particular coordinate system, of the four points. That r is independent of the coordinate system is established by substituting for the x_j^i their values in terms of the y_j^i obtained from (1.2) and showing that the resulting expression reduces to the original form with y's in place of the x's.

1.3. Examples of projective spaces. Since an equivalence class is determined by any one of its members, to construct a projective space on a given set of points all that is necessary is to construct one projective coordinate system in the set of points. Hence each of the examples in §1.1 determines a projective space. The space of Example 3 is the well-known projective plane. (We shall use the usual terms *line* and *plane* for spaces of dimensions one and two respectively.) Example 4 gives a method of visualizing the projective plane as a bounded subset of the euclidean plane. From Example 6 we see that an S_0 consists of a single point.

It should be observed that a given set of points may serve as the basis for more than one projective space. Thus if we alter Example 4 by replacing $1 - x^2 - y^2$ by, say, $\sqrt{1 - x^2 - y^2}$, we obtain a different S_2, since the relation between the two systems of coordinates is not expressible in the form (1.1). More complicated examples can be given of a set of points serving as the basis for two projective spaces of different dimensions.

1.4. Exercises. 1. If K is a finite field consisting of q elements, then SK_n has $1 + q + q^2 + \cdots + q^n$ points.

2. Show that if K is the field of two elements a set S of three points can be the basis of one and only one SK_1. Is this true for the seven points of an SK_2?

3. Write (P_1P_2, P_3P_4) for the cross-ratio of the four points P_1, P_2, P_3, P_4 in this order. Then

   (i) $(P_1P_2, P_3P_4) = (P_2P_1, P_4P_3) = (P_3P_4, P_1P_2) = (P_4P_3, P_2P_1) = r$.

   (ii) $(P_1P_2, P_4P_3) = 1/r$.
       $(P_1P_3, P_2P_4) = 1 - r$.
       $(P_1P_3, P_4P_2) = 1/(1 - r)$.
       $(P_1P_4, P_2P_3) = (r - 1)/r$.
       $(P_1P_4, P_3P_2) = r/(r - 1)$.

   (iii) The only cases in which there are less than six distinct cross-ratios of four points are

   (a) Harmonic points, where $r = -1$, $1/2$, 2;

   (b) Equianharmonic points, where r has two values which are the roots of the equation $x^2 - x + 1 = 0$.

§2. Linear Subspaces

2.1. Linear dependence of points. Since in a given coordinate system the points of S_n are represented by $(n + 1)$-tuples of numbers, we can apply the theory of linear dependence to points. The first thing to notice is that the results are independent of the coordinate system. For suppose the points P^α, $\alpha = 1, \cdots, m$, are dependent in terms of their coordinates (x_i^α) in a certain coordinate system. That is, suppose there exist numbers c_α, not all zero, such that

$$\Sigma c_\alpha x_i^\alpha = 0, \quad i = 0, \cdots, n.$$

If we transfer to another coordinate system by (1.1), we then have

$$\Sigma_\alpha c_\alpha y_j^\alpha = \Sigma_{\alpha, i} c_\alpha a_j^i x_i^\alpha = \Sigma_i a_j^i (\Sigma_\alpha c_\alpha x_i^\alpha) = 0.$$

Hence the points P^α are dependent in terms of their coordinates (y_j^α). Since the relation between the two coordinate systems is symmetric, the two types of linear dependence are equivalent, and so we can speak of the dependence of points without reference to any particular coordinate system. Dependence of points is thus a geometric property.

2.2. Frame of reference. There is an interesting and useful interpretation of a coordinate system in terms of linear dependence. This can be obtained from equation (1.1) by regarding $(a_0^i, \cdots, a_n^i)$ as the $\mathcal{S}'$-coordinates of a point P^i. Then (1.1) expresses the dependence of the point X on the points $P^0, \cdots, P^n$, and the $\mathcal{S}$-coordinates (x) of X are just the constants of dependence. The points $P^0, \cdots, P^n$ are themselves independent, since $|a_j^i| \neq 0$, and so their $\mathcal{S}$-coordinates are respectively $(1, 0, 0, \cdots, 0)$, $(0, 1, 0, \cdots, 0)$, $\cdots$, $(0, 0, 0, \cdots, 1)$.

Conversely, if $(a_0^i, \cdots, a_n^i)$ are $\mathcal{S}'$-coordinates of $n + 1$ independent points P^i, then any point X is dependent on these, and the constants of dependence are coordinates of X in a system $\mathcal{S}$.

It must be noticed that $\mathcal{S}$ is determined not only by the points P^i but also by the particular sets of coordinates used to represent these points. This ambiguity in the determination of $\mathcal{S}$ is usually removed in the following way. Let P^* be a point dependent on no n of $P^0, \cdots, P^n$. Then if $(b_0, \cdots, b_n)$ are $\mathcal{S}$-coordinates of P^* we must have $b_i \neq 0$, $i = 0, \cdots, n$. Now a change in the $\mathcal{S}'$-coordinates of P^i, say from (a_j^i) to $(\rho_i a_j^i)$, multiplies b_i by $1/\rho_i$. Hence there is a unique choice of the ρ_i, that is, a unique choice of $\mathcal{S}'$-coordinates of the P^i, for which P^* has $(1, 1, \cdots, 1)$ as its $\mathcal{S}$-coordinates. We condense these conclusions into

THEOREM 2.1. *Given any $n + 2$ points of S_n, no $n + 1$ of which are dependent, there is a unique coordinate system in which these points have* *the coordinates* $(1,0,\cdots,0)$, $(0,1,\cdots,0),\cdots$, $(0,0,\cdots,1)$, $(1,1,\cdots,1)$ *in a given order.*

The ordered set of $n + 2$ points is said to be the *frame of reference* of the coordinate system so determined. The choice of the point $(1,1,\cdots,1)$ (the "unit point") is usually not of much importance, but we shall often find it helpful to choose the points $(1,0,\cdots,0),\cdots,(0,0,\cdots,1)$, which we call the "vertices of reference," in convenient positions.

2.3. Linear subspaces. The investigation of the geometry of a space consists mainly in the determination of the properties of certain of its subsets. In the case of the projective space the simplest subsets are those which correspond to lines in a plane, or lines and planes in 3-space. We shall define these in terms of linear dependence.

Consider the subset S' of points of S_n dependent on $r + 1$ independent points P^α, $\alpha = 0,\cdots,r$, of S_n. We shall set up an r-dimensional projective coordinate system in S'. Since the P^α are independent, there exist, by Theorem I-4.2(ii), $n - r$ points $P^{r+1},\cdots,P^n$ such that $P^0,\cdots,P^n$ are independent. Take these points as the vertices of reference of a coordinate system in S_n. It is then obvious that a point $X = (x_0,\cdots,x_n)$ of S_n lies in S' if and only if $x_{r+1} = \cdots = x_n = 0$. If we associate with a point X of S' the $(r + 1)$-tuple $(x_0,\cdots,x_r)$, this association is clearly an r-dimensional coordinate system over K in S', and so defines an r-dimensional projective space S_r whose points are the points of S'. We shall call an S_r determined in this way a *linear subspace* (or merely a *subspace*) of S_n.

The basic properties of subspaces are expressed in the following theorems.

THEOREM 2.2. $r + 1$ *independent points of* S_n *lie in one and only one subspace of dimension* r.

PROOF. By definition, $r + 1$ independent points P^α of S_n lie in at least one r-dimensional subspace S_r. Let S'_r be any r-dimensional subspace containing the P^α. We notice first that S_r and S'_r consist of the same points; for since the P^α lie in S'_r every linear combination of them does also, which implies $S_r \subset S'_r$; and conversely, every point of S'_r is a linear combination of the $r + 1$ independent points P^α, so that $S'_r \subset S_r$. Now let X be a point of S_r and S'_r, having coordinates $(x_0,\cdots,x_r)$ in S_r and $(y_0,\cdots,y_r)$ in S'_r. From the definition of a linear subspace there exist two coordinate systems in S_n for which X has coordinates $(x_0,\cdots,x_r, 0,\cdots,0)$ and $(y_0,\cdots,y_r, 0,\cdots,0)$ respectively. These systems are related by the equations (1.1). But when applied to points of S_r and S'_r, for which $x_{r+1} = \cdots = x_n = y_{r+1} = \cdots = y_n = 0$ this becomes

$$y_\beta = \Sigma_{\alpha=0}^r a_\beta^\alpha x_\alpha, \quad \beta = 0,\cdots,r.$$

Moreover, $|a_\beta^\alpha|$ cannot be zero, for if it were, the independent points P^α would be dependent in their y-coordinates. Hence the coordinate systems in S_r and S'_r are equivalent, and so the two spaces are identical.

For the values $r = 1$ and $r = 2$ this theorem is the projective analogue of the familiar propositions of euclidean geometry that a line is determined by two points and a plane by three non-collinear (that is, independent) points.

THEOREM 2.3. *If S_r is a subspace of S_n, for any coordinate system $\mathcal{S}$ of S_r there is a system $\mathcal{S}'$ of S_n such that the $\mathcal{S}'$-coordinates of any point of S_r consist of its $\mathcal{S}$-coordinates followed by $n - r$ zeros.*

PROOF. Let $P^0, \cdots, P^r$, P^* be the frame of reference of $\mathcal{S}$. For the vertices of reference of $\mathcal{S}'$ take $P^0, \cdots, P^r, P^{r+1}, \cdots, P^n$ as in the definition of a subspace. Then every point of S_r has $\mathcal{S}'$-coordinates of form $(x_0, \cdots, x_r, 0, \cdots, 0)$ and in particular the $\mathcal{S}'$-coordinates of P^* are $(\rho_0, \cdots, \rho_r, 0, \cdots, 0)$ with $\rho_\alpha \neq 0$. Proper choice of the unit point of $\mathcal{S}'$ will then give $\rho_\alpha = 1$. The system $\mathcal{S}_0$ in S_r obtained by taking the first $r + 1$ of the $\mathcal{S}'$-coordinates then has the same frame of reference as $\mathcal{S}$, and so $\mathcal{S}_0$ and $\mathcal{S}$ are identical.

We shall find Theorem 2.3 to be useful in investigating further properties of subspaces. One immediate consequence is

THEOREM 2.4. *If S_r is a subspace of S_n, points of S_r are dependent in S_n if and only if they are dependent in S_r.*

This property of subspaces is very convenient, for it enables us largely to ignore the particular subspace our points are lying in when we discuss their dependence.

2.4. Dimensionality. Since an n-dimensional space S_n cannot contain more than $n + 1$ independent points it cannot have a subspace of dimension greater than n. S_n has exactly one subspace of dimension n, namely the space S_n itself. A subspace of S_n of dimension $n - 1$ is called a *hyperplane* of S_n. Thus the hyperplanes of S_1 are points, those of S_2 are lines, and those of S_3, planes.

It is convenient to regard the empty set as a linear subspace of dimension -1. This convention fits in with Theorem 2.2, and will be useful in avoiding special cases in some of our later theorems (Theorem 2.8, in particular).

2.5. Relations between subspaces. We shall now consider relations between the subspaces of a given S_n.

THEOREM 2.5 (i) *If S_s is a subspace of S_r, and S_r a subspace of S_n, then S_s is a subspace of S_n.*

(ii) *If S_r and S_s are subspaces of S_n, and if all points of S_s lie in S_r, then S_s is a subspace of S_r.*

PROOF. (i) This follows immediately from a double application of Theorem 2.3.

(ii)   By a double application of Theorem I-4.2(ii) we can obtain independent points $P^0,\cdots,P^n$ of S_n such that $P^0,\cdots,P^s$ are in S_s and $P^0,\cdots,P^r$ are in S_r. Using these points as vertices of reference in the three spaces, we see as in the proof of Theorem 2.3 that by a suitable choice of unit points in S_r and S_s, the S_n coordinates of a point in S_r (or S_s) consist of their S_r- (or S_s-) coordinates followed by $n - r$ (or $n - s$) zeros. Considering then the relation between the S_r- and the S_s-coordinates, we see that S_s is a subspace of S_r.

THEOREM 2.6.   *If a subspace of S_n contains $r + 1$ independent points of a subspace S_r of S_n, it contains all points of S_r.*

The proof is left to the reader.

THEOREM 2.7.   *Given any subset S of S_n there is a unique subspace S_r of least dimension which contains S.*

PROOF.   Let $r + 1$ be the maximum number of independent points of S, let $P^0 \cdots,P^r$ be a set of independent points of S, and let S_r be the subspace determined by $P^0,\cdots,P^r$. ($r = -1$ if S is the empty set.) Then every point of S is dependent on $P^0,\cdots,P^r$, and so S is contained in S_r. Since $P^0,\cdots,P^r$ are independent they cannot be contained in any S_s with $s < r$. If S'_r is any subspace of dimension r containing S it must contain S_r since it contains $r + 1$ independent points of S_r. Hence it must coincide with S_r.

S is said to *span* S_r.

THEOREM 2.8.   If S_s and S_t together span S_r, the points common to S_s and S_t are the points of an S_{s+t-r}.

PROOF.   Let $q + 1$ be the maximum number of independent points common to S_s and S_t, ($q = -1$ if S_s and S_t have no common points), and let $P^0,\cdots,P^q$ be $q + 1$ such points. By Theorems 2.5 and 2.6 the S_q determined by $P^0,\cdots,P^q$ is a subspace of S_s and S_t. Moreover it contains all their common points, for if it did not the set $P^0,\cdots,P^q$ could be enlarged. Hence the points common to S_s and S_t form an S_q, and we have only to show that $q = s + t - r$.

Let $Q^{q+1},\cdots,Q^s$ be points of S_s such that $P^0,\cdots,P^q, Q^{q+1},\cdots,Q^s$ are independent; and let $R^{q+1},\cdots,R^t$ be points of S_t such that $P^0,\cdots,P^q, R^{q+1},\cdots,R^t$ are independent. Then the entire set of points P, Q, and R is independent. If not, since the set of P's and Q's is independent, there must be a combination of the R's expressible in terms of the P's and Q's. This combination must be a point of S_q, for the R's are in S_t and the P's and Q's in S_s, and so must be expressible as a combination of the P's alone. This contradicts the assumption that the P's and R's are independent. The S_{s+t-q} determined by the P's, Q's, R's is therefore spanned by S_s and S_t, and so $r = s + t - q$, or $q = s + t - r$.

The S_q common to S_s and S_t is called their *intersection*, and the S_r

which they span is their *join*. Theorem 2.8 can now be stated in the following symmetrical form: The sum of the dimensions of two subspaces is equal to the sum of the dimensions of their intersection and their join.

One useful consequence of Theorem 2.8 is that an S_r and an S_s in S_n must have in common a space of at least $r + s - n$ dimensions. The familiar intersection properties of lines in a plane, and of lines and planes in an S_3, follow from this.

We leave to the reader the proof of the following theorem which will be needed later.

THEOREM 2.9. *Let S_r and S_s be subspaces of S_n and let $P^0, \cdots, P^r$ be independent points of S_r and $Q^0, \cdots, Q^s$ independent points of S_s. Then $P^0, \cdots, P^r, Q^0, \cdots, Q^s$ are independent if and only if S_r and S_s have no common point.*

2.6. Exercises. 1. If a hyperplane of S_n does not contain a given S_r of S_n, it intersects the S_r in an S_{r-1}.

2. The intersection of r hyperplanes of S_n is a space of dimension at least $n - r$.

3. For any coordinate systems in S_n and a subspace S_r, the relation between S_n-coordinates $(x_0, \cdots, x_n)$ and S_r-coordinates $(y_0, \cdots, y_r)$ of a point of S_r is given by

$$y_\alpha = \Sigma_{i=0}^n a_\alpha^i x_i, \quad \alpha = 0, \cdots, r,$$

where the matrix $\| a_\alpha^i \|$ is of rank $r + 1$.

4. The points of the S_1 of §1.1, Example 1, are points of the S_2 of Example 2. Is S_1 a linear subspace of S_2?

5. If K is a finite field with q elements, the number of S_r in SK_n is

$$\frac{(q^{n+1} - 1)(q^n - 1) \cdots (q^{n-r+1} - 1)}{(q^{r+1} - 1)(q^r - 1) \cdots (q - 1)}.$$

§3. DUALITY

3.1. Hyperplane coordinates. One of the most interesting aspects of plane projective geometry is the theory of duality, which says in effect that the roles of points and lines can be interchanged in the development of this geometry. We are now in a position to show that a similar duality holds in any S_n. The first thing to do is to set up a coordinate system for the hyperplanes of S_n.

We consider a definite coordinate system in S_n. Let π be a hyperplane, determined by the independent points $P^\alpha = (a_i^\alpha)$, $\alpha = 0, \cdots, n - 1$. The equations $\Sigma_i u^i a_i^\alpha = 0$ have then a non-trivial solution b^i, unique to within a common non-zero multiple (Theorems I-4.1 and

I-4.3). Since every point of π is dependent on the P's, the homogeneous linear expression $\Sigma b^i x_i$ vanishes for every point (x) of π. Conversely, given any set of $n + 1$ numbers b^i, not all zero, the equation $\Sigma b^i x_i = 0$ has n independent solutions (a_i^α), $\alpha = 0, \cdots, n - 1$, and any solution is a combination of these. That is, the non-trivial solutions of $\Sigma b^i x_i = 0$ are precisely the points of a hyperplane. $\Sigma b^i x_i = 0$ is called an *equation* of the hyperplane, and the b's are *coordinates* of the hyperplane. The procedure above shows that these coordinates satisfy conditions (A) and (B) of a projective coordinate system. To see that (C) is also satisfied let $\Sigma b^i x_i = 0$ and $\Sigma c^i x_i = 0$ be equations of the same hyperplane. Then these equations must have n independent common solutions, and this is so if and only if the b's and the c's are dependent, that is, if and only if $b^i = \rho c^i$ for some $\rho \neq 0$.

The equivalence class of coordinate systems determined by the system just defined, together with the set of hyperplanes of S_n, is then an n-dimensional projective space over K, and will be denoted by S_n^*.

The construction of S_n^* was given in terms of a particular coordinate system in S_n; we shall now show that the same S_n^* is obtained regardless of which coordinate system in S_n we use. Let a new coordinate system in S_n be defined by (1.1), and let $\Sigma b^i x_i = 0$, $\Sigma c^i y_i = 0$ be the equations of a hyperplane π in the two systems. Then a point (y) is in π if and only if $\Sigma_{i,j} b^i A_i^j y_j = 0$; that is, $\Sigma_j (\Sigma_i A_i^j b^i) y_j = 0$ is the equation of π in the y-system. Hence there is a $\rho \neq 0$ such that

$$c^j = \Sigma_i \rho A_i^j b^i,$$

and $|\rho A_i^j| = \rho^{n+1} a^{-1} \neq 0$. These equations tell us that the coordinate system for the hyperplanes of S_n determined by the y-system in S_n is equivalent to that determined by the x-system. They therefore belong to the same equivalence class and so determine the same S_n^*.

3.2. Dual spaces. S_n^* is called the *dual* space of S_n. As the word dual is usually used in mathematics in a reciprocal sense, we might expect that the dual of S_n^* is S_n. This is not strictly so, for an element of the dual of S_n^* would be a hyperplane of S_n^*, that is, a set of hyperplanes of S_n, and, therefore, certainly not a point of S_n. To emphasize the reciprocity of the relation between S_n and S_n^* we shall think of the elements of S_n^* not as subsets of S_n but as individual entities, and instead of saying that a point lies in a hyperplane, we shall say that the corresponding elements of S_n and S_n^* are *incident*. From the definition of S_n^* we see that to each coordinate system of S_n there corresponds a coordinate system of S_n^* such that if $P = (a_i)$ and $\pi = (b^i)$ in these coordinate systems then P and π are incident if and only if $\Sigma a_i b^i = 0$. Two coordinate systems so related will be said to *correspond*. It is not difficult to see that each coordinate system in S_n^* has a corresponding system in S_n. For let S and S^* be corresponding systems, and let S_1^* be any other system in S_n^*. If (ξ^i) and (η^i) are coordinates of the same point in S^* and S_1^* respectively we have relations

$$\eta^j = \Sigma_i a_i^j \xi^i, \quad j = 0, \cdots, n.$$

If S_1 is defined in terms of S by

$$y_j = \Sigma_i A_j^i x_i,$$

then S_1 is seen to correspond to S_1^*.

Expressed in terms of incidence and corresponding coordinate systems, the relation between S_n and S_n^* is thus completely symmetric.

3.3. Dual subspaces. From the duality relation it follows that the hyperplanes of S_n which constitute the points of a hyperplane $\Sigma a_i \xi^i = 0$ of S_n^* have the unique common point (a) if corresponding coordinate systems are used. This is a special case of the following theorem.

THEOREM 3.1. *The hyperplanes of S_n which contain a given subspace S_r constitute an S_{n-r-1}^* of S_n^*.*

PROOF. Using corresponding coordinate systems, let S_r be determined by the independent points (a^α), $\alpha = 0, \cdots, r$. The hyperplane (ξ) contains the (a^α), and hence S_r, if and only if

$$(3.1) \qquad\qquad \Sigma_i a_i^\alpha \xi^i = 0.$$

Since the (a^α) are independent these equations have $n - r$ independent solutions (ξ_β), $\beta = 0, \cdots, n - r - 1$. Hence the solutions of (3.1) are just those hyperplanes (ξ) which are dependent on the (ξ_β), that is, they constitute an S_{n-r-1}^*.

S_{n-r-1}^* is called the *dual* of S_r. We must be careful to distinguish between the dual of S_r when S_r is thought of as the primary space, and the dual of S_r when S_r is thought of as a subspace of a space S_n. In the first case the dual is of dimension r and consists of all the hyperplanes of S_r; in the second case it is of dimension $n - r - 1$ and consists of all the hyperplanes of S_n that contain S_r. This double usage of the term "dual" is somewhat unfortunate, but it rarely causes confusion. As a special case of the latter usage we see that S_n, considered as a subspace of itself, has as its dual the empty set S_{-1}^* of S_n^*.

The following theorem is merely the dual of Theorem 2.1, but it is important enough to be stated separately.

THEOREM 3.2. *Given any $n + 2$ hyperplanes of S_n, no $n + 1$ of which are dependent, there is a unique coordinate system in which these have the equations*

$$x_0 = 0, \quad x_1 = 0, \cdots, \quad x_n = 0, \quad x_0 + x_1 + \cdots + x_n = 0,$$

in a given order.

It is evident that each vertex of reference is the intersection of n "sides of reference," and dually that each side of reference is the join of n vertices of reference.

3.4. Exercises. 1. Given any coordinate systems in S_n and S_n^*, there exist constants α_j^i, with $|\alpha_j^i| \neq 0$, such that a point (a_i) and a hyperplane (b^i) are incident if and only if $\Sigma_{i,j}\alpha_j^i a_i b^i = 0$.

2. The duals of the intersection and the join of two subspaces are respectively the join and the intersection of the duals of the two subspaces.

3. The S_{r+1}'s of S_n which contain a fixed S_r of S_n can be considered as the points of an S_{n-r-1}. (Compare with §1.1, Example 3.)

§4. AFFINE SPACES

4.1. Affine coordinates. In investigating certain problems in algebraic geometry we shall find it a distinct disadvantage that the correspondence between points and their sets of coordinates is not one-to-one. Because of this we shall define another type of coordinate system, in which the correspondence is one-to-one.

Let $a_0, \cdots, a_n$ be the coordinates of a point P in a projective coordinate system $\mathfrak{S}$ in S_n. If $a_0 \neq 0$, the n numbers $a_1/a_0, \cdots, a_n/a_0$ are said to be the coordinates of P in the *affine coordinate system* corresponding to $\mathfrak{S}$. The following properties of an affine coordinate system follow at once:

(A′) A point P has coordinates in the given affine system if and only if P does not lie on the hyperplane π, $x_0 = 0$, of the associated projective system.

This hyperplane is often called, for obvious reasons, the *hyperplane at infinity* of the affine system. The vertex of reference $(1,0,\cdots,0)$ not on the hyperplane at infinity is called the *origin* of the system, and the lines joining the origin to the other vertices of reference are the *axes*.

(B′) The affine coordinate system is a one-to-one correspondence between the points of $S_n - \pi$ (that is, the points of S_n not in π) and all n-tuples of numbers.

A change of projective coordinates (1.1) which takes the equation $x_0 = 0$ into $y_0 = 0$ can be put in the form

$$y_0 = x_0,$$

$$y_j = \Sigma_{i=1}^n a_j^i x_i + b_j x_0, \quad j = 1, \cdots, n.$$

Hence

(C′) If two affine coordinate systems have the same hyperplane at infinity they are related by equations,

$$y_j = \Sigma_{i=1}^n a_j^i x_i + b_j, \quad j = 1, \cdots, n,$$

where $|a_j^i| \neq 0$.

Conversely, any set of equations of this type defines a change of affine coordinate systems. Two affine systems related in this way will be said to be equivalent.

The points of $S_n - \pi$, together with an equivalence class of affine coordinate systems, constitute an *n-dimensional affine space* A_n over K.

4.2. Relation between affine and projective spaces. We have defined A_n as a subspace of S_n. The reason for this procedure is that we shall be primarily interested in the projective space, and shall use the affine space only as an auxiliary concept. It is evident, however, that A_n could be defined intrinsically in the same manner as S_n was defined, using (B′) and (C′) to define the appropriate coordinate systems and transformations. Historically, affine space, which is essentially euclidean space with no notions of distance and angle, was known long before projective space, and projective space was originally defined by adding points at infinity to affine space.

4.3. Subspaces of affine space. From its definition, A_n lies in a unique S_n. Conversely, however, S_n contains many distinct A_n's; for evidently any hyperplane of S_n may be chosen as the hyperplane at infinity of an appropriate A_n. We shall see later that it is just this arbitrariness of choice that enables us to make such good use of the affine coordinates.

Let A_n be an affine space in S_n with π as the hyperplane at infinity. If S_r is a linear subspace of S_n not lying in π, the intersection of S_r with π is an S_{r-1}, a hyperplane π' of S_r. The points of S_r which lie in A_n are, therefore, just the points of $S_r - \pi'$, and these can be considered in a unique way as an affine space A_r. A_r will be called a linear subspace of A_n. The properties of intersections and joins of linear subspaces of A_n are not nearly so simple as those of subspaces of S_n, due to the existence of *parallel* subspaces, subspaces which when considered as lying in S_n have all their intersections on the hyperplane at infinity. It was the desire to eliminate the exceptional properties of these parallel subspaces that led to the invention of projective space.

Subspaces of A_n may also be defined in terms of linear dependence. However, the affine coordinates do not lend themselves readily to these considerations, and we shall have little occasion to use them in this connection. It should be noticed, though, that a hyperplane in A_n still has an equation, which is linear but not necessarily homogeneous. This is an immediate consequence of the relation between projective and affine coordinates.

Finally, there is no duality in A_n. For two points of A_n are always incident with a line, while two hyperplanes may be parallel and so incident with no A_{n-2}.

4.4. Lines in affine space. The one aspect of linear dependence which we shall consider in affine coordinates is the dependence of points on a line. If (a) and (b) are projective coordinates of two points, any point (x) on their join L is given by

$$(4.1) \qquad x_i = sa_i + tb_i, \quad i = 0, \cdots, n,$$

and (s,t) may be considered to be projective coordinates in L. We may, first of all, introduce affine coordinates in L, and write

$$(4.2) \qquad x_i = a_i + ub_i, \quad i = 0, \cdots, n,$$

u being the affine coordinate. (b) is then the point at infinity and cannot be represented in the form (4.2). In many cases it is convenient to introduce a fictitious value of u, usually designated by ∞, in terms of which (b) can be expressed by (4.2). By writing $u = \infty$ we really mean that we are returning to (4.1) and putting $s = 0$, $t \neq 0$.

If we introduce affine coordinates in S_n, (4.2) becomes

$$(4.3) \qquad x_i = (a_i + ub_i)/(a_0 + ub_0), \quad i = 1, \cdots, n.$$

Finally, if (b) is a point on the hyperplane at infinity, in which case (a) is not on this hyperplane, we have $b_0 = 0$, $a_0 \neq 0$, and (4.3) becomes

$$(4.4) \qquad x_i = a_i + ub_i, \quad i = 1, \cdots, n.$$

Equations (4.4) are called *parametric* equations of the line.

4.5. Exercises. 1. If $(a_i^0), \cdots, (a_i^r)$ are independent points of a subspace A_r of A_n, the points of A_r are given by

$$x_i = (1 - \Sigma_\alpha t_\alpha)a_i^0 + \Sigma_\alpha t_\alpha a_i^\alpha, \quad i = 1, \cdots, n,$$

for all finite values of the t_α. The correspondence between the points of A_r and the sets $(t_1, \cdots, t_r)$ is a coordinate system of A_r, and every coordinate system of A_r is obtainable in this way.

2. We define two subspaces A_r and A_s, $s \leqslant r$, of A_n to be parallel if the S_{s-1} at infinity of A_s is contained in the S_{r-1} at infinity of A_r.

(i)   For a fixed r, parallelism between A_r's of A_n is an equivalence relation.

(ii) Given an A_r in A_n and a point P not in A_r there is one and only one A_r' through P parallel to A_r.

(iii) For $s < r$, A_s is parallel to A_r if and only if it is parallel to some A_s' contained in A_r.

§5. PROJECTION

5.1. Projection of points from a subspace. The simplest type of projection, from which projective geometry gets its name, is the following. Let π be a hyperplane of S_n and P any point not in π. Then for any point A distinct from P the line AP will intersect π in a single point A'. A' is said to be the *projection* of A from P into π. If S is any set of points not containing P the projection of S from P into π is the set of the projections of all points of S.

This process can easily be generalized. Let S_r, $0 \leqslant r \leqslant n - 1$, and S_{n-r-1} be two subspaces of S_n having no common points. (That such pairs of subspaces exist for each r will be shown later.) For any point A not on S_{n-r-1}, the join of A and S_{n-r-1} is an S_{n-r} which intersects S_r in an S_s. Now S_s and S_{n-r-1} span S_n and do not intersect, since otherwise S_r and S_{n-r-1} would intersect. Hence $s = 0$. S_s is, therefore, a point A' of S_r, and we say that A' is the projection of A from S_{n-r-1} into S_r. S_{n-r-1} is called the *center* of projection. As in the preceding paragraph we can now define the projection from S_{n-r-1} into S_r of any set having no points on S_{n-r-1}.

To see the relation between the coordinates of A and those of A' we shall first choose a special coordinate system in S_n. Let $P^0, \cdots, P^r$ be independent points of S_r and $P^{r+1}, \cdots, P^n$ independent points of S_{n-r-1}. Then $P^0, \cdots, P^n$ are independent (Theorem 2.9). (Conversely if $P^0, \cdots, P^n$ are independent, the spaces spanned by $P^0, \cdots, P^r$ and $P^{r+1}, \cdots, P^n$ do not intersect, and this proves the existence of non-intersecting pairs S_r and S_{n-r-1} for any r from 0 to $n - 1$.) Now if we take the P^α as the vertices of reference of a coordinate system in S_n, the relation between the coordinates of A and A' is very simple. S_r is defined by $x_{r+1} = \cdots = x_n = 0$, and S_{n-r-1} by $x_0 = \cdots = x_r = 0$. If A has coordinates (a_i), then any point of the join of A and S_{n-r-1} has coordinates $(\lambda a_i + \mu b_i)$, where (b_i) is a point of S_{n-r-1}. Since A' is such a point, its coordinates are of this form. However, A' is also a point of S_r, and so its last $n - r$ coordinates are zero. Its first $r + 1$ coordinates are

$$\lambda a_0 + \mu b_0, \cdots, \lambda a_r + \mu b_r.$$

But since (b_i) is a point of S_{n-r-1} we have $b_0 = \cdots = b_r = 0$. Hence A' has the coordinates $(a_0, \cdots, a_r, 0, \cdots, 0)$. In other words, the passage from A to A' consists merely in replacing the last $n - r$ coordinates of A by zero.

5.2. Exercises. 1. In any coordinate systems in S_n and S_r, if (y) are the coordinates in S_r of the projection of (x), then

$$y = \Sigma_{i=0}^{n} a_\alpha^i x_i, \quad \alpha = 0, \cdots, r,$$

the matrix $\| a_\alpha^i \|$ being of rank $r + 1$. (Compare with §2.6, Exercise 3.)

2. A projection from S_{n-r-1} into S_r has the same result as a succession of projections from $n - r$ independent points of S_{n-r-1} into $n - r$ suitably chosen independent hyperplanes containing S_r.

3. Let S_r, S_r', S_{n-r-1} be subspaces of S_n such that S_{n-r-1} intersects neither S_r nor S_r'. Then the correspondence $P \leftrightarrow P'$ between the points of S_r and S_r' defined by projection from S_{n-r-1} is one-to-one and has the following properties:

(i)   Points $P^1, \cdots, P^k$ are dependent if and only if $P^{1\prime}, \cdots, P^{k\prime}$ are dependent.

(ii)   The projection of any S_s of S_r is an S_s' of S_r', and conversely.

(iii)   There exist coordinate systems in S_r and S_r' in which corresponding points have the same coordinates.

(This correspondence between the points of S_r and S_r' is called a *perspectivity* with center S_{n-r-1}.)

4. The one-to-one correspondence defined by a succession of perspectivities has the properties (i), (ii), and (iii) of Exercise 3. Conversely, any one-to-one correspondence between the points of two subspaces S_r and S_r' of S_n which has these properties can be obtained by a succession of perspectivities. (Such a correspondence is called a *projectivity*.)

§6. LINEAR TRANSFORMATIONS

6.1. Collineations. Equations (1.1) were introduced to define the passage from one coordinate system to another. We thought of (x) and (y) as coordinates of the same point P in different coordinate systems. However, we can put another interpretation on the equations by regarding (x) and (y) as coordinates of *different* points in the *same* coordinate system. Then equations (1.1) give us a rule whereby to each point (x) there is made to correspond a unique point (y), which may or may not coincide with (x). Thus the equations determine a single-valued transformation of the set of points S into itself. Because of the existence of the inverse transformation (1.2) the correspondence between (x) and (y) is one-to-one. Such a one-to-one transformation of a projective space into itself, defined by linear equations, is called a *collineation*. We shall find it convenient to represent the collineation (1.1) by a single letter, say T, and the transform (y) of (x) by $T(x)$.

Since change of coordinates and collineation are merely different interpretations of the same algebraic process, every property of one can be interpreted as a property of the other. Thus from §2.1 we obtain at once

THEOREM 6.1. *Points (x^α) are dependent if and only if their transforms $T(x^\alpha)$ are dependent.*

As an immediate corollary we have

THEOREM 6.2. *A collineation transforms any linear subspace into a linear subspace of the same dimension.*

6.2. Exercises. 1. We define the product of two collineations

$$T_1, \quad y_j = \Sigma_i a_j^i x_i,$$

and

$$T_2, \quad y_j = \Sigma_i b_j^i x_i,$$

to be the transformation

$$T_2 T_1, \quad y_j = \Sigma_i c_j^i x_i,$$

where

$$c_j^i = \Sigma_k b_j^k a_k^i.$$

Prove that the set of all collineations in S_n forms a group (§I-2.1) with respect to this operation of multiplication.

2. Any $n + 2$ points of S_n, no $n + 1$ of which are dependent, can be transformed by a unique collineation into any other $n + 2$ such points. (Compare with Theorem 2.1.)

3. The collineation (1.1) in S_n induces the collineation

$$v^i = \Sigma_i A_i^j u^i$$

in S_n^*.

4. A transformation T is said to be an *involution* if $TT(x) = (x)$ for all points (x) but $T(x) \neq (x)$ for at least one point (x). Show that a collineation in S_1 is an involution if and only if $a_0^0 + a_1^1 = 0$.

III. Plane Algebraic Curves

In the present chapter we shall investigate some of the simpler properties of algebraic curves lying in a plane. We shall be concerned with the points of a fixed SK_2, where K is an algebraically closed field of characteristic zero. Many of our arguments will apply to a more general ground field, but the investigation of such extensions of the results will be left to the reader.

Additional material relating to the contents of this chapter will be found in the following works:

B. L. van der Waerden, *Einführung in die Algebraische Geometrie*, Springer, Berlin, 1939.

J. L. Coolidge, *Algebraic Plane Curves*, Oxford, 1931.

§1. PLANE ALGEBRAIC CURVES

1.1. Reducible and irreducible curves. Consider a definite projective coordinate system in S_2, and let $F(x) = F(x_0, x_1, x_2)$ be an irreducible homogeneous polynomial of degree $n > 0$ in x_0, x_1, x_2 with coefficients in K. If one set of coordinates (a) of a point P satisfies the equation $F(x) = 0$ then all sets will, since $F(\rho a_0, \rho a_1, \rho a_2) = \rho^n F(a_0, a_1, a_2)$. The set of all such points P is called an *irreducible algebraic curve*, and the equation $F(x) = 0$ is the *equation of the curve* in the given coordinate system. If we transform to a new coordinate system by (II-1.1) and let $G(y)$ be the polynomial obtained by substituting $\Sigma_j A_i^j y_j$ for x_i in $F(x)$, then the y-coordinates of a point satisfy $G(y) = 0$ if and only if its x-coordinates satisfy $F(x) = 0$. Hence $G(y) = 0$ is the equation of the same curve in the new coordinates. Since the passage from F to G is reversible, the reducibility of G would imply that of F, and so G is irreducible. Hence an irreducible algebraic curve is a geometric entity, its definition being independent of the coordinate system employed.

From Theorem I-9.7 it follows that the equation of an irreducible curve is unique to within a constant factor. For if $F(x) = 0$ and $G(x) = 0$ define the same irreducible curve, then F and G are each irreducible and $F(a) = 0$ if and only if $G(a) = 0$. Hence $F(x)$ and $G(x)$ divide each other, and so there is a non-zero constant ρ such that $G(x) = \rho F(x)$. As the equations $F(x) = 0$ and $\rho F(x) = 0$ obviously define the same set of points we shall regard them as identical equations.

That this property of an irreducible curve depends on the algebraic closure of K is evident from an example. Let K be the field of all real numbers, which is not algebraically closed. Then $F = x_0^2 + x_1^2 + x_2^2$ and $G = x_0^4 + x_1^4 + x_2^4$ are irreducible and vanish at the same set of points of S_2, namely at the empty set.

Any homogeneous polynomial $F(x)$ of degree n has a factorization $F = F_1 F_2 \cdots F_r$ into irreducible homogeneous factors unique to within constant multiples. The set of irreducible curves $C_1, \cdots, C_r$ whose equations are $F_1(x) = 0, \cdots, F_r(x) = 0$ will be said to be an algebraic curve C whose equation is $F(x) = 0$, and the irreducible curves $C_1, \cdots, C_r$ are called *components* of C. It should be noted that these components need not be distinct; for example, the curve whose equation is $x_0^3 x_1^2 = 0$ has five components. An irreducible curve appearing more than once as a component of C is said to be a *multiple* component of C. Curves with multiple components have certain undesirable properties, and are often excluded from consideration. There is no harm in doing this if a curve is to be considered merely as a subset of S_2.

An irreducible curve may now be thought of as a curve with one component. Accordingly, a curve with two or more components is said to be *reducible*. The concepts of reducibility, components, and multiple components, are easily seen not to depend on the coordinate system in which they are expressed.

For brevity, we shall usually use the phrase "the curve $F(x) = 0$," or "the curve F," instead of "the curve whose equation is $F(x) = 0$."

1.2. Curves in the affine plane. Let $F(x) = 0$ be a curve C which does not have $x_0 = 0$ as a component. Then x_0 is not a factor of $F(x)$, and there is an associated non-homogeneous polynomial $F(1,x,y)$ of the same degree. We shall ordinarily write $f(x,y)$ for $F(1,x,y)$. $f(x,y) = 0$ will be called the equation of C in the corresponding affine coordinate system. We notice that if (a,b) are the affine coordinates of a point of C, then $f(a,b) = 0$, and conversely. The solutions of $f(x,y) = 0$ are, therefore, those points of C which are not on the line at infinity.

The use of the affine equation of a curve enables us to make use of the advantages of affine coordinates mentioned in §II-4. In fact, most of our investigations will be carried out in appropriate affine coordinates. It must not be forgotten, however, that the affine representation of a curve is incomplete in that it omits the points at infinity, and that it is merely a tool for investigating the properties of the complete curve in the projective plane.

Our freedom in choosing the line at infinity in the affine plane will be very useful in the sequel. At present, we notice merely that any curve C has an affine representation. For since K is infinite there is an infinite number of lines in S_2, and hence there is one line which is not a component of C and which can, therefore, be made the line at infinity.

1.3. Exercises. 1. Where possible, express the equation of the curve

$$x_0^2 x_2 - x_0 x_1^2 + x_0 x_2^2 - 2x_0 x_1 x_2 - x_1^2 x_2 - 2x_1 x_2^2 = 0$$

in each of the following coordinate systems:

(i)   A system with $(1,1,-1)$, $(1,0,-2)$, $(1,0,0)$, $(0,1,0)$ for its frame of reference.

(ii)   Any affine system having $x_0 + x_2 = 0$ as its line at infinity.

(iii)   An affine system with $x_0 + x_2 = 0$ and $x_1 + x_2 = 0$ as axes, $x_2 = 0$ as line at infinity, and $(0,0,1)$ as unit point.

What are the components of this curve?

2. A *hypersurface* in S_r, $r \geqslant 1$, is the set of points satisfying an equation $F(x_0, \cdots, x_r) = 0$, F being a homogeneous polynomial of degree $n \geqslant 1$. Generalize the definitions and results of §1 to hypersurfaces.

§2. SINGULAR POINTS

2.1. Intersection of curve and line. Let C be an algebraic curve with equation $F(x) = 0$, F being a homogeneous polynomial of degree n. If (a) and (b) are distinct points, a point (x) lies on the line L joining (a) and (b) if and only if $x_i = a_i s + b_i t$ for some s and t. The values of s and t for which such a point also lies on C are the roots of $F(as + bt) = 0$. There are now two cases to consider.

(i)   If $F(as + bt)$ is identically zero in s and t then every point of L is a point of C. Let the coordinate system be chosen so that L is the line $x_0 = 0$. Then $F(0,c_1,c_2) = 0$ for all c_1,c_2 in K, and so $F(0,x_1,x_2) = 0$ (Theorem I-7.4). That is, x_0 is a factor of F, and L is a component of C.

(ii)   If $F(as + bt)$ is not identically zero in s and t it is a homogeneous polynomial of degree n in these variables. By Theorem I-10.8, $F(as + bt) = 0$ is satisfied by precisely n ratios $s:t$, an r-fold root being counted as r roots. Each such value of $s:t$ determines a unique point common to L and C. It will be convenient to count as r points a point of intersection corresponding to an r-fold root of $F(as + bt) = 0$.

These results can be condensed into

THEOREM 2.1. *If the equation of a curve C is of degree n, a line either is a component of C or has precisely n points (properly counted) in common with C.*

The degree of the defining equation of a curve has thus a simple geometric significance, and it is called the *order* of the curve. For a curve with no multiple components we can prove the following stronger theorem.

THEOREM 2.2. *If C is a curve of order n with no multiple components,* *then through any point P not on C there pass lines which intersect C in n distinct points.*

PROOF. Choose a coordinate system in which $P = (0,0,1)$, and let $f(x,y) = 0$ be the equation of C in the associated affine coordinates. For the parametric equations of a line L_α through P we have

$$x = \alpha, \quad \alpha \in K,$$
$$y = t.$$

Assigning finite values to t gives us all points on L_α except P; since we are interested only in the intersections of L_α and C, and since P is not on C, this exception causes no trouble. The intersections of L_α with C are given by the roots of $f(\alpha,t) = 0$. Since $(0,0,1)$ is not on the curve, this equation is of degree n in t. Let us assume that for all α this equation has a multiple root in t. Let $R(x)$ be the discriminant of $f(x,y)$ with respect to y. Then since $R(\alpha)$ is the resultant of $f(\alpha,t)$ with respect to t (§I-9.2), we have $R(\alpha) = 0$ for all α. Hence $R(x) = 0$ (Theorem I-7.3), and so $f(x,y)$ has a multiple factor (Theorem I-9.4); that is, C has a multiple component.

For a curve with no multiple components we may, therefore, define the order as the maximum number of distinct intersections with a line. This definition is wholly geometric.

A curve of order one is obviously a line, and every line is a curve of order one. Curves of orders 2, 3, 4, $\cdots$, n, are called conics, cubics, quartics, $\cdots$, n-ics.

2.2. Multiple points. We now wish to investigate more carefully the intersections of L and C at a particular point P of C. To this end we choose an affine coordinate system in which P has coordinates (a,b), and C the equation $f(x,y) = 0$. The parametric equations of L may be put in the form

$$(2.1) \qquad x = a + \lambda t, \quad y = b + \mu t,$$

L being determined by the ratio $\lambda:\mu$. The intersections of L and C are then determined by the roots of $f(a + \lambda t, b + \mu t) = 0$. Expanding the left hand side in a Taylor series in t, we obtain, since $f(a,b) = 0$,

$$(f_x\lambda + f_y\mu)t + \frac{1}{2!}(f_{xx}\lambda^2 + 2f_{xy}\lambda\mu + f_{yy}\mu^2)t^2 + \cdots = 0,$$

where $f_x, f_y, \cdots$ are the values at P of the derivatives of f.

Case 1. Suppose f_x and f_y are not both zero. Then every line through P has a single intersection with C at P, with the one exception corresponding to the value of $\lambda:\mu$ which makes $f_x\lambda + f_y\mu = 0$. This line is called the *tangent* to C at P.

Case 2. Suppose $f_x = f_y = 0$ but not all of f_{xx}, f_{xy}, f_{yy} are zero. Then every line through P has at least two intersections at P, and at most two lines, corresponding to the roots of

$$(2.2) \qquad f_{xx}\lambda^2 + 2f_{xy}\lambda\mu + f_{yy}\mu^2 = 0,$$

have more than two. These exceptional lines are called tangents to C at P, and if (2.2) has a double root we shall say that there are two coincident tangents.

Case r. Suppose that all derivatives of f up to and including the $(r - 1)$-th vanish at P but that at least one r-th derivative does not vanish at P. Then every line through P has at least r intersections with C at P, and precisely r such lines, properly counted, have more than r intersections. The exceptional lines, the *tangents* to C at P, correspond to the roots of

$$f_{x^r}\lambda^r + \binom{r}{1} f_{x^{r-1}y}\lambda^{r-1}\mu + \cdots + \binom{r}{r} f_{y^r}\mu^r = 0,$$

and are counted with multiplicities equal to the multiplicities of the corresponding roots of this equation. P is said to be a point of C of *multiplicity* r, or an r-fold point.

Since $f(x,y)$ is not identically zero there must be some derivative of order less than or equal to n which does not vanish at P. Hence Case r must occur for some r with $1 \leqslant r \leqslant n$.

It will sometimes be convenient to refer to a point not on C as a point of C of multiplicity zero.

A point of C of multiplicity one is called a *simple* point of C, one of multiplicity two, a *double* point, etc. A point of multiplicity r is *ordinary* if the r tangents at the point are distinct.

A point of multiplicity two or more is said to be *singular*. It is evident that a necessary and sufficient condition that a point (a,b) be singular is that $f(a,b) = f_x(a,b) = f_y(a,b) = 0$. We shall find that the singular points play a very important role in the theory of algebraic curves. By a non-singular curve we mean a curve with no singular points.

In investigating singular points the following theorem is very useful.

THEOREM 2.3. *If $f(x,y)$ has no terms of degree less than r and has some terms of degree r, then the origin is an r-fold point of $f = 0$ and the curve defined by equating to zero the terms of f of degree r has as its components the tangents to f at the origin.*

The proof follows at once from the definitions.

In terms of projective coordinates the criteria for singular points can be put in a more convenient form.

THEOREM 2.4. *P is an r-fold point of $F(x) = 0$ if and only if all the $(r - 1)$-th derivatives of F, but not all the r-th derivatives, vanish at P.*

PROOF. We may assume that P is not on $x_0 = 0$, since this situation can always be attained by a permutation of the coordinates. If $x_0 \mid F$ then F has no affine equation, but $f(x,y) = F(1,x,y) = 0$ is the affine equation of a curve which differs from F only in lacking $x_0 = 0$ as a component. Since this component obviously has no effect on the multiplicity of the curve at the point P we can treat $f(x,y) = 0$ as the affine equation of F. $f(a,b) = 0$ if and only if $F(1,a,b) = 0$. Also,

$$f_x(x,y) = F_{x_1}(1,x,y), \quad f_y(x,y) = F_{x_2}(1,x,y),$$

and so

$$f_x(a,b) = f_y(a,b) = 0$$

if and only if

$$F_{x_1}(1,a,b) = F_{x_2}(1,a,b) = 0.$$

But

$$x_0 F_{x_0} + x_1 F_{x_1} + x_2 F_{x_2} = nF,$$

and so

$$F(1,a,b) = F_{x_1}(1,a,b) = F_{x_2}(1,a,b) = 0$$

if and only if

$$F_{x_0}(1,a,b) = F_{x_1}(1,a,b) = F_{x_2}(1,a,b) = 0.$$

Continuing this process we find that

$$f(a,b) = f_x(a,b) = f_y(a,b) = f_{x^2}(a,b) = \cdots = f_{y^r}(a,b) = 0$$

if and only if

$$F_{x_0^r}(1,a,b) = F_{x_0^{r-1}x_1}(1,a,b) = \cdots = F_{x_2^r}(1,a,b) = 0.$$

The theorem now follows at once.

As a corollary of this theorem we see that a point (a) of $F(x) = 0$ is singular if and only if $F_0(a) = F_1(a) = F_2(a) = 0$. (We shall usually find it convenient to write F_i, F_{ij}, etc. for $\partial F/\partial x_i$, $\partial^2 F/\partial x_i \partial x_j$, etc.) For the non-singular points the following theorem is useful.

THEOREM 2.5. *If (a) is a non-singular point of $F(x) = 0$, the equation of the tangent to F at (a) is*

$$\Sigma F_i(a)x_i = 0.$$

The proof is left to the reader, as is also the proof of the following generalization of Theorem 2.2, which will be needed later.

THEOREM 2.6. *If C is a curve of order n with no multiple components, then through any point P of C of multiplicity r there pass lines which intersect C in n-r distinct points other than P.*

We also leave to the reader the proof that the various concepts defined in this section, namely multiplicity of intersection of a line and a curve, multiplicity of a point, tangent, and multiplicity of a tangent, are all independent of the coordinate system used in defining them, and so are geometric concepts.

2.3. Remarks on drawings. At this point it is convenient to interpolate some remarks regarding the use of drawings to illustrate geometric propositions. In any branch of geometry a drawing is merely a means of suggesting certain geometrical relations, and the more relations it suggests the greater is its value. Now all (or nearly all) drawings are made on a flat surface which is most suggestive of a portion of an affine plane AR_2, where R is the field of real numbers. Geometrical properties of this space can, therefore, be represented fairly accurately by drawings.

In our work with algebraic curves we are interested in an SK_2, K being algebraically closed. The fact that we are working in a projective space instead of an affine one will not seriously diminish the suggestiveness of our drawings; the main trouble is that R is not algebraically closed. Many of our most important results are vitally dependent on the closure of K, and a drawing will be of little help in investigating these. However, if one keeps this fact in mind it will be found that a suitable drawing will often throw some light on a complicated situation.

If $f(x,y)$ is a polynomial over R we can consider the equation $f(x,y) = 0$ as defining a curve C_1 in AR_2, and also a curve C_2 in AK_2, where K is the field of all complex numbers. Since $K \supset R$ evidently $AK_2 \supset AR_2$, and the points of C_1 are points of C_2. We usually say that C_1 consists of the "real" points of C_2. In our drawings of algebraic curves in the plane we draw C_1 and try to infer from it something about C_2.

2.4. Examples of singular points. We shall now give some simple examples of singular points of curves. In each of these the singularity has been placed at the origin, so that Theorem 2.3 can be applied.

Example 1. $x^3 - x^2 + y^2 = 0$. (Fig. 2.1.) The origin is an ordinary double point with the distinct tangents $x + y = 0$ and $x - y = 0$. An ordinary double point is called a *node*.

Example 2. $x^3 + x^2 + y^2 = 0$. (Fig. 2.2.) Here the origin is also a node, with tangents $x + iy = 0$ and $x - iy = 0$. The difference in the drawings of the two curves is of course due to the fact that their real

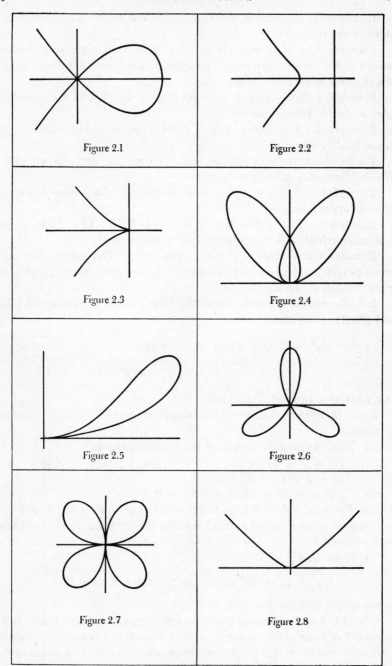

Figure 2.1

Figure 2.2

Figure 2.3

Figure 2.4

Figure 2.5

Figure 2.6

Figure 2.7

Figure 2.8

points are quite different in the two cases. The origin is an "isolated" point of the real curve.

Example 3. $x^3 - y^2 = 0$. (Fig. 2.3.) Here the origin is a double point but not an ordinary one. This type of singularity is called a *cusp*. We shall see more about cusps later.

Example 4. $2x^4 - 3x^2y + y^2 - 2y^3 + y^4 = 0$. (Fig. 2.4.) Another type of double point, a *tacnode*.

Example 5. $x^4 + x^2y^2 - 2x^2y - xy^2 + y^2 = 0$. (Fig. 2.5.) A "ramphoid" cusp.

Points of multiplicity greater than two can be very complicated. We shall consider only three samples.

Example 6. $(x^2 + y^2)^2 + 3x^2y - y^3 = 0$. (Fig. 2.6.) The origin is an ordinary triple point.

Example 7. $(x^2 + y^2)^3 - 4x^2y^2 = 0$. (Fig. 2.7.) The origin is of multiplicity four with its tangents coincident in pairs.

Example 8. $x^6 - x^2y^3 - y^5 = 0$. (Fig. 2.8.) The origin has one triple tangent and two simple tangents. Notice that the real curve is quite smooth at the singular point.

2.5. Exercises. 1. Investigate the singularities at $(1,0,0)$, $(0,1,0)$, and $(0,0,1)$ of the curve

$$x^2y^5 - x^5y^2 - 2xy^5z + x^5z^2 + y^5z^2 - x^3yz^3$$

$$+ 2\alpha x^2y^2z^3 - xy^3z^3 = 0, \quad \alpha \in K.$$

$(z,x,y$ are used instead of $x_0,x_1,x_2)$.

Note. In all numerical problems take K to be the field of all complex numbers.

2. Find the singular points of the following curves:

(i) $xz^2 - y^3 + xy^2 = 0$.

(ii) $(x + y + z)^3 - 27 xyz = 0$.

(iii) $x^2y^2 + 36xz^3 + 24yz^3 + 108z^4 = 0$.

3. For what values of k has the curve $x^3 + y^3 + z^3 + k(x + y + z)^3 = 0$ one or more singular points? Locate the singular points for each such value of k.

4. Show that

$$xy^2 + yz^2 + zx^2 + x^2y + y^2z + z^2x + kxyz = 0$$

is non-singular unless $k = 2$, 3, or 6.

5. If C has components $C_1, C_2, \cdots$ not necessarily distinct, and if P is a point of multiplicity r_i for C_i, $r_i \geqslant 0$, then P is a point of C of multiplicity $r = r_1 + r_2 + \cdots$. In particular, every point of an s-fold component of C is a point of C of multiplicity at least s.

6. Prove that the equation of a curve with no multiple components is determined by the points of the curve.

7. If K is the complex field and P a non-singular point of the curve F then the above definition of the tangent to F at P agrees with the classical one, that is, the tangent at P is the limiting position of a line PQ as Q approaches P along F.

8. Show that for each $n > 0$ there exist non-singular curves of order n.

9. By considering the intersections of a line with a hypersurface, define multiplicity of a point on a hypersurface, and extend Theorems 2.1 (modified), 2.2, 2.4, and 2.6 to hypersurfaces.

10. A hypersurface F is said to be a *cone* with a point V as a *vertex* if F contains every line joining V to any point of F. Extend Theorem 2.3 to hypersurfaces, replacing the last phrase "has as its components $\cdots$" by "is a cone consisting of all the lines tangent to F at the origin."

11. Prove that if (a) is a non-singular point of a hypersurface F the tangent cone to F at (a) is a hyperplane whose equation is $\Sigma F_i(a)x_i = 0$.

§3. Intersection of Curves

3.1. Bezout's Theorem. Much of the theory of algebraic curves depends upon the investigation of the intersections of two curves, and in this connection a certain theorem of Bezout is of basic importance. Bezout's Theorem appears in various forms throughout all branches of algebraic geometry, and not only in the theory of curves. At present we shall prove only a weak form of this theorem.

Theorem 3.1. *If two curves, of orders m and n, have more than mn common points, they have a common component.*

Proof. Let F and G be two curves, of orders m and n, having more than mn common points. Select any set of $mn + 1$ of these points and join each pair of selected points by a line. Since there is only a finite number of such lines there is a point P not on any of the lines nor on F or G. Choose a coordinate system in which $P = (0,0,1)$. Then

$$(3.1) \quad \begin{aligned} F(x) &= A_0 x_2^m + A_1 x_2^{m-1} + \cdots + A_m, \\ G(x) &= B_0 x_2^n + B_1 x_2^{n-1} + \cdots + B_n, \end{aligned}$$

where A_0, B_0 are non-zero constants and A_i, B_i, $i > 0$, are homogeneous polynomials of degree i in x_0, x_1. By Theorem I-10.9 the resultant R of F and G with respect to x_2 either is zero or is a homogeneous polynomial of degree mn in x_0, x_1. $R(c_0, c_1) = 0$ if and only if there is a c_2 such that $F(c) = G(c) = 0$. That is, the first two coordinates c_0, c_1 of any point common to F and G satisfy $R(x_0, x_1) = 0$. But each of the $mn + 1$

selected points has a different value of $c_0:c_1$, since no pair of them is collinear with $(0,0,1)$. Hence $R(x_0,x_1)$ is zero, and so F and G have a common factor.

In §2.1 we defined the multiplicity of intersection of a curve and a line in such a way that the number of intersections, counted according to their multiplicities, was exactly the order of the curve. From the way in which the degree of the resultant was used in the above proof it is not difficult to see how one could define the multiplicity of intersection of two curves so that the number of intersections would be precisely mn, assuming the curves have no common component. One need only define the multiplicity of intersection at a point as the multiplicity of the corresponding root of $R(x_0,x_1) = 0$. There are two drawbacks to such a procedure, however. In the first place, it is difficult to show that the so-defined multiplicity is independent of the coordinate system used to define it; and secondly, the complicated form of the resultant makes it hard to tell much about the nature of its roots. We shall, therefore, not use this method, but shall postpone the discussion of multiplicity of intersection of two curves until we have developed a more suitable technique. The following result, however, will be of use.

THEOREM 3.2. *If $F(x)$ and $G(x)$ have the form* (3.1) *and if $P = (a_0,a_1,a_2)$ is a point of multiplicity r for F and s for G, then the resultant $R(x_0,x_1)$ of F and G with respect to x_2, if it is not zero, has $a_0:a_1$ as a root of multiplicity at least rs.*

PROOF. Since $(0,0,1)$ is not a point of F or G, at least one of a_0,a_1 is not zero, say $a_0 \neq 0$. Then if we make the change of coordinates

$$x_0^{'} = x_0/a_0, \quad x_1^{'} = x_1 - a_1x_0/a_0, \quad x_2^{'} = x_2,$$

the point P becomes $(1,0,a_2)$ and the resultant with respect to $x_2^{'}$ of the transformed equation is $R(a_0x_0^{'}, x_1^{'} + a_1x_0^{'})$, which has the root $1:0$ to the same multiplicity as $R(x_0,x_1)$ has the root $a_0:a_1$. Hence we can assume without loss of generality that $a_0 = 1$, $a_1 = 0$. We shall next show that we can assume that $a_2 = 0$. For consider the resultant of $F(x_0,x_1,x_2 + \lambda x_0)$ and $G(x_0,x_1,x_2 + \lambda x_0)$ with respect to x_2. This is a polynomial $R(x_0,x_1,\lambda) = c_0 + c_1\lambda + \cdots + c_N\lambda^N$, $N \geqslant 0$, where $c_i \in K[x_0,x_1]$. Since $c_0 = R(x_0,x_1,0)$ is the resultant of $F(x)$ and $G(x)$, we have $c_0 \neq 0$. Suppose that $N > 0$, $c_N \neq 0$. Then there exist constants α_0,α_1 such that $c_0(\alpha_0,\alpha_1)c_N(\alpha_0,\alpha_1) \neq 0$. Since K is algebraically closed there is a constant λ_0 for which $R(\alpha_0,\alpha_1,\lambda_0) = 0$, and so the polynomials $F(\alpha_0,\alpha_1,x_2 + \lambda_0\alpha_0)$ and $G(\alpha_0,\alpha_1,x_2 + \lambda_0\alpha_0)$ have a common zero α_2. Therefore $F(\alpha_0,\alpha_1,x_2)$ and $G(\alpha_0,\alpha_1,x_2)$ have a common zero $\alpha_2 + \lambda_0\alpha_0$, which is impossible since $R(\alpha_0,\alpha_1,0) \neq 0$. It follows that $R(x_0,x_1,\lambda)$ does not involve λ. Hence if we make the change of coordinates, $x_0^{'} = x_0$, $x_1^{'} = x_1$, $x_2^{'} = x_2 - a_2x_0$,

P has coordinates $(1,0,0)$ and the resultant of the new equations is the same as that of the old.

We now pass to affine coordinates. Since the origin is an r-fold point of f and an s-fold point of g, we can write these polynomials in the forms

$$f = f_0 x^r + f_1 x^{r-1} y + \cdots + f_r y^r + f_{r+1} y^{r+1} + \cdots,$$

$$g = g_0 x^s + g_1 x^{s-1} y + \cdots + g_s y^s + g_{s+1} y^{s+1} + \cdots,$$

the f_i, g_i being polynomials in x. Hence

$$R(x) = \begin{vmatrix} f_0 x^r & f_1 x^{r-1} & \cdots\cdots & f_r & f_{r+1} & \cdots\cdots & f_m & & \\ & f_0 x^r & \cdots\cdots & f_{r-1}x & f_r & \cdots\cdots & f_{m-1} & f_m & \\ & & \cdots\cdots\cdots\cdots\cdots\cdots\cdots\cdots\cdots & & & & & & \\ & & & & f_0 x^r & \cdots\cdots\cdots\cdots & & & f_m \\ g_0 x^s & g_1 x^{s-1} & \cdots & g_s & g_{s+1} & \cdots\cdots & g_{n-1} & g_n & \\ & & \cdots\cdots\cdots\cdots\cdots\cdots\cdots\cdots\cdots & & & & & & \\ & & & & g_0 x^s & \cdots\cdots\cdots\cdots\cdots & & & g_n \end{vmatrix}.$$

If we multiply the first row by x^s, the second row by $x^{s-1}, \cdots$, the s-th row by x, the first row of g's by $x^r, \cdots$, the r-th row of g's by x, we find that the $(r + s + 1 - i)$-th power of x can be factored from the i-th column. Hence $R(x)$ is divisible by x to the power

$$\Sigma_{i=1}^{r+s} i - \Sigma_{i=1}^{r} i - \Sigma_{i=1}^{s} i$$

$$= \frac{(r + s)(r + s + 1)}{2} - \frac{r(r + 1)}{2} - \frac{s(s + 1)}{2} = rs.$$

The following theorem is an important application of Theorem 3.2.

THEOREM 3.3. *If two curves, of orders m and n, have no common components and have multiplicities r_i and s_i at their common points P_i, $i = 1, 2, \cdots$, $\Sigma r_i s_i \leqslant mn$.*

PROOF. As in the proof of Theorem 3.1 we choose coordinates so that the curves have equations of the form (3.1), and so that no two points of intersection of the two curves lie on a line of the form $\alpha_1 x_0 - a_0 x_1 = 0$. Then to a point (a_0, a_1, a_2) of multiplicities r_i and s_i for the two curves there corresponds a root $a_0 : a_1$ of $R(x_0, x_1)$ of multiplicity at least $r_i s_i$. Since by the choice of the coordinate system no two common points of F and G can give the same ratio $a_0 : a_1$, the roots of $R(x_0, x_1)$ corresponding to distinct intersections are distinct. Hence $R(x_0, x_1)$ has at least $\Sigma r_i s_i$ roots, counted with the proper multiplicity, and so $\Sigma r_i s_i \leqslant mn$.

Theorem 3.3 is useful in proving the reducibility of curves possessing certain singularities. For example, a cubic with two double points must have as a component the line joining them, for otherwise its intersections with this line could not satisfy the inequality. Similarly we can see that an irreducible curve of order n with an $(n-1)$-fold point can have no other singularity. Before considering more general questions of this sort we must investigate some other properties of curves.

3.2. Determination of intersections. The method of proving Theorem 3.1 suggests a means of finding the points common to two curves. That is, we choose coordinates so that the curves have the form (3.1), get the resultant with respect to x_2, determine the ratios $x_0 : x_1$ for which the resultant vanishes, and for each of these ratios determine the common solutions of (3.1).

The first step of this process is often an unfortunate one, since one frequently encounters curves which have simple equations or intersect at convenient points, such as the vertices of reference, and a change of coordinates usually spoils both these properties. Fortunately, however, it is not necessary to make such a transformation, for the same process applied to any pair of equations will give all points of intersection not at $(0,0,1)$, as is easily seen. The point $(0,0,1)$ can then be investigated to see if it is common to the two curves.

3.3. Exercises. 1. Find the intersections of the following pairs of curves.

(a) $x(y^2 - xz)^2 - y^5 = 0,$

  $y^4 + y^3 z - x^2 z^2 = 0.$

(b) $x^3 - y^3 - 2xyz = 0,$

  $2x^3 - 4x^2 y - 3xy^2 - y^3 - 2x^2 z = 0.$

(c) $x^4 + y^4 - y^2 z^2 = 0,$

  $x^4 + y^4 - 2y^3 z - 2x^2 yz - xy^2 z + y^2 z^2 = 0.$

§4. LINEAR SYSTEMS OF CURVES

4.1. Linear systems. Any curve of order n has an equation of the form $\Sigma a_{ijk} x_0^i x_1^j x_2^k = 0$, the summation being over all non-negative values of i, j, k for which $i + j + k = n$. Such a curve is uniquely determined by its coefficients, and conversely such a curve determines its coefficients to within a common factor.[*] Hence the coefficients a_{ijk} can be considered to be projective coordinates of the curve, and the set of curves may be thought of as comprising the points of an S_N. N is one less than the number of terms in the summation, and is readily found to be $n(n + 3)/2$.

---

[*] In this theory multiplicity of components must be taken into account; e.g., $x_1^2 x_2 = 0$ and $x_1 x_2^2 = 0$ are different cubics.

A change of coordinates (II-1.1) in S_2 replaces $\Sigma a_{ijk} x_0^i x_1^j x_2^k$ by

$$\Sigma a_{ijk} (\Sigma A_0^\alpha y_\alpha)^i (\Sigma A_1^\beta y_\beta)^j (\Sigma A_2^\gamma y_\gamma)^k = \Sigma b_{pqr} y_0^p y_1^q y_2^r.$$

Here

$$b_{pqr} = \Sigma_{ijk} M_{pqr}^{ijk} a_{ijk},$$

where the M's are polynomials in the A's. This is a transformation in S_N of type (II-1.1), and since we can pass similarly from the y's to the x's its determinant must be different from zero. Hence the coordinate systems in S_N induced by two systems in S_2 are equivalent, and so S_N is uniquely determined.

The curves which constitute the points of a subspace S_R of S_N are said to form a *linear system* of dimension R. Such a system is determined by $R + 1$ independent curves of it, and we can write the equations of the curves of the system in the form $\Sigma_0^R \lambda_i F_i(x) = 0$, where the F_i are linearly independent homogeneous polynomials of degree n. Since, by duality, an S_R is also determined by $N - R$ independent hyperplanes containing it, we can specify linear systems in this manner also. The equation of a hyperplane in S_N is said to be a *linear condition* on the curves of order n, and a curve "satisfies" this condition if it is a point of the hyperplane. Since N hyperplanes always have at least one common point, a curve can always be found satisfying any N, or less, linear conditions. More generally, a curve of any given R-dimensional system can be found satisfying R, or less, conditions. Of course, such a curve may be reducible or have multiple components.

The most important type of linear condition arises on requiring that a curve have a given point as a point of multiplicity at least r, $r \geqslant 1$. The necessary and sufficient condition for this is that all the $(r - 1)$-th derivatives of the polynomial vanish at the point. There are $r(r + 1)/2$ of these derivatives, and their values at the point are homogeneous linear polynomials in the a_{ijk}. Hence $r(r + 1)/2$ linear conditions are imposed on the curve by this requirement. A point of multiplicity $\geqslant r$ for all the curves of a linear system is called a *base point* of multiplicity r of the system.

4.2. Base points. Each simple base point $(r = 1)$ imposes one linear condition on the curves of order n. Hence we might expect the system of all curves of order n with k assigned simple base points to be of dimension $N - k$. This is not always the case, however. Consider, for example, a system of conics $(n = 2, N = 5)$ with four simple base points. If three of these points are on a line L any conic containing them must have L as a component, by Theorem 3.3. Hence if the fourth point is also on L it will impose no extra condition on the conics. In this case the system is of dimension 2, consisting of all reducible conics with L as one component and an arbitrary line as the other.

An example not involving reducible curves is provided by cubics ($n = 3$, $N = 9$). Two cubics C_1 and C_2 can be found intersecting in nine distinct points (for instance let each cubic consist of three lines). Then the 1-dimensional system $\lambda_1 C_1 + \lambda_2 C_2$ has these nine points as base points, although $N - 9 = 0$.

These examples illustrate the general situation. If the k base points lie on one or more curves of rather low order they may not impose independent conditions on the curves of a given order n. A similar situation holds for base points of higher multiplicities. However, it can be shown that for given positions and multiplicities of the base points the conditions they impose are independent if n is sufficiently large. As we shall have no occasion to use this fact we refer the interested reader to Severi-Loeffler, *Vorlesungen über algebraische Geometrie*, Teubner, Berlin, 1921, p. 114, for its proof.

Linear systems of 1, 2, and 3 dimensions are called *pencils*, *nets*, and *webs* respectively. A pencil has the important property that all of its curves pass through all the points common to any two independent curves of it. We shall give one application of this property.

THEOREM 4.1. *If two curves of order n intersect in n^2 points, and if exactly mn of these lie on an irreducible curve of order m, then the remaining $n(n - m)$ lie on a curve of order $n - m$.*

PROOF. Let F_1 and F_2 be two curves of order n, intersecting in n^2 points, and let G be an irreducible curve of order m containing exactly mn of these points. A curve of the pencil $\lambda_1 F_1 + \lambda_2 F_2$ can be found passing through an arbitrarily assigned point. Choose this point on G. Then G and $\lambda_1 F_1 + \lambda_2 F_2$ have at least $mn + 1$ common points and so have a common component, which must be G since G is irreducible. Thus $\lambda_1 F_1 + \lambda_2 F_2 = GH$ passes through the n^2 points, and so H, which is of order $n - m$, contains the $n(n - m)$ points which G does not.

An important special case of this theorem is

THEOREM 4.2. (Pascal's Theorem) *The pairs of opposite sides of a hexagon inscribed in an irreducible conic meet in three collinear points.*

PROOF. Let $L_1, \cdots, L_6$ be the successive sides of the inscribed hexagon. (Fig. 4.1.) The two cubics $L_1 L_3 L_5$ and $L_2 L_4 L_6$ intersect in the six vertices of the hexagon and the three points of intersection of opposite sides of the hexagon. The required result, therefore, follows at once from Theorem 4.1.

4.3. Upper bounds on multiplicities. From Theorem 3.3 we can obtain some information about the effect of singularities on the structure of a curve. Consider a cubic with two double points. Applying Theorem 3.3 to the intersection of the cubic with the line joining the double points we see that the cubic must contain the line as a component. A less obvious example is provided by a quartic with four double points. There is a conic passing through these points and a fifth point of the quartic. By Theorem 3.3 the quartic has a component in common with the conic, and hence is composite.

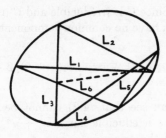

Figure 4.1

These examples suggest that there is a limit to the number and complexity of the singularities of an irreducible curve. The following theorems determine this limit.

THEOREM 4.3. *If a curve of order n with no multiple components has multiplicities r_i at points P_i, then*

$$(4.1) \qquad n(n - 1) \geqslant \Sigma r_i(r_i - 1).$$

PROOF. Choose coordinates so that no vertex of the triangle of reference is on the curve $F = 0$. Then the partial derivative F_0 is not identically zero. Also, F has no factor not containing x_0, and since in addition F has no multiple factors, F can have no factor in common with F_0. Now the curve $F_0(x) = 0$ has P_i for a point of multiplicity at least $r_i - 1$, for every $(r_i - 2)$-th derivative of F_0 is an $(r_i - 1)$-th derivative of F, and so vanishes at P_i. Applying Theorem 3.3 to the intersections of $F = 0$ and $F_0 = 0$ at the points P_i we obtain the desired inequality.

If F is composed of n distinct concurrent lines it has one singular point of multiplicity n, and the equality holds in (4.1). Hence the inequality (4.1) cannot be bettered.

THEOREM 4.4. *If an irreducible curve C of order n has multiplicities r_i at points P_i, then*

$$(4.2) \qquad (n - 1)(n - 2) \geqslant \Sigma r_i(r_i - 1).$$

PROOF. Since C has no multiple components, we have by the previous theorem,

$$\Sigma r_i(r_i - 1)/2 \leqslant n(n - 1)/2 \leqslant (n - 1)(n + 2)/2.$$

Hence there is a curve C' of order $n - 1$ having an $(r_i - 1)$-fold point at P_i and passing through

$$(n - 1)(n + 2)/2 - \Sigma r_i(r_i - 1)/2$$

simple points of C. Since C is irreducible and C' is of lower order than C, the two curves can have no common component, and so by Theorem 3.3,

$$n(n - 1) \geqslant \Sigma r_i (r_i - 1) + (n - 1)(n + 2)/2 - \Sigma r_i (r_i - 1)/2.$$

This reduces to (4.2).

Once again we can see that (4.2) cannot be improved, since the equality holds for the irreducible curve $x^n + y^{n-1} = 0$, which has an $(n - 1)$-fold point at the origin.

4.4. Exercises. 1. The system of conics on four base points is a pencil if the points are not collinear. [If the system had dimension > 1 a curve could be found containing two arbitrarily chosen points. Show that this is impossible.]

2. For given values of n and k, with $0 \leqslant k \leqslant N + 1$, there exist k points such that the system of curves of order n with these as simple base points is of dimension $N - k$. [Use induction on k.]

3. If a curve of order n with k distinct components has multiplicities r_i at points P_i then

$$(n - 1)(n - 2)/2 + k - 1 \geqslant \Sigma r_i(r_i - 1)/2.$$

[Use induction on k.]

4. Construct a net of quartics with thirteen simple base points. [First construct a web with twelve base points.]

5. The hypersurfaces of order n in S_r form an S_N with $N = \binom{r+n}{r} - 1$.

§5. RATIONAL CURVES

5.1. Sufficient condition for rationality. In elementary analytic geometry curves are often specified by expressing the coordinates of their points as functions of a parameter. We have already made use of this process in the case of a straight line, for equations (2.1) do just this. In general we shall consider the case in which the defining functions are rational functions over K. We shall see later (§VI-7.2) that this can be done only for a special class of curves, which are, therefore, known as *rational* curves.

We define an irreducible curve $f(x,y) = 0$ to be rational if there exist two rational functions $\phi(\lambda), \psi(\lambda) \in K(\lambda)$ such that

(i)   For all but a finite set of $\lambda_0 \in K$, $(\phi(\lambda_0), \psi(\lambda_0))$ is a point of f;

(ii)   With a finite number of exceptions, for every point (x_0, y_0) of f there is a unique $\lambda_0 \in K$ such that $x_0 = \phi(\lambda_0), y_0 = \psi(\lambda_0)$.

It is impossible to avoid having a finite number of exceptions in these conditions. They arise from two sources. One is the fact that a rational function is not defined for all values of the variable, and the other is the presence of singular points on the curve f. Consider, for example, the curve of §2.4, Example 8. If we put

$$\phi(\lambda) = (\lambda^2 + 1)/\lambda^5, \quad \psi(\lambda) = (\lambda^2 + 1)/\lambda^6,$$

it is easy to verify that (i) and (ii) hold. The exceptional value of λ_0 in (i) is $\lambda_0 = 0$; the exceptional point in (ii) is the singularity $(0,0)$, since to this point there correspond two values of λ, $\pm i$.

We shall prove here only one theorem concerning rational curves.

THEOREM 5.1. *An irreducible curve of order n with points of multiplicity r_i is rational if*

$$(n - 1)(n - 2) = \Sigma r_i(r_i - 1).$$

PROOF. Consider the linear system of curves of order $n - 1$ with each r_i-fold point of the given curve f as an $(r_i - 1)$-fold base point, and having in addition $2n - 3$ simple base points on f. For the dimension R of this system we have

$$R \geqslant (n - 1)(n + 2)/2 - \Sigma r_i(r_i - 1)/2 - (2n - 3) = 1.$$

Suppose $R > 1$. Then there is a curve g of the system containing two points of f not already among the base points of the system. Applying Theorem 3.3 to f and g we find that they must have a common component, since

$$\Sigma r_i(r_i - 1) + (2n - 3) + 2 > n(n - 1).$$

This is impossible since f is irreducible and g is of lower degree than f. Hence $R = 1$. The curves of S_R, with one exception, can, therefore, be expressed in the form $g_1 + \lambda g_2 = 0$ for suitable values of λ.

We choose affine coordinates so that

$$f = ay^n + \cdots, \quad a \neq 0,$$
$$g_1 = by^{n-1} + \cdots, \quad b \neq 0,$$
$$g_2 = cy^{n-1} + \cdots, \quad c \neq 0,$$

and so that no intersection of f and g_1 is at infinity. Let $R(x,\lambda)$ be the resultant with respect to y of f and $g_1 + \lambda g_2$. We have

$$R(x,\lambda) = b_0(\lambda) + b_1(\lambda)x + \cdots + b_N(\lambda)x^N,$$

where $N = n(n - 1)$. Now $R(x,0)$ is the resultant of f and g_1, and is of degree $n(n - 1)$. Hence $b_N(0) \neq 0$, and so $b_N(\lambda_0) = 0$ for at most a finite set of values λ_0. We exclude this set of values in the remaining discussion. Then f and $g_1 + \lambda_0 g_2$ have no intersections at infinity. Now by Theorem 3.2, the equation $R(x,\lambda_0) = 0$ has a root a_i of multiplicity at least $r_i(r_i - 1)$ at each r_i-fold point (a_i,b_i) of f, and has a simple root c_j at each of the $2n - 3$ chosen simple points (c_j,d_j) of f. Since

$$\Sigma r_i(r_i - 1) + 2n - 3 = n(n - 1) - 1$$

we have thus accounted for all but one of the roots of $R(x,\lambda_0) = 0$. The remaining root is, therefore,

$$\phi(\lambda_0) = -\frac{b_{N-1}(\lambda_0)}{b_N(\lambda_0)} - \Sigma r_i(r_i - 1)a_i - \Sigma c_j.$$

We thus obtain a certain rational function $\phi(\lambda)$. By proceeding similarly with the resultant with respect to x we obtain another rational function $\psi(\lambda)$. We shall show that these functions satisfy the properties given in the definition of a rational curve.

(i)   For each of the non-excluded values of λ_0 we have by the construction of $\phi(\lambda_0)$ and $\psi(\lambda_0)$ that $(\phi(\lambda_0), \psi(\lambda_0))$ is a point of f.

(ii)   If (x_0,y_0) is a point of f not on g_2 there is a unique λ_0 such that $g_1 + \lambda_0 g_2 = 0$ contains (x_0,y_0), namely $\lambda_0 = -g_1(x_0,y_0)/g_2(x_0,y_0)$. Hence $R(\lambda_0,x) = 0$ has x_0 as a root, and so $x_0 = \phi(\lambda_0)$. Similarly, $y_0 = \psi(\lambda_0)$. Since there is only a finite set of points of f which are on g_2, this completes the proof of the theorem.

That there exist rational curves for which $\Sigma r_i(r_i - 1) < (n - 1) \cdot (n - 2)$ can be shown by an example. The quartic $(x^2 - y)^2 - y^3 = 0$ has as its only singularity a double point at the origin. However, it is a rational curve, for

$$\phi(\lambda) = \frac{\lambda^2 - 1}{\lambda^3}, \quad \psi(\lambda) = \frac{(\lambda^2 - 1)^2}{\lambda^4}$$

satisfy (i), and since we have

$$\lambda = \frac{\psi - \phi^2}{\phi\psi},$$

(ii) is satisfied.

A complete analysis of rational curves will be obtained in Chapter VI.

5.2. Exercises. 1. For a curve of order n with an $(n-1)$-fold point (a,b) the curves $g_1 + \lambda g_2 = 0$ in the above proof can be replaced by the lines

$$(y - b) - \lambda(x - a) = 0.$$

2. Carry out the proof of Theorem 5.1 for $n > 2$, using curves of order $n - 2$ with an $(r_i - 1)$-fold point at each r_i-fold point of f and passing through $n - 3$ simple points of f.

3. Expressed in projective coordinates the condition for an irreducible curve F to be rational is the existence of homogeneous polynomials $G_i(\lambda,\mu)$, $i = 0,1,2$, of the same degree, such that

   (i)   For all but a finite set of ratios $\lambda_0 : \mu_0$, $(G_i(\lambda_0,\mu_0))$ is a point of F;

   (ii)   With a finite set of exceptions, to each point (a) o⁻ F there corresponds a unique ratio $\lambda_0 : \mu_0$ such that $\rho a_i = G_i(\lambda_0,\mu_0)$, $\rho \neq 0$.

4. A curve with no multiple components which satisfies (i) and (ii) is irreducible, and hence rational.

§6. Conics and Cubics

6.1. Conics. As illustrations of some of the results we have ob⁻ tained we shall apply them to the simplest curves, namely to those of orders less than four. Curves of order one, that is, lines, have no interesting properties from this point of view, so we shall commence with the conics.

For a conic we have $(n-1)(n-2) = 0$. Hence every irreducible conic C is non-singular and rational. If $g_1 + \lambda g_2 = 0$ is a pencil of lines with base point at a point of C the coordinates of the residual intersection are rational functions of λ which serve as a rational parametrization of the curve. On choosing two tangent lines and the line joining their points of contact as the sides of reference the equation is easily seen to reduce to $x_0^2 - ax_1x_2 = 0$, and a may be made 1 by choosing the unit point on the curve.

A reducible conic is either a pair of lines or a line counted twice. The following theorem is often useful in determining whether a conic is reducible or not.

THEOREM 6.1. *The conic*

$$F = \Sigma_{i,j=0}^2 a_{ij}x_ix_j = 0,$$

where $a_{ij} = a_{ji}$, *is reducible if and only if the determinant* $|a_{ij}| = 0$.

PROOF. By the remarks above, F is reducible if and only if it has a singular point; that is, if and only if the equations $F_i = 0$, $i = 0,1,2$, have a non-trivial solution. But $F_i = 2\Sigma_j a_{ij}x_j$, and so $F_i = 0$ have a common solution if and only if $|a_{ij}| = 0$.

6.2. Cubics. We now pass to the more interesting case of the cubics. The following theorem gives an interesting property of cubics which will be generalized later (Theorem IV-7.3).

THEOREM 6.2. *If two cubics intersect in exactly nine points every cubic on eight of these points is on the ninth.*

PROOF. Let F_1 and F_2 be two cubics having the distinct intersections $P_1, \cdots, P_9$, and let F be a cubic containing $P_1, \cdots, P_8$. If F is dependent on F_1 and F_2, then $F = \lambda F_1 + \mu F_2$ for some λ, μ and hence F contains F_9, since F_1 and F_2 do. If F, F_1 and F_2 are independent, then λ, μ, ν may be chosen so that $\lambda F_1 + \mu F_2 + \nu F$ contains any two given points. We shall show that this leads to a contradiction.

(i) Of the nine points P_i no four can lie on a line, for such a line would be a common component of F_1 and F_2. Similarly, no seven of the nine points can lie on a conic. Suppose that P_1, P_2, P_3 lie on a line L. Then $P_4, \cdots, P_8$ are on a unique conic Q, for if two conics have five common points they have a common component, the remaining components can have only one intersection not on this line, and so the other four points must be collinear. Let A be a point on L distinct from P_1, P_2, P_3,

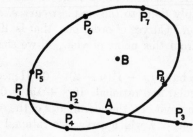

Figure 6.1

and let B be a point not on Q or L, (Fig. 6.1). Now $\lambda F_1 + \mu F_2 + \nu F$ contains $P_1, \cdots, P_8$, and if λ, μ, ν are chosen so that it contains A and B it will necessarily have L as a component. The other component (or components) must, therefore, be Q, and this is impossible since neither Q nor L contains B.

(ii) Suppose that $P_1, \cdots, P_6$ lie on a conic Q; then P_7, P_8 lie on a line L. By taking A as another point of Q and B as a point on neither Q nor L we can obtain a contradiction as in (i).

(iii) If no three of $P_1, \cdots, P_8$ are on a line and no six on a conic let L be the line P_1P_2 and Q the conic on $P_3, \cdots, P_7$. Taking A and B on L and proceeding as in (i) we again obtain a contradiction, since P_8 is on neither Q nor L. This exhausts all the possibilities, and so the theorem is proved.

One consequence of this theorem is to remove the restriction of irreducibility in Theorem 4.1 in the case $n = 3$, $m = 2$. For if a conic contains six of the nine intersections of two cubics, the cubic consisting of this conic and the line joining two of the remaining three intersections must also contain the third. The proof of Theorem 4.2 can then be applied as well to reducible conics, giving us the Theorem of Pappus.

6.3. Inflections of a curve. Cubics are the simplest curves which can have points of inflection. We shall call such a point a *flex* for short, and shall first investigate its properties in general.

We define a flex of a curve F to be a non-singular point of F at which the tangent line has three or more intersections with F. By this definition every simple point of a line component of F is a flex; this is a degenerate case in which we shall not be interested, and we shall consider only curves having no line components.

THEOREM 6.3. *The flexes of F are its non-singular points which are intersections with the curve*

$$H(x) = |F_{ij}(x)| = 0.$$

This curve is called the *Hessian* of F.

PROOF. Let (a) be a simple point of F, and (b) any other point. Then

$$F(as + bt) = F(a)s^n + \Sigma F_i(a)b_i s^{n-1}t + \tfrac{1}{2}\Sigma F_{ij}(a)b_i b_j s^{n-2}t^2 + \cdots.$$

Let L be the line $\Sigma F_i(a)x_i = 0$ and Q the conic $\Sigma F_{ij}(a)x_i x_j = 0$. Then by §2.1, (a) is a flex if and only if L is a component of Q; that is, if and only if $\Sigma F_{ij}(a)b_i b_j = 0$ whenever $\Sigma F(a)b_i = 0$. Hence if (a) is a flex, Q is reducible and $H(a) = 0$, (Theorem 6.1). Conversely, if $H(a) = 0$, Q is reducible. Now in any case, Q contains (a), for

$$\Sigma F_{ij}(a)a_i a_j = n(n - 1)F(a) = 0$$

by Euler's Theorem (Theorem I-10.3); also L is tangent to Q at (a), for this tangent has as its equation

$$\Sigma F_{ij}(a)a_i x_j = 0,$$

and by Euler's Theorem this is

$$(n - 1)\, \Sigma F_j(a)x_j = 0.$$

Hence if Q is reducible it must contain L, and it follows that (a) is a flex.

If F is of order $n \geqslant 3$, H is of order $3(n - 2) > 0$, and so must intersect F in at least one point. Hence:

THEOREM 6.4. *Every non-singular curve of order $\geqslant 3$ has at least one flex.*

It is easy to see that a non-singular conic has no flexes.

6.4. Normal form and flexes of a cubic. Returning to the cubics, we first prove

THEOREM 6.5. *By a proper choice of the coordinate system any non-singular cubic C can be put in the form*

$$(6.1) \qquad\qquad y^2 = g(x),$$

where $g(x)$ is a cubic polynomial with distinct roots.

PROOF. By Theorem 6.4, C has at least one flex. Choose this as the point $(0,0,1)$, and let the flex tangent be $x_0 = 0$. In affine coordinates C then has the equation

$$(6.2) \qquad\qquad x^3 + \phi(x,y) = 0,$$

where ϕ is of degree two. ϕ must involve a term ay^2, $a \neq 0$, for if it did not $(0,0,1)$ would be a singular point. Hence if (6.2) is solved for y we obtain

$$(6.3) \qquad\qquad y = \alpha x + \beta \pm \sqrt{g(x)},$$

where $g(x)$ is a cubic polynomial in x. The transformation $\bar{y} = y - \alpha x - \beta$, $\bar{x} = x$ then reduces (6.3) to (6.1). If $g(x)$ had a multiple root r, a further transformation $\bar{\bar{x}} = \bar{x} - r$, $\bar{\bar{y}} = \bar{y}$ would put the equation in the form

$$\bar{\bar{y}}^2 = \bar{\bar{x}}^2 \, (\gamma \bar{\bar{x}} - \delta),$$

and the curve would have a singular point at the origin.

We now can prove one of the most interesting properties of a cubic.

THEOREM 6.6. *A non-singular cubic has nine flexes, which have the property that every line joining two of them contains a third.*

PROOF. By a transformation of the type $x' = \alpha x + \beta$, $y' = y$, the equation (6.1) of the cubic may be put in the form

$$f = y^2 - x^3 - ax^2 - bx = 0,$$

with $b(a^2 - 4b) \neq 0$ since $x^3 + ax^2 + bx = 0$ has distinct roots. By direct computation of the Hessian we find that

$$h = (y^2 + bx)(3x + a) - (ax + b)^2.$$

Eliminating y between f and h we obtain

$$k(x) = 3x^4 + 4ax^3 + 6bx^2 - b^2 = 0.$$

This equation has four distinct roots, for

$$k' = 12(x^3 + ax^2 + bx)$$

and the resultant of k and k' is found to be

$$b^4(a^2 - 4b)^2 \neq 0.$$

For each of these values of x there are two values of y, since none of these values of x satisfies $x^3 + ax^2 + bx = 0$. Since we started with a flex at infinity we therefore have nine altogether. The last part of the theorem now follows at once. For given any two flexes, one of them can be taken as $(0,0,1)$, and then if the other one is $(1,a,b)$, we see that $(1,a,-b)$ must also be a flex. These three flexes are then collinear.

The configuration formed by the nine flexes of a cubic has been the subject of many investigations. Some of its properties are given in the exercises below, and the interested reader will find reference to others in the *Encyklopädie der mathematischen Wissenschaften*, III, 2.1, pp. 475–479.

6.5. Exercises. 1. Let three conics Q_1, Q_2, Q_3 have the four non-collinear points $P_1, \cdots, P_4$ in common, and let three lines L_1, L_2, L_3 have a fifth point P_5 in common. Let L_i intersect Q_i in distinct points A_i, B_i, none of which coincide with any P_j. Then there is a unique cubic through the eleven points $P_1, \cdots, P_5, A_1, A_2, A_3, B_1, B_2, B_3$.

2. Show by an example that all the quartics on thirteen points do not necessarily contain another point. [Use §4.4, Exercise 4.]

3. An irreducible cubic with an ordinary double point has three flexes, which are collinear. Its equation can be put in the form $y^2 = x^2(x + 1)$.

4. An irreducible cubic having a double point with coincident tangents has one flex. Its equation can be put in the form $y^2 = x^3$.

5. The flexes of a non-singular cubic form a set of nine non-collinear points with the property that a line joining any two of the points passes through a third (Theorem 6.6). Show that by properly choosing the coordinate system any such set of points can be given the coordinates

$$(0,1,-1) \quad (-1,0,1) \quad (1,-1,0)$$

$$(0,1,\alpha) \quad (\alpha,0,1) \quad (1,\alpha,0)$$

$$(0,1,\beta) \quad (\beta,0,1) \quad (1,\beta,0).$$

α and β are the two roots of $x^2 - x + 1 = 0$.

6. Any cubic passing through the nine points of Exercise 5 necessarily has the form

$$x^3 + y^3 + z^3 + 3mxyz = 0.$$

This cubic is singular if and only if $m = \infty, -1, \alpha,$ or β, and in these cases it degenerates into three lines. If the cubic is irreducible these nine points are its flexes.

7. If F is a non-singular cubic and H its Hessian, every cubic of the form $aF + bH$, with four exceptions, is non-singular and has the same flexes as F.

8. A non-singular cubic is transformed into itself by a group of eighteen collineations.

9. A quadric (second order) hypersurface Q in S_r has an equation of the form $\Sigma a_{ij} x_i x_j = 0$, $a_{ij} = a_{ji}$. It has a singular point if and only if $|a_{ij}| = 0$. If it has a singular point it is a cone with this point as a vertex. More generally, if the matrix $\|a_{ij}\|$ is of rank s, the singular points of Q constitute an S_{r-s}, each point of which is a vertex. If $s = 2$, Q consists of two hyperplanes; if $s = 1$, Q consists of a hyperplane counted twice.

§7. ANALYSIS OF SINGULARITIES

7.1. Need for analysis of singularities. In our considerations of multiple points we have been concerned only with the multiplicities of the points. The following example will suggest the need of further investigation of these points. The curve

$$x^4 + x^2 y^2 - y^2 - 2a^2 x^2 + a^4 = 0$$

is irreducible for any value of a, and for $a \neq 0$ it has ordinary double points at $(\pm a, 0)$ as well as one at the infinite point on the y-axis. It is, therefore, rational for $a \neq 0$ (Theorem 5.1), and in fact we may take

$$(7.1) \quad \phi(\lambda) = \frac{\lambda^2 - 1}{\lambda^2 + 1}, \quad \psi(\lambda) = \frac{(1 - a^2)(\lambda^4 - 1) - 2\lambda^2(1 + a^2)}{2\lambda(\lambda^2 + 1)}.$$

For $a = 0$ the curve has only two double points, one at the origin and one at infinity, but the former is not ordinary. It is obvious that this curve is also rational, for if we put $a = 0$ in (7.1) we have a rational parametrization. These considerations suggest that we regard the singularity at the origin as two "coincident" or "neighboring" double points, so that we can still apply Theorem 5.1 in some extended sense. One of the general methods of defining such neighboring singularities is by means of quadratic transformations.

7.2. Quadratic transformations. We consider two projective planes S_2 and S_2', and a relation between their points defined by

$$(7.2) \qquad\qquad y_i = x_j x_k,$$

where $i, j, k = 0, 1, 2$, and i, j, k, are all different; x_0, x_1, x_2 are the coordinates of a point of S_2 in some specified coordinate system, and (y) is similarly a point of S_2'. We call the correspondence set up by (7.2) a *quadratic transformation* of S_2 into S_2', and denote it by the letter T. The transform (y) of (x) may then be denoted by $T(x)$. T has the following properties:

(i) Each point of S_2, with the exception of $(1,0,0),(0,1,0)$, and $(0,0,1)$, is transformed into a unique point of S_2'. The three exceptional points are called *fundamental points* of the transformation, and their transforms are not defined by (7.2).

(ii) Any non-fundamental point of the line $x_i = 0$ is transformed into the point $y_i = 1$, $y_j = 0$, $y_k = 0$. These three lines are called *irregular lines** of the transformation.

Designate by T' the corresponding transformation

$$x_i = y_j y_k$$

from S_2' to S_2. It of course also has properties similar to (i) and (ii). We also have

(iii) If (x) is a point not on an irregular line of T, then $(y) = T(x)$ is not on an irregular line of T', and $T'(y) = (x)$.

Since the analogous property holds for T' we see that T and T' set up a one-to-one correspondence between the points of S_2 and S_2' not on any irregular line, and that T and T' are inverse transformations of these points.

7.3. Transformation of a curve. If

$$F(x_0,x_1,x_2) = F(x_i) = 0$$

is a curve in S_2, the transforms of its points will satisfy the equation

$$G(y_i) = F(y_j y_k) = F(y_1 y_2, y_2 y_0, y_0 y_1) = 0.$$

We shall refer to the curve G as the *algebraic* transform of F. But to see the precise geometric relation between F and G we must consider what happens when F contains a fundamental point. Take the simple case in which F is a line $L = \Sigma a_i x_i$.

Case 1. If no $a_i = 0$, L is not on any fundamental point, and so each point of L has a unique transform. These transforms lie on the conic $C = \Sigma a_i y_j y_k$, which contains the fundamental points of T' but has no other points in common with the irregular lines. It is then easy to see that the correspondence between L and C is one-to-one, the fundamental points on C corresponding to the intersections of L with the irregular lines of T, and the rest of the points being taken care of by (iii).

Case 2. Let $L = x_1 + \lambda x_2$ be a line on one fundamental point. Its

---

* These are usually referred to as "fundamental lines" in the literature. O. Zariski (*Trans. Amer. Math. Soc.*, *53* (1943), 515) has pointed out that this double use of the word "fundamental" can cause confusion, and has proposed the use of the term "irregular."

algebraic transform is $y_2y_0 + \lambda y_0y_1$, a reducible conic consisting of the line $L' = y_2 + \lambda y_1$ and the irregular line y_0. As in Case 1 we can show that the transformation between L and L' is one-to-one. We are, therefore, led to regard L' as the true geometric transform of L, the extra component y_0 being merely an extraneous factor introduced in the algebra.

Case 3. If $L = x_0$ is an irregular line its algebraic transform y_1y_2 is a pair of irregular lines. But every point of L whose transform is defined is transformed into $(1,0,0)$, and so we regard the transform of L to be this single point. This is an unpleasant situation which we shall avoid by never considering curves having irregular lines as components.

From these special cases we are led to the following definition. Let $F(x) = 0$ be a curve having no irregular line as a component, and let

$$G(y) = F(y_1y_2, y_2y_0, y_0y_1)$$

be the algebraic transform of F. If $G(y) = \pi(y)F'(y)$, where π is a product of powers of the y_i, and F' is not divisible by any y_i, we say that F' is the transform of F by T. We then have the following theorem.

THEOREM 7.1. *If F' is the transform of F by T then F is the transform of F' by T'. With a finite number of exceptions the points of F and F' are in one-to-one correspondence, and the components of F and F' also correspond.*

PROOF. We have

(7.3) $$F(y_1y_2, y_2y_0, y_0y_1) = \pi_1(y)F'(y_0, y_1, y_2);$$

and similarly

(7.4) $$F'(x_1x_2, x_2x_0, x_0x_1) = \pi_2(x)F''(x_0, x_1, x_2),$$

where F'' is the transform of F' by T'. Replacing y_i in (7.3) by x_jx_k we obtain

$$F(x_0^2x_1x_2, x_0x_1^2x_2, x_0x_1x_2^2) = \pi_3(x)F'(x_1x_2, x_2x_0, x_0x_1)$$
$$= \pi_4(x)F''(x_0, x_1, x_2),$$

the π's indicating products of powers of the variables. But since F is homogeneous

$$F(x_0^2x_1x_2, x_0x_1^2x_2, x_0x_1x_2^2) = (x_0x_1x_2)^nF(x_0, x_1, x_2).$$

Since neither F nor F'' is divisible by any x_i we must have $F'' = F$. The one-to-one correspondence between the points now follows from (iii), since F and F' have only a finite set of points in common with the irregular lines. The correspondence between the factors of F and F' is an immediate consequence of (7.3) and (7.4).

7.4. Transformation of a singularity. As indicated in §7.1, we are going to be interested in the effects of a quadratic transformation on the singular points of a curve. Before considering the general case we refer to the example of Case 2 above. In the correspondence between L and L', the fundamental point $P = (1,0,0)$ on L corresponds to the point $(0,1,-\lambda)$ in which L' intersects the irregular line $y_0 = 0$. By giving different values to λ we may make P correspond to different points of $y_0 = 0$. Hence, in a sense, to the points of the irregular line $y_0 = 0$ correspond the *directions* at the fundamental point $(1,0,0)$. We shall now see that this correspondence applies to any curve, so that to the intersections of F' with an irregular line correspond the tangents to F at the corresponding fundamental point.

THEOREM 7.2. *Let F be a curve of order n, having an r_i-fold point, $r_i \geqslant 0$, at the fundamental point $x_j = x_k = 0$ $(i,j,k,$ all different), no tangent at any of these points being an irregular line. Then*

(i) *The algebraic transform G of F has the line $y_i = 0$ as an r_i-fold component, and so F' is of order $2n - \Sigma r_i$.*

(ii) *There is a one-to-one correspondence, preserving multiplicities, between the tangents to F at $x_j = x_k = 0$ and the non-fundamental intersections of F' with $y_i = 0$.*

(iii) *F' has multiplicity $n - r_j - r_k$ at $y_j = y_k = 0$, the tangents being distinct from the irregular lines and corresponding to the non-fundamental intersections of F with $x_i = 0$.*

PROOF. We concentrate on the fundamental point $(1,0,0)$. F must have the form

$$F(x) = x_0^{n-r_0}A_{r_0}(x_1 x_2) + x_0^{n-r_0-1}A_{r_0+1}(x_1,x_2) + \cdots + A_n(x_1,x_2),$$

where A_p is a homogeneous polynomial of degree p and $A_{r_0}A_n \neq 0$. Hence

$$G = F(y_j y_k) = y_1^{n-r_0}y_2^{n-r_0}A_{r_0}(y_2 y_0, y_0 y_1) + \cdots + A_n(y_2 y_0, y_0 y_1)$$
$$= y_1^{n-r_0}y_2^{n-r_0}y_0^{r_0}A_{r_0}(y_2,y_1) + \cdots + y_0^n A_n(y_2,y_1).$$

Hence $y_0^{r_0}$ is the highest power of y_0 that can be factored from G, and since y_1 and y_2 can be treated similarly, (i) is proved. To prove (ii) we merely note that the tangents to F at $(1,0,0)$ are the components of the curve $A_{r_0}(x_1,x_2) = 0$, while the intersections of F' with $y_0 = 0$ are the roots of

$$y_1^{n-r_0-r_1}y_2^{n-r_0-r_2}A_{r_0}(y_2,y_1) = 0.$$

The stated correspondence is then obvious. As for (iii), we have

$$F' = y_1^{n-r_0-r_1}y_2^{n-r_0-r_2}A_{r_0}(y_2,y_1) + \cdots + y_0^{n-r_0}y_1^{-r_1}y_2^{-r_2}A_n(y_2,y_1),$$

and the multiplicity of F' at $(1,0,0)$ is the degree of the polynomial

$$B(y_1,y_2) = y_1^{-r_1}y_2^{-r_2}A_n(y_2,y_1),$$

which is of course $n - r_1 - r_2$. Furthermore, the tangents here are the components of the curve $B(y_1,y_2) = 0$. If one of these were irregular $A_n(y_2,y_1)$ would be divisible by, say, y_1 to a power $r > r_1$. In that case F would have r intersections with the line $x_0 = 0$ at $(0,1,0)$, which would mean that one of the tangents here is the irregular line $x_0 = 0$, contrary to assumption. The last part of (iii) now follows by applying (ii) to the transformation T'.

As a slight check on the correctness of this theorem we can consider the effect of applying T followed by T'. T changes n,r_0,r_1,r_2 into

$$n' = 2n - r_0 - r_1 - r_2, \quad r_0' = n - r_1 - r_2,$$

$$r_1' = n - r_2 - r_0, \quad r_2' = n - r_0 - r_1,$$

respectively. T' will change n',r_0',r_1',r_2', into n'',r_0'',r_1'',r_2'', defined similarly. By direct substitution we find that $n'' = n,r_i'' = r_i$, as must be the case.

Since the transformation T transforms real points into real points, Theorem 7.2 can be well illustrated by a figure. In Figure 7.1 is shown a curve F obtained from

$$x_1(x_1^4 + x_2^4 - 2x_0x_1x_2^2) = 0$$

by a change of coordinates, and its transform F'. In the new coordinate system we have

$$n = 5, \quad r_0 = 4, \quad r_1 = 0, \quad r_2 = 1.$$

Hence

$$n' = 10 - 4 - 0 - 1 = 5, \quad r_0' = 5 - 0 - 1 = 4,$$

$$r_1' = 5 - 1 - 4 = 0, \quad r_2' = 5 - 4 - 0 = 1.$$

The four tangents to F at $(1,0,0)$ are coincident in pairs, and so F' has two double intersections with $y_0 = 0$. F has four simple intersections with $x_0 = 0$, and so F' has four distinct tangents at $(1,0,0)$.

There is no great difficulty in extending Theorem 7.2 by removing the restriction on the tangents at the fundamental points. As we shall have no occasion to use this extension, its precise wording and proof are left to the reader.

The following theorem will complete our investigation of the behavior of singular points under a quadratic transformation.

THEOREM 7.3. *An r-fold point of F not on an irregular line is transformed into an r-fold point of F', and the tangents at these two points correspond in multiplicities.*

PROOF. We may assume that the given r-fold point P is the unit point, so that its transform P' has the same coordinates. For if $P = (a_0, a_1, a_2)$ and we introduce new coordinates

$$x'_i = a_i^{-1} x_i, \quad y'_i = a_i y_i,$$

then the equations of the quadratic transformation have the same form $y'_i = x'_j x'_k$, and in the new coordinates $P = (1,1,1)$. Since G and F'

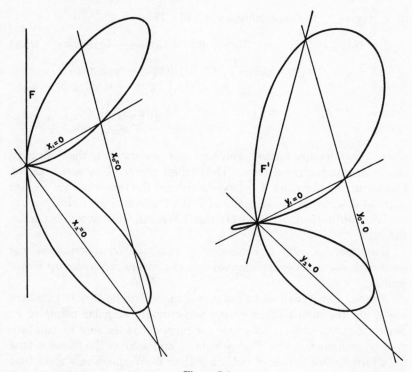

Figure 7.1

differ only by components which do not contain P', it will be sufficient to prove the theorem for G instead of F'. Let

$$z_0 = x_0, \quad z_1 = x_1 - x_0, \quad z_2 = x_2 - x_0$$

define a change of coordinates in S_2. Then P has z-coordinates $(1,0,0)$, and so

$$F(x) = F_1(z) = z_0^{n-r} A_r(z_1, z_2) + \cdots + A_n(z_1, z_2)$$
$$= x_0^{n-r} A_r(x_1 - x_0, x_2 - x_0) + \cdots + A_n(x_1 - x_0, x_2 - x_0).$$

Hence

$$G(y) = y_1^{n-r} y_2^{n-r} A_r(y_2 y_0 - y_1 y_2, \ y_0 y_1 - y_1 y_2) + \cdots$$
$$+ A_n(y_2 y_0 - y_1 y_2, \ y_0 y_1 - y_1 y_2).$$

We make a similar change of coordinates

$$w_0 = y_0, \quad w_1 = y_0 - y_1, \quad w_2 = y_0 - y_2$$

in S_2' to give P' the w-coordinates $(1,0,0)$. Then

$$G(y) = G_1(w) = (w_0 - w_1)^{n-r}(w_0 - w_2)^{n-r} A_r(w_0 w_1 - w_1 w_2, w_0 w_2 - w_1 w_2)$$
$$+ (w_0 - w_1)^{n-r-1}(w_0 - w_2)^{n-r-1} A_{r+1}(w_0 w_1 - w_1 w_2, w_0 w_2 - w_1 w_2)$$
$$+ \cdots + A_n(w_0 w_1 - w_1 w_2, \ w_0 w_2 - w_1 w_2)$$

$$= w_0^{2n-r} A_r(w_1, w_2) + (\cdots) + w_0^{2n-r-1} A_{r+1}(w_1, w_2) + (\cdots)$$
$$+ \cdots + w_0^n A_n(w_1, w_2) + (\cdots),$$

where $(\cdots)$ denotes terms involving lower powers of w_0 than occur in the preceding indicated term. The highest power of w_0 occurs in the first term, and therefore $A_r(w_1, w_2)$ determines the tangents at P'. Since $A_r(z_1, z_2)$ determines the tangents at P the theorem is proved.

7.5. Reduction of singularities. We can now prove our main theorem.

THEOREM 7.4. *By a succession of quadratic transformations any irreducible curve can be transformed into one having only ordinary singularities.*

PROOF. Let us define the *index* of a curve F to be $\Sigma(r_i - 1)$, where the r_i are the multiplicities of the non-ordinary singular points of F. Since the theorem is trivially true for curves of index zero we can proceed by induction, so let F have index I and assume the theorem true for all irreducible curves of index less than I. We need only show that F can be transformed into a curve of index less than I.

Let P be a non-ordinary r-fold point of F. There exists a coordinate system in which

    (i) P has coordinates $(1,0,0)$;

    (ii)   The lines $x_1 = 0$ and $x_2 = 0$ each intersect F in $n - r$ distinct points other than P (Theorem 2.6);

    (iii)   The line $x_0 = 0$ intersects $x_1 x_2 F$ in $n + 2$ distinct points (Theorem 2.2).

F then has the form required for the application of Theorem 7.2, with $r_0 = r$, $r_1 = r_2 = 0$. On transforming F by the transformation T we therefore obtain an irreducible curve F' with the following properties:

(iv) F' is of order $2n - r$ (Theorem 7.2 (i));

(v)   Any singularity of F other than P is transformed into one of the same multiplicity; if it is ordinary its transform is ordinary (Theorem 7.3);

(vi) F' has three new ordinary singularities, one of order n and two of order $n - r$ (Theorem 7.2 (iii));

(vii)   Corresponding to P, F' has certain points P'_α, $\alpha = 1, \cdots, k$, on the irregular line $y_0 = 0$ (Theorem 7.2 (ii)).

The singularities of F' arising from (v) and (vi) cause no change in the index of the curve. But if r'_α is the multiplicity of P'_α, then the index of F' is less than that of F by an amount

$$h \geqslant (r - 1) - \Sigma_{\alpha=1}^{k}(r'_\alpha - 1).$$

Now from Theorem 7.2 (ii), $\Sigma r'_\alpha \leqslant r$, for the number of intersections of $y_0 = 0$ with F' at the P'_α, which is certainly $\geqslant \Sigma r'_\alpha$, is equal to the sum of the multiplicities of F at P, which is r. Hence

$$h \geqslant (r - 1) - (\Sigma r'_\alpha - k) \geqslant (r - 1) - (r - k) = k - 1 \geqslant 0,$$

and $h = 0$ only if $k = 1$ and $r'_1 = r$. If the inequality holds F' has index $< I$ and the theorem is proved. If the equality holds we treat F' as we did F, applying a quadratic transformation with P' as the fundamental point, and continue this process until the index is finally lowered. To see that such a lowering eventually occurs consider the curve F_{p+1} obtained from F by a sequence of $p + 1$ transformations for each of which $h = 0$. F_{p+1} has order $n_{p+1} = 2n_p - r$ and among its singular points are the following: two of each of the multiplicities $n - r$, $n_1 - r$, $\cdots$, $n_p - r$, and one of each of the multiplicities $n, n_1, \cdots, n_p$. By Theorem 4.4 the integer

$$M_{p+1} = (n_{p+1} - 1)(n_{p+1} - 2) - 2\Sigma_{i=0}^{p}(n_i - r)(n_i - r - 1)$$
$$- \Sigma_{i=0}^{p} n_i (n_i - 1),$$

where $n_0 = n$, must be non-negative. But we find that

$$M_{p+1} - M_p = - r(r - 1) \leqslant -2,$$

since $r \geqslant 2$, and so p cannot be arbitrarily large. This completes the proof of the theorem.

This theorem, besides being interesting in itself, is very useful in investigating certain properties of curves, particularly those connected with the theory of linear series (Chapter VI). At present we point out one application to the study of rational curves. It is easy to see that a quadratic transform of a rational curve is again rational. Hence the sufficiency condition of Theorem 5.1 can be applied to the simplified curve obtained by the application of Theorem 7.4. It is shown in §VI-5.3 that in this case the condition is also necessary, so that we have a complete characterization of rational curves.

By making use of the inequality stated in §4.4, Exercise 3, Theorem 7.4 can be extended to include any curve with distinct components. We need merely add $k - 1$ to M_p to make the above proof apply.

7.6. Neighboring points. By means of quadratic transformations we can give an interesting and useful description of a complicated singularity. Let P be an r-fold point of a curve F with distinct components. If P is one of the fundamental points of the transformation of Theorem 7.2, the point P is replaced on the transformed curve F' by points $P'_1, P'_2, \cdots, P'_k$ of multiplicities $r'_1, r'_2, \cdots, r'_k$. We express this situation in other words by saying that *in the first neighborhood of P, F has points $P_1, \cdots, P_k$, of multiplicities $r'_1, \cdots, r'_k$.* It must be realized that these "neighboring points" P_α are not points at all, in the ordinary sense of the word, but are merely a verbal device used to describe a certain property of the curve F. Thus the statement that the curve F in Figure 7.1 has one double and one simple point in its first neighborhood means neither more nor less than that F' has one double and one simple point on the line $y_0 = 0$, exclusive of the fundamental points.

This verbal device is useful because it turns out that the neighboring points can be assigned properties similar to those of ordinary points. We first of all define P'_α to be the transform of P_α by the transformation T. With this convention, each point of F' is the transform of one or more points of F, including those in the first neighborhood of P. Also every point of F is transformed into a point of F' except P, which simply disappears. Since, for a specific transformation T, the position of P'_α depends on the direction of the corresponding tangent to F at P, we shall say that the "position" of the neighboring point P_α is determined by this tangent. Two curves F_1 and F_2 with a common point P shall, therefore, be said to have a common point P_α in the first neighborhood of P if they have a common tangent at P; or, in other words, if their transforms F'_1 and F'_2 by the same transformation T have the common point P'_α.

This terminology is easily extended. If F' has a point P_β of multiplicity r''_β in the first neighborhood of P'_α we shall say that this point is the transform of an r''_β-fold point P_β of F in the first neighborhood of P_α and in the *second* neighborhood of P. This process can obviously be extended to define points of F in neighborhoods of arbitrarily high order.

Examples. 1. If P is a simple point of F it can have only one corresponding point P' on F'. That is, a simple point of F has just one point of F, also simple, in its first neighborhood. It follows immediately, then, that the same is true of every neighborhood, and so the analysis of neighboring points can be stopped whenever a simple point is reached.

2. Let P be an ordinary r-fold point of F. On F', P is replaced by r simple points $P'_1, \cdots, P'_r$. Hence P has r simple points in its first neighborhood.

3. In §7.1 we saw that the curve $x^4 + x^2y^2 - y^2 = 0$ had at the origin a double point P which was not ordinary but which seemed to take the place of two ordinary double points. To apply our quadratic transformation to P we want first of all to change the coordinates, as the x-axis is tangent to the curve at P. A convenient change is to replace y by $y - x$; then introducing the projective coordinates we have

$$F = x_1^4 + x_1^2(x_2 - x_1)^2 - (x_2 - x_1)^2 x_0^2.$$

Then

$$F' = y_2^2 y_0^2 + y_0^2(y_1 - y_2)^2 - (y_1 - y_2)^2 y_1^2,$$

and on this curve the point $P' = (0,1,1)$ corresponds to P. Replacing y_2 by $y'_2 + y_1$, F' becomes

$$(y_1 + y'_2)^2 y_0^2 + y_0^2 y_2'^2 - y_1^2 y_2'^2 = 0,$$

and P' is $(0,1,0)$. F', therefore, has an ordinary double point at P', and so the singularity of F at P consists of a double point with a double point in its first neighborhood and two simple points in its second neighborhood. This type of singularity is known as a *tacnode*. (See §2.4, Example 4.)

4. Let P be the origin on the curve $y^2 + x^3 = 0$, §2.4, Example 3. As above, we replace this by

$$F = x_1^3 + (x_2 - x_1)^2 x_0,$$

and find that

$$F' = y_2^2 y_0 + (y_1 - y_2)^2 y_1,$$

or

$$(y'_2 + y_1)^2 y_0 + y_2'^2 y_1 = 0,$$

on which the one point P' corresponding to P is at $(0,1,0)$. P' is a simple point of F'. Thus a cusp consists of a double point with one simple point in its first neighborhood.

An immediate consequence of Theorem 7.4 is the fact that *there are at most a finite number of singular points in the neighborhoods of any point of an irreducible curve.* Hence the analysis of a singularity in terms of neighboring singularities is a finite process, and leads to a complete classification of all singular points. There is one objection to this process, however, which the critical reader may have already noticed. In reducing a singularity there is at each step a wide variety of choice in the selection of the coordinates and hence of the transformation T. We have given no proof that the final analysis of the singularity is independent of this choice. Such a proof can be given, but it is quite long and complicated, and it involves ideas which we have not yet taken up. As we shall have no occasion to use this result we shall not give the proof; the interested reader is referred to van der Waerden, *Einführung in die algebraische Geometrie*, Chapter IX.

7.7. Intersections at neighboring points. Even without assuming the uniqueness of the analysis of a singularity we can prove two interesting properties of the singularities of a curve. We first make a slight extension of the method of determining neighboring singularities of a curve F. By Theorem 7.4 there is a finite sequence of quadratic transformations $T_1, T_2, \cdots, T_k$, such that if F_{p+1} is the transform of F_p by T_p (starting with $F_1 = F$) then T_p satisfies the conditions (i), (ii), (iii), in the proof of Theorem 7.4 with respect to F_p; furthermore, F_{k+1} has only ordinary multiple points, and hence no neighboring singularities (see Example 2 above). Each of the transformations T_p has a vital effect on only one singularity of the corresponding F_p; any other singular point P of F_p is transformed into a singular point P' of F_{p+1} of the same multiplicity. We adopt the further convention that T_p transforms a point of F_p in the r-th neighborhood of P into a point of the same multiplicity in the r-th neighborhood of P'. This is in accord with Theorem 7.3. The sequence of transformations $T_1, T_2, \cdots, T_k$, then serves to define all the neighboring singularities of the curve F in the manner described in §7.6.

In this method of defining the neighboring singularities of F there is a choice not only in the selection of the irregular lines of the individual transformations T_p but also of the order in which the singularities are chosen as fundamental points. Here again we shall make no attempt to prove the invariance of the definition but shall always consider the neighboring singularities as defined with respect to a particular sequence of transformations.

In the same way we can define the neighboring points common to two curves. If F and G have no common components and if neither has a multiple component there is a sequence of transformations which eliminates the non-ordinary singularities of the curve FG. This sequence then not only reduces the singularities of F and G separately, but also reduces F and G to curves F_{k+1} and G_{k+1} having no common tangents at any of their intersections, and hence having no common neighboring points. We can then define, in an obvious way, the common neighboring points of F and G with respect to this sequence of transformations.

We now prove an extension of Theorem 4.4.

THEOREM 7.5. *Let* $r_1, r_2, \cdots$ *be the multiplicities of all the singular points* (*including the neighboring ones*) *of an irreducible curve F of order n. Then*

$$(n - 1)(n - 2) \geqslant \Sigma r_i(r_i - 1).$$

PROOF. The neighboring singularities of F are defined with respect to a certain sequence of transformations $T_1, \cdots, T_k$. Consider the effect of T_1 on the number

$$N = (n - 1)(n - 2) - \Sigma r_i(r_i - 1).$$

Let the fundamental point P of T_1 on F have multiplicity r_1. Then F_2 is of order $2n - r_1$, and has singularities of multiplicities $r_2, r_3, \cdots$ which are the transforms of the non-fundamental ones of F plus those in the neighborhood of P, and in addition has three ordinary singularities of multiplicities $n, n - r_1, n - r_1$. The singularity of F of order r_1 disappears completely. Hence for F_2 we have

$$N_2 = (2n - r_1 - 1)(2n - r_1 - 2) - [\Sigma r_i(r_i - 1) - r_1(r_1 - 1)]$$
$$- n(n - 1) - 2(n - r_1)(n - r_1 - 1),$$

which reduces to N. Similarly we obtain $N_{k+1} = N_k = \cdots = N_2 = N$. But F_{k+1} has no neighboring singularities, and so by Theorem 4.4, $N_{k+1} \geqslant 0$. Hence $N \geqslant 0$, which proves the theorem.

We have actually proved a stronger theorem than the one stated. We have shown that the non-negative integer N associated with the curve F and the sequence of transformations $T_1, T_2, \cdots$ remains unchanged when these transformations are successively applied to F. We shall see later that N is invariant under a much more general type of transformation, and is, in fact, the most important invariant of an irreducible curve.

A similar extension of Theorem 3.3 can be made.

THEOREM 7.6. *Let F and G be two curves, of orders m and n, having no common components and neither F nor G having any multiple components, and let F and G have multiplicities r_i, s_i at their common points, including the neighboring ones. Then* $mn \geqslant \Sigma r_i s_i$.

PROOF. Proceeding as in the proof of Theorem 7.5, if we let

$$N = mn \overset{!}{-} \Sigma r_i s_i,$$

then

$$N_2 = (2m - r_1)(2n - s_1) - [\Sigma r_i s_i - r_1 s_1] - mn - 2(m - r_1)(n - s_1)$$
$$= N.$$

Hence, as before, $N_{k+1} = N$. But $N_{k+1} \geqslant 0$ by Theorem 3.3, and so $N \geqslant 0$.

Here again we have proved more than was indicated in the statement of the theorem. By a careful examination of the resultant $R(x)$ in Theorem 3.2 it can be shown that if F and G have no common tangent at a common point then there corresponds to this point a root of the resultant of multiplicity exactly rs. However, a simpler proof of this fact will be given later (Theorem IV-5.10). Applying this to F_{k+1} and G_{k+1} we find that $N_{k+1} = 0$. Hence $N = 0$ and $\Sigma r_i s_i$ actually equals mn.

7.8. Exercises. 1. After a change of coordinates in the x- and y-planes, the equations (7.2) of the quadratic transformation become

$$y_i = G_i(x), \quad i = 0,1,2,$$

where the G_i are independent conics having three common non-collinear points. Conversely, if G_0, G_1, G_2 are three such conics then the transformation $y_i = G_i(x)$ can be reduced to the form (7.2) by proper choice of coordinate systems.

2. If $r_1, r_2, \cdots$ are the multiplicities of the singular points, including the neighboring ones, of an irreducible curve of order n, then the curve is rational if $(n - 1)(n - 2) = \Sigma r_i(r_i - 1)$.

3. The ramphoid cusp (§2.4, Example 5), is a double point with one double point in the first neighborhood and one simple point in the second.

4. Analyze the singularities of each of the following curves.

(a) $x_0(x_1^2 - x_0 x_2)^2 - x_1^5 = 0$.

(b) $x_1^4 + x_1^3 x_2 - x_0^2 x_2^2 = 0$.

5. Verify that for the two curves of Exercise 4 we have $\Sigma r_i s_i = mn$.

IV. Formal Power Series

Let K be the real or the complex field and let the curve $f(x,y) = 0$ have a non-singular point at (x_0,y_0). Then at least one of $f_x(x_0,y_0)$, $f_y(x_0,y_0)$ is different from zero, and we may assume that $f_y(x_0,y_0) \neq 0$. From the implicit function theorem it follows that there is a function $y(x)$, analytic in some neighborhood of x_0, such that

(i) $y(x_0) = y_0$,

(ii) $f(x,y(x)) = 0$,

(iii) For every point (x,y) of f in a suitable neighborhood of (x_0,y_0), $y = y(x)$.

$y(x)$ can be expressed as a power series in $x - x_0$, the series converging in a neighborhood of x_0.

If K is a complex field, and (x_0,y_0) is any point of f, singular or not, one can show (see, for example, E. Picard, *Traité d'Analyse*, Gauthier-Villars, Paris, Vol. II, Chapter 13, or van der Waerden, *Einführung in die Algebraische Geometrie*, §14), that there exists a finite number of pairs of functions $x(t)$, $y(t)$, analytic in a neighborhood of $t = 0$, such that

(i) $x(0) = x_0$, $y(0) = y_0$,

(ii) $f(x(t), y(t)) = 0$,

(iii) For every point (x,y) of f, other than (x_0,y_0), in a suitable neighborhood of (x_0,y_0), there is exactly one of the pairs of functions and a unique value of t in its region of definition such that $x = x(t)$, $y = y(t)$.

Such parametrizations of the portion of a curve in the neighborhood of one of its points have proved very useful in investigations of the structure of singular points and of the intersections of curves at singular points. In the present chapter we shall use the so-called formal power series to obtain an analogous development, as far as this is possible, over a more general ground field.

§1. FORMAL POWER SERIES

1.1. The domain and the field of formal power series. In §I-5 a polynomial over a domain D was defined to be a formal finite sum, $a_0 + a_1x + \cdots + a_nx^n$, the a_i belonging to D and x being an indeterminate. If we allow infinite sums of this type, $a_0 + a_1x + \cdots + a_nx^n + \cdots$, we obtain a set of quantities which are called *formal power series* over D. They can be added and multiplied just like polynomials, and they constitute a domain $D[x]'$. $D[x]' \supset D[x]$, for the power series with only a finite number of non-zero coefficients are essentially polynomials. We adopt the same abbreviations of notation as were used for polynomials.

THEOREM 1.1. $a_0 + a_1x + \cdots$ *is a unit in* $D[x]'$ *if and only if* a_0 *is a unit in* D.

PROOF. If a_0 is a unit define $b_0, b_1, \cdots, b_n, \cdots$ by

$$a_0b_0 = 1,$$
$$a_0b_1 + a_1b_0 = 0,$$
$$a_0b_2 + a_1b_1 + a_2b_0 = 0,$$
$$\cdots$$
$$a_0b_n + a_1b_{n-1} + \cdots + a_nb_0 = 0,$$
$$\cdots$$

Then

(1.1) $$(a_0 + a_1x + \cdots)(b_0 + b_1x + \cdots) = 1.$$

Conversely, if (1.1) holds, then $a_0b_0 = 1$ and a_0 is a unit.

THEOREM 1.2. *If* K *is a field, any element of the quotient field* $K(x)'$ *of* $K[x]'$ *can be written in the form*

$$\frac{a_0 + a_1x + \cdots}{x^h}, \; h \geqslant 0.$$

PROOF. If

$$f = \frac{b_0 + b_1x + \cdots}{c_0 + c_1x + \cdots} \in K(x)',$$

let h be the least integer for which $c_h \neq 0$. Since K is a field c_h is a unit, and so $c_h + c_{h+1}x + c_{h+2}x^2 + \cdots$ has an inverse $d_0 + d_1x + \cdots$. Then

$$f = \frac{(b_0 + b_1x + \cdots)(d_0 + d_1x + \cdots)}{x^h(c_h + c_{h+1}x + \cdots)(d_0 + d_1x + \cdots)} = \frac{a_0 + a_1x + \cdots}{x^h}.$$

We can conveniently write

$$f = x^{-h}(a_0 + a_1x + \cdots) = a_0x^{-h} + a_1x^{-h+1} + \cdots.$$

That is, $K(x)'$ consists of formal power series with a finite number of terms with negative exponents. These can be added and multiplied just like elements of $K[x]'$. Every non-zero element of $K(x)'$ can be expressed uniquely in the form

$$f = x^k(a_0 + a_1x + \cdots),$$

where k is an integer and $a_0 \neq 0$. k is said to be the *order* of f, and will be indicated by $O(f)$. We readily find that

(i) $O(fg) = O(f) + O(g)$,

(ii) $O(f \pm g) \geqslant \min [O(f), O(g)]$; moreover the equality holds whenever $O(f) \neq O(g)$.

It will be convenient to define $O(0) = \infty$, where the symbol ∞ has the properties $\infty > n$, $\infty + n = n + \infty = \infty$, for any integer n, and $\infty + \infty = \infty$. Then (i) and (ii) hold for all elements f and g of $K(x)'$.

1.2. Substitution in power series. In the applications of power series to algebraic curves there is no need to consider power series over an arbitrary domain; hence we shall assume from now on that our set of constants is a field K. Many of our theorems will be true, with perhaps slight alterations, over more general domains, but these extensions will be left to the reader.

The theory of polynomials centers chiefly around the process of factoring, and we might expect a similar situation to hold for power series. However, things turn out to be much simpler in $K[x]'$ than in $K[x]$, for from Theorem 1.1 it follows at once that any non-zero element of $K[x]'$ is associate to a power of x, and hence that $f \mid g$ if and only if $O(f) \leqslant O(g)$.

The substitution of a constant for the indeterminant x in a power series is usually meaningless. However, if the series has only a finite number of non-zero coefficients it is essentially an element of $K(x)$, and so substitution is possible. Also, if $f(x) = a_0 + a_1x + \cdots \in K[x]'$, we can define $f(0) = a_0$. But in other cases it is difficult to give a satisfactory meaning to $f(a)$ unless there is some notion of continuity in K by means of which the convergence of an infinite series can be defined.

We can, however, define a substitution of one power series into another, and this will prove to be an important process. To carry out this process systematically, we shall use the notion of *congruence*. Two elements, f and g, of $K[x]'$ are said to be congruent modulo x^m, written $f \equiv g \pmod{x^m}$, if $f - g$ is divisible by x^m. Other ways of expressing this are to say that $O(f - g) \geqslant m$, or that the first m coefficients of f and g are equal. The fundamental properties of congruences are stated in

THEOREM 1.3. (i) *Congruence modulo x^m is an equivalence relation.*

(ii) *If*

$$f_1 \equiv f_2, \quad g_1 \equiv g_2 \pmod{x^m},$$

then

$$f_1 \pm g_1 \equiv f_2 \pm g_2, \quad f_1 g_1 \equiv f_2 g_2 \pmod{x^m}.$$

(iii) *If $f \equiv g \pmod{x^m}$ for arbitrarily large m, then $f = g$.*

(iv)   *If f_1 and f_2 are polynomials, if $O(g_1), O(g_2) > 0$, and if $f_1 \equiv f_2$, $g_1 \equiv g_2$ (mod x^m), then $f_1(g_1) \equiv f_2(g_2)$ (mod x^m).*

(v)   *If $f_1, f_2, \cdots$ are elements of $K[x]'$ such that*

$$f_{m+1} \equiv f_m \pmod{x^m}, \quad m = 1, 2, \cdots,$$

then there is a unique $f \in K[x]'$ such that

$$f_m \equiv f \pmod{x^m}, \quad m = 1, 2, \cdots.$$

PROOF.   (i), (ii), and (iii) follow at once from the last comment of the preceding paragraph. For (iv) we write $f_1 = f_2 + x^m f_3$, where f_3 is a polynomial. By repeated application of (ii) we have

$$f_1(g_1) \equiv f_2(g_2) + g_2^m f_3(g_2) \pmod{x^m}.$$

Since

$$O(g_2^m f_3(g_2)) = m O(g_2) + O(f_3(g_2)) \geqq m,$$

this gives the desired result. To prove (v) note that we must have

$$f_1 = a_{10} + a_{11}x + a_{12}x^2 + \cdots,$$

$$f_2 = a_{10} + a_{21}x + a_{22}x^2 + \cdots,$$

$$f_3 = a_{10} + a_{21}x + a_{32}x^2 + \cdots,$$

$$f_m = a_{10} + a_{21}x + \cdots + a_{m,m-1}x^{m-1} + a_{mm}x^m + \cdots.$$

Hence if we put

$$f = a_{10} + a_{21}x + \cdots + a_{m+1,m}x^m + \cdots,$$

then $f_m \equiv f$ (mod x^m) for all m. If g is any other element of $K[x]'$ such that $f_m \equiv g$ (mod x^m) for all m, then by (i) $f \equiv g$ (mod x^m) for all m, and so $f = g$, by (iii). Hence f is unique.

Let $f, g \in K[x]'$ and let $O(g) > 0$. Let f_m and g_m, $m = 1, 2, \cdots$, be polynomials such that

$$f_m \equiv f, \quad g_m \equiv g \pmod{x^m}.$$

(f_m and g_m may be taken to be the sum of the first m terms of f and g respectively.) Then

$$f_{m+1} \equiv f_m, \quad g_{m+1} = g_m \pmod{x^m},$$

and by Theorem 1.3 (ii),

$$f_{m+1}(g_{m+1}) = f_m(g_m) \pmod{x_m}.$$

Hence there is a unique $h \in K[x]'$ such that

$$f_m(g_m) = h \pmod{x^m}, \quad m = 1, 2, \cdots.$$

If we start with a different set of polynomials f'_m and g'_m, we have

$$f'_m(g'_m) = f_m(g_m) \pmod{x^m},$$

and so h is uniquely determined. We write $h = f(g)$.

$f(g)$ is easily computed by formal expansion. If

$$f = a_0 + a_1 x + \cdots,$$
$$g = b_1 x + b_2 x^2 + \cdots,$$

then

$$f(g) = a_0 + a_1 g + a_2 g^2 + a_3 g^3 + \cdots$$
$$= a_0 + a_1 b_1 x + (a_1 b_2 + a_2 b_1^2) x^2$$
$$+ (a_1 b_3 + 2a_2 b_1 b_2 + a_3 b_1^3) x^3 + \cdots.$$

The useful properties of substitutions are stated in the following theorem:

THEOREM 1.4. (i) *For a fixed g, the correspondence $f \to f(g)$ is a homomorphism of $K[x]'$ into itself.*

(ii) *If $fg \neq 0$, $O(f(g)) = O(f)O(g)$.*

(iii) *If $O(g) > 0$, $O(h) > 0$, the result of substituting h in $f(g)$ is the same as that of substituting $g(h)$ in f.*

PROOF. (i) and (ii) are immediate consequences of the definition of $f(g)$. To prove (iii) let $k = f(g)$ and $l = g(h)$, let f_m, g_m, h_m, be polynomials congruent modulo x^m to the corresponding power series, and put $k_m = f_m(g_m)$, $l_m = g_m(h_m)$.

Then

$$k_m(h_m) = f_m(l_m).$$

But

$$k_m \equiv k, \quad h_m \equiv h, \quad f_m \equiv f, \quad l_m \equiv l \pmod{x^m},$$

and so

$$k_m(h_m) \equiv k(h), \quad f_m(l_m) \equiv f(l) \pmod{x^m},$$

from which follows

$$k(h) \equiv f(l) \pmod{x^m}.$$

Since this is true for arbitrary m, we must have $k(h) = f(l)$, which proves (iii).

We shall be particularly interested in the substitutions $f(g)$ in which $O(g) = 1$. These have the following properties.

THEOREM 1.5. *If* $O(g) = 1$, *and* $f' = f(g)$, *then*

(i) $O(f') = O(f)$.

(ii)   *There is a* g', $O(g') = 1$, *such that* $f = f'(g')$ *for every* $f \in K[x]'$.

PROOF. (i) is a special case of Theorem 1.4 (ii). To prove (ii) let $g = b_1x + b_2x^2 + \cdots$, $b_1 \neq 0$. If $g' = c_1x + c_2x^2 + \cdots$, we have

$$
\begin{aligned}
g(g') &= b_1g' + b_2g'^2 + \cdots \\
&= b_1c_1x + (b_1c_2 + b_2c_1^2)x^2 + (b_1c_3 + 2b_2c_1c_2 + b_3c_1^3)x^3 + \cdots \\
&\quad + (b_1c_n + P_n(b_2,\cdots,b_n,c_1,\cdots,c_{n-1}))x^n + \cdots,
\end{aligned}
$$

where P_n is a polynomial in the indicated arguments. If we therefore define c_1 by $b_1c_1 = 1$, and c_n, $n > 1$, by the recursion formula

$$c_n = -b_1^{-1}P_n(b_2,\cdots,b_n,c_1,\cdots,c_{n-1}),$$

we shall have $g(g') = x$. The required conclusion now follows from Theorem 1.4 (iii).

The conclusions of Theorem 1.5 may also be stated as follows: The homomorphism $f \to f(g)$ is an isomorphism over K of $K[x]'$ into itself (i.e. an *automorphism* of $K[x]'$ over K) which preserves the orders of the elements. We leave to the reader the proof of the converse theorem, that every order-preserving automorphism of $K[x]'$ over K is of the form $f \to f(g)$. We shall not need this theorem in our later work.

1.3. Derivatives. Just as for polynomials, if $f = \Sigma a_nx^n \in K[x]'$, we define the *derivative* of f to be $f' = \Sigma na_nx^{n-1}$.

To see that the properties of derivatives of polynomials extend to power series, we note first that $f_1 \equiv f_2 \pmod{x^m}$ implies $f_1' \equiv f_2' \pmod{x^{m-1}}$. Consider then, for example, the derivative of fg. Let f_m, g_m be polynomials such that

$$f \equiv f_m, \quad g \equiv g_m \pmod{x^m}, \quad m = 1,2,\cdots.$$

Then

$$fg \equiv f_mg_m \pmod{x^m},$$

and so

$$
\begin{aligned}
(fg)' &\equiv (f_mg_m)' \pmod{x^{m-1}} \\
&= f_mg_m' + f_m'g_m \\
&\equiv fg' + f'g \pmod{x^{m-1}}
\end{aligned}
$$

Since this is true for all m we must have

$$(fg)' = fg' + f'g.$$

The other formal properties of derivatives (see §I-8) can be obtained similarly.

1.4. Exercises. 1. Let $f \in D[x]'$ and define $|f|$ to be $2^{-\nu}$, $\nu = O(f)$. Then

   (i) $|fg| = |f| \, |g|$,

   (ii) $|f \pm g| \leqslant \max [\, |f|, |g| \,]$.

   (iii) $|f| = 0$ if and only if $f = 0$.

2. Using the above definition of absolute value and applying the usual definitions of analysis, prove the following:

   (i)   A sequence of power series f_n has a limit f if and only if $\lim_{n \to \infty} (f_{n+1} - f_n) = 0$.

   (ii) $\lim_{n \to \infty} \Sigma_{i=1}^{n} f_i$ exists if and only if $\lim_{n \to \infty} f_n = 0$.

   (iii) $a_0 + a_1 x + \cdots = \lim_{n \to \infty} (a_0 + a_1 x + \cdots + a_n x^n)$; that is, $D[x]$ is everywhere dense in $D[x]'$.

3. With this definition of absolute value, if $f_n(x)$ is a sequence of polynomials converging to $f(x)$, and if $|g(x)| < 1$, then $f_n(g)$ converges to $f(g)$.

4. The derivative $f'(x)$ of $f(x)$ can be defined as

$$\lim_{h(x) \to 0} \frac{f(x + h(x)) - f(x)}{h(x)}.$$

§2. PARAMETRIZATIONS

2.1. Parametrization of a curve. In our future work we shall use power series in an auxiliary variable t. We shall find it convenient to use dashed letters ($\bar{a}$, $\bar{x}$, etc.) for elements of $K(t)'$. An element of $K(t)'$ need not always be represented as a dashed letter—for instance, t is an element of $K(t)'$—but every dashed letter will be an element of $K(t)'$ (or of a closely related type of field to be introduced later).

Let $F(x) = 0$ be the equation of an algebraic curve C in the projective plane over a field K which is algebraically closed and of characteristic zero. If $\bar{x}_0, \bar{x}_1, \bar{x}_2$ are elements of $K(t)'$, we say that they are the coordinates of a *parametrization* of C provided

   (i) $F(\bar{x}) = 0$,

   (ii) There is no $\bar{e} \neq 0$, such that $\bar{e}\bar{x}_i \in K$, $i = 0,1,2$.

If $(\bar{x}_0, \bar{x}_1, \bar{x}_2)$ are the coordinates of a parametrization of C so are $(\bar{e}\bar{x}_0, \bar{e}\bar{x}_1, \bar{e}\bar{x}_2)$, where $\bar{e} \neq 0$. As in the case of points (§II-1.1), we regard these triads as being coordinates of the same parametrization.

In passing to a new coordinate system the coordinates of a parametrization are to be subjected to the same transformation as the coordinates of a point. It follows that the defining conditions (i) and (ii) are satisfied in all coordinate systems if they are satisfied in one. We adopt the same abbreviations in speaking of parametrizations as in speaking of points; that is, we say, "the parametrization $(\bar{x})$," instead of, "the parametrization whose coordinates in the given system are $(\bar{x})$."

As a matter of fact, the parametrizations can in a certain sense be considered as actual points of C. We need merely consider the equation $F(x) = 0$ as defining a curve C' in the projective plane over the ground field $K(t)'$. Then the points of C' consist of all points of C plus all parametrizations of C.

If $(\bar{x})$ is any parametrization of C, let $h = -\min O(\bar{x}_i)$. Then if $\bar{y}_i = t^h \bar{x}_i$, $(\bar{y})$ is the same parametrization, and $\bar{y}_i \in K[t]'$ with at least one $O(\bar{y}_i) = 0$. Then $\bar{y}_i(0) = a_i$ exists, and at least one $a_i \neq 0$. The point (a) is called the *center* of the parametrization. It is evident that the coordinates of the center behave like point coordinates under change of coordinates, and so a parametrization has a unique center.

If $\bar{x}_0 \neq 0$, and we define $\bar{x} = \bar{x}_1/\bar{x}_0$, $\bar{y} = \bar{x}_2/\bar{x}_0$, then $(\bar{x},\bar{y})$ can be considered to be the corresponding affine coordinates of the parametrization. Conversely, if $\bar{x}$ and $\bar{y}$ satisfy the conditions

(i) $f(\bar{x},\bar{y}) = F(1,\bar{x},\bar{y}) = 0$,

(ii) $\bar{x}$ and $\bar{y}$ are not both elements of K,

then $(1,\bar{x},\bar{y})$ are the projective coordinates of a parametrization of C. In the relations between the two types of coordinates the parametrizations again behave exactly like points.

If $(\bar{x})$, $\bar{x}_i \in K[t]'$, is a parametrization, and if $O(\bar{t}) > 0$, $\bar{t} \neq 0$, then $(\bar{y})$, where $\bar{y}_i = \bar{x}_i(\bar{t})$, is also a parametrization with the same center. If $O(\bar{t}) = 1$, the two parametrizations will be said to be equivalent. By Theorems 1.4 and 1.5, the property of equivalence is reflexive, symmetric and transitive, and so any parametrization determines a unique equivalence class.

If $\bar{x}_i \in K(t^r)'$ for some $r > 1$, we can simplify the power series by replacing t^r by a new variable, t'. Such a parametrization, or one equivalent to it, will be said to be *reducible*. We shall be chiefly concerned with irreducible parametrizations, and we shall need a criterion for determining whether or not a given parametrization is reducible. The following theorem provides such a criterion.

THEOREM 2.1. *The parametrization*

$$\bar{x} = t^n, \quad \bar{y} = a_1 t^{n_1} + a_2 t^{n_2} + \cdots,$$

where

$$0 < n, 0 < n_1 < n_2 < \cdots, \quad a_i \neq 0,$$

is reducible if and only if the integers $n, n_1, n_2, \cdots$ have a common factor greater than 1.

PROOF. The sufficiency of the condition is obvious. To prove the necessity let us suppose that there exists a $\bar{t}$, with $O(\bar{t}) = 1$, such that $\bar{x}(\bar{t}), \bar{y}(\bar{t}) \in K[t^r]'$, $r > 1$. We shall show first that $\bar{t}/t \in K[t^r]'$. If this were not so $\bar{t}$ would have the form

$$\bar{t} = t(b_0 + b_1 t^r + \cdots + b_h t^{hr} + c t^s + \cdots),$$

where $b_0 c \neq 0$ and $r \nmid s$. Then

$$\bar{x}(\bar{t}) = t^n[(b_0 + \cdots + b_h t^{hr}) + c t^s + \cdots]^n$$

$$= t^n(b_0 + \cdots + b_h t^{hr})^n + n c t^{n+s}(b_0 + \cdots + b_h t^{hr})^{n-1} + \cdots.$$

Since by assumption $\bar{x}(\bar{t}) \in K[t^r]'$, we must have $r \mid n$, since $\bar{x}(\bar{t})$ begins with the term $b_0^n t^n$. Then

$$\bar{x}(\bar{t}) - t^n(b_0 + \cdots + b_h t^{hr})^n = n c t^{n+s} b_0^{n-1} + \cdots$$

is an element of $K[t^r]'$, which is impossible since $r \nmid (n + s)$. Hence $\bar{t} = t\bar{z}$, with $\bar{z} \in K[t^r]'$.

Now suppose that at least one of $n_1, n_2, \cdots$ is not divisible by r, and let n_{h+1} be the first n_i not so divisible. Then

$$\bar{y}(\bar{t}) - (a_1 t^{m_1} \bar{z}^{m_1} + \cdots + a_h t^{m_h} \bar{z}^{n_h}) = a_{h+1} t^{n_{h+1}}(b_0 + b_1 t^r + \cdots)^{n_{h+1}} + \cdots$$

$$= a_{h+1} b_0^{n_{h+1}} t^{n_{h+1}} + \cdots.$$

The left-hand side of this equation is a member of $K[t^r]'$ and the right-hand side is not. This contradiction implies that r must be a factor of all the n_i, and so the theorem is proved.

The usefulness of Theorem 2.1 follows from

THEOREM 2.2. *In a suitable coordinate system any given parametrization is equivalent to one of the type*

$$\bar{x} = t^n, \quad \bar{y} = a_1 t^{n_1} + a_2 t^{n_2} + \cdots,$$

$$0 < n, \, 0 < n_1 < n_2 < \cdots.$$

PROOF. Choosing the center of the parametrization as the origin of an affine coordinate system, the parametrization becomes

$$\bar{x}_1 = t^n(b_0 + b_1 t + \cdots), \quad n > 0,$$

$$\bar{y}_1 = t^m(c_0 + c_1 t + \cdots), \quad n_1 > 0.$$

with at least one of b_0, c_0 different from zero. By interchanging axes, if necessary, we can assume that $b_0 \neq 0$. Now let

$$\bar{t} = d_1 t + d_2 t^2 + \cdots, \quad d_1 \neq 0,$$

and let

$$\bar{x} = \bar{x}_1(\bar{t}), \quad \bar{y} = \bar{y}_1(\bar{t}).$$

Then

$$
\begin{aligned}
\bar{x} &= t^n (d_1 + d_2 t + \cdots)^n \, [b_0 + b_1(d_1 t + \cdots) + \cdots] \\
&= t^n [d_1^n b_0 + (n d_1^{n-1} d_2 b_0 + d_1^{n+1} b_1) t + \cdots \\
&\quad + (n d_1^{n-1} d_i b_0 + P_i(b_1, \cdots, b_i, d_1, \cdots, d_{i-1})) t^i + \cdots],
\end{aligned}
$$

where P_i is a polynomial in its arguments. Defining $d_1, d_2, \cdots$, successively by

$$
\begin{aligned}
d_1^n &= b_0^{-1}, \\
d_2 &= -(n d_1^{n-1} b_0)^{-1} d_1^{n+1} b_1, \\
d_i &= -(n d_1^{n-1} b_0)^{-1} P_i, \quad i = 3, 4, \cdots,
\end{aligned}
$$

we have $\bar{x} = t^n$. $(\bar{x}, \bar{y})$ is then a parametrization of the required type.

2.2. Place of a curve. An equivalence class of irreducible parametrizations will be called a *place* of the curve C. The common center of the parametrizations is the *center* of the place.

The motivation for this definition can be seen by referring to the remarks at the beginning of this chapter. Considering only the case in which K is the complex field, the power series expansions of the functions $x(t), y(t)$ provide a pair of formal power series which are the coordinates of a parametrization of f with center (x_0, y_0). The functions $x(t), y(t)$ are not unique, but it can be shown that if $x_1(t), y_1(t)$ are any other pair such that $(x(t), y(t))$ and $(x_1(t), y_1(t))$ give the same set of points as t varies in appropriate neighborhoods of zero, then there is a function $z(t)$, analytic in a neighborhood of zero and such that $z(0) = 0$, $z'(0) \neq 0$, for which

$$x_1(t) = x(z(t)), \quad y_1(t) = y(z(t)).$$

That is, the parametrizations $(x(t), y(t))$ and $(x_1(t), y_1(t))$ are equivalent. Finally, the fact that a point sufficiently close to (x_0, y_0) is obtained from a unique value of t, requires that any such parametrization $(x(t), y(t))$ be irreducible. Thus a place of a curve is an algebraic counterpart of a *branch* of a curve over the complex field, a branch being a set of all points $(x(t), y(t))$ obtained by allowing t to vary within some neighborhood of zero within which $x(t)$ and $y(t)$ are analytic.

Returning to the purely algebraic case, it is easy to see that the center of any place of C is a point of C. For if $(\bar{x})$ is a parametrization of the place, with $\bar{x}_i = a_i + b_i t + \cdots$, not all $a_i = 0$, then $F(\bar{x}) = 0$, and so $F(\bar{x}) \equiv 0 \pmod{t}$. But $\bar{x}_i \equiv a_i \pmod{t}$, and so $F(a) \equiv 0 \pmod{t}$, and this obviously implies $F(a) = 0$. The converse of this property is of fundamental importance in the theory of algebraic curves. It is stated in

THEOREM 2.3. *Every point of C is the center of at least one place of C.*

The proof of this theorem is quite long, and will be given in several stages.

§3. FRACTIONAL POWER SERIES

3.1. The field $K(x)^*$ of fractional power series. We shall prove Theorem 2.3 by showing the existence of parametrizations of the type $(t^n, \bar{y}(t))$. In discussing these it is convenient to make a slight extension of the notion of power series. Let us use instead of the indeterminate t, the symbol $x^{1/n}$. We introduce a relation between the symbols $x^{1/n}$, $n = 1, 2, \cdots$, by defining

$$x^{1/1} = x, \quad (x^{1/rn})^r = x^{1/n}, \quad x^{m/n} = (x^{1/n})^m.$$

From these it follows that

$$x^{rm/rn} = x^{m/n}.$$

A parametrization of the type mentioned above can now be written in the form $(x, \bar{y})$, where $\bar{y}$ is an element of some $K(x^{1/n})'$ and $f(x, \bar{y}) = 0$.

From the relation $(x^{1/rn})^r = x^{1/n}$ it follows that $K(x^{1/n})' \subset K(x^{1/rn})'$. Consider the union of all the fields $K(x^{1/n})'$, $n = 1, 2, \cdots$, that is, the set of all elements belonging to any of these fields. We denote this set by $K(x)^*$. If $\bar{y}$ and $\bar{z}$ are two elements of $K(x)^*$ then for some m and n, $\bar{y} \in K(x^{1/m})'$, $\bar{z} \in K(x^{1/n})'$. Hence $\bar{y}, \bar{z} \in K(x^{1/mn})'$, and so their sum, product, and quotient (if $\bar{z} \neq 0$) likewise belong to $K(x^{1/mn})'$, and hence to $K(x)^*$. It follows that $K(x)^*$ is a field.

If

$$\bar{a}(x) = a_1 x^{m_1/n_1} + a_2 x^{m_2/n_2} + \cdots \in K(x)^*,$$

where

$$a_i \neq 0, \quad m_1/n_1 < m_2/n_2 < \cdots,$$

we define the order of $\bar{a}(x)$ to be m_1/n_1. The set of elements of $K(x)^*$ of non-negative order is a domain $K[x]^*$. If $\bar{a}(x) \in K[x]^*$, the coefficient of x^0 in $\bar{a}(x)$ will be designated by $\bar{a}(0)$. Obviously $\bar{a}(0) \neq 0$ if and only if $O(\bar{a}(x)) = 0$.

3.2. Algebraic closure of $K(x)^*$. The basic theorem concerning parametrizations of algebraic curves can now be stated as follows.

THEOREM 3.1. $K(x)^*$ *is algebraically closed.*

PROOF. We wish to show that if $f(x,y)$ is an element of $K(x)^*[y]$ but not of $K(x)^*$, then there is a $\bar{y} \in K(x)^*$ such that $f(x,\bar{y}) = 0$. In order to motivate some of the steps in the construction of such a $\bar{y}$ we shall first consider necessary conditions on $\bar{y}$ if it is to be a root of $f(x,y) = 0$.

Let $f(x,\bar{y}) = 0$, where $\bar{y} \in K(x)^*$, and

$$(3.1) \qquad f(x,y) = \bar{a}_0 + \bar{a}_1 y + \cdots + \bar{a}_n y^n,$$

with $\bar{a}_i \in K(x)^*$, $\bar{a}_n \neq 0$, $n > 0$. If $O(\bar{a}_i) = \alpha_i < \infty$ we put $\bar{a}_i = a_i x^{\alpha_i} + \cdots$. $\bar{y}$ can be zero if and only if $\bar{a}_0 = 0$. Hence we consider only the case $\bar{y} \neq 0$. We can then write $\bar{y}$ in the form

$$(3.2) \qquad \bar{y} = c_1 x^{\gamma_1} + c_2 x^{\gamma_1 + \gamma_2} + c_3 x^{\gamma_1 + \gamma_2 + \gamma_3} + \cdots,$$

with $c_i \neq 0$, $\gamma_2 > 0$, $\gamma_3 > 0, \cdots$; there may be a finite or an infinite set of c_i. For the moment let us abbreviate this expression to $\bar{y} = x^{\gamma}(c + \bar{y}_1)$, where we have put $\gamma = \gamma_1$, $c = c_1$, $\bar{y}_1 = c_2 x^{\gamma_2} + \cdots$. Then

$$f(x,\bar{y}) = \bar{a}_0 + \bar{a}_1 x^{\gamma}(c + \bar{y}_1) + \cdots + \bar{a}_n x^{n\gamma}(c + \bar{y}_1)^n$$

$$= \bar{a}_0 + c\bar{a}_1 x^{\gamma} + \cdots + c^n \bar{a}_n x^{n\gamma} + g(x,\bar{y}_1),$$

where g contains all the terms involving $\bar{y}_1$. Since $O(\bar{y}_1) = \gamma_2 > 0$, each term appearing in g has order greater than that of some one of the $c^i \bar{a}_i x^{i\gamma}$. Since a necessary condition for $f(x,\bar{y}) = 0$ is that the terms of lowest order cancel, we must have

(i)   At least two of the $c^i \bar{a}_i x^{i\gamma}$ have the same order, this order being no greater than the order of any other $c^i \bar{a}_i x^{i\gamma}$; that is, there are at least two indices, j and k, such that

$$O(c^j \bar{a}_j x^{j\gamma}) = O(c^k \bar{a}_k x^{k\gamma}) \leqslant O(c^i \bar{a}_i x^{i\gamma}), \quad i = 0, \cdots, n,$$

or

$$(3.3) \qquad \alpha_j + j\gamma = \alpha_k + k\gamma \leqslant \alpha_i + i\gamma, \quad i = 0, \cdots, n.$$

(ii)   The coefficients of all terms of lowest order must cancel; that is,

$$(3.4) \qquad \Sigma a_h c^h = 0.$$

the summation being over all values of h for which $a_h + h\gamma = a_j + j\gamma$.

To determine possible values of γ satisfying (3.3) we use the so-called Newton polygon. In a cartesian coordinate system we plot the points P_i with coordinates $u = i, v = \alpha_i$. (We omit P_i if $\alpha_i = \infty$.) Condition

(3.3) then states that there is a β such that all P_i lie on or above the line L, $v + \gamma u = \beta$, and at least two P_i lie on L. If, then, we join P_0 to P_n with a convex polygonal arc each of whose vertices is a P_i and such that no P_i lies below the arc then the segments of this arc are the only possible choices for L. Figure 3.1 shows the Newton polygon for an

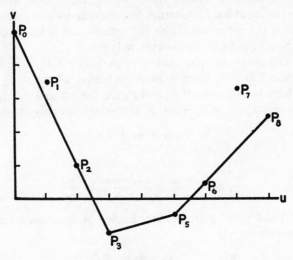

Figure 3.1

equation with $n = 8$, $\alpha_0 = 5$, $\alpha_1 = 7/2$, $\alpha_2 = 1$, $\alpha_3 = -1$, $\alpha_4 = \infty$, $\alpha_5 = -1/2$, $\alpha_6 = 1/2$, $\alpha_7 = 10/3$, $\alpha_8 = 5/2$. (If $\bar{a}_0 = \cdots = \bar{a}_{e-1} = 0$, $\bar{a}_e \neq 0$, so that f has e zero roots, we start the polygon at P_e instead of P_0.) The possible values of γ are thus determined by the slopes of the segments of the Newton polygon. For a given value of γ, and hence a given L, the value of c must satisfy (3.4) where P_h lies on L.

We have thus determined necessary conditions on the γ_1 and c_1 in (3.2). To do the same for γ_2 and c_2 we put

$$f_1(x,y_1) = x^{-\beta}f(x,x^{\gamma_1}(c_1 + y_1)),$$

and consider the root $\bar{y}_1$ of $f_1(x,y_1) = 0$. (The factor $x^{-\beta}$ can be omitted in the definition of f_1, but its use simplifies some later considerations.) The same procedure can be applied, with the one exception that since $\gamma_2 > 0$ we consider only those segments of the Newton polygon which have negative slopes. The process can be continued to give conditions on all the γ_i and c_i.

We are now in a position to prove Theorem 3.1 by showing that the above process can be carried out on any polynomial of the form (3.1) to construct a root of the equation $f(x,y) = 0$. We have three things to show; first, that at each stage of the process equation (3.4) has a non-zero solution; second, that after the first stage the Newton polygon has a segment of negative slope; and third, that after a certain stage all the γ_i have a common denominator.

The first condition follows from the algebraic closure of K, for $\Sigma a_h c^h = 0$, having at least two terms, has one or more non-zero solutions. To show that the other conditions are satisfied we must make a more thorough investigation of the Newton polygon.

In the first place, we note that since each $\bar{a}_i$, $i = 0, \cdots, n$, is an element of some $K(x^{1/n_i})'$, there is an m such that all the $\bar{a}_i \in K(x^{1/m})'$. Hence we have $\alpha_i = m_i/m$. If P_j and P_k are the left and the right hand ends of the segment L, $v + \gamma_1 u = \beta_1$ of the Newton polygon, then

$$\alpha_j + j\gamma_1 = \alpha_k + k\gamma_1,$$

or

$$\gamma_1 = \frac{\alpha_j - \alpha_k}{k - j} = \frac{m_j - m_k}{m(k - j)} = \frac{p}{mq},$$

where $q > 0$ and p and q are integers having no common factor. If P_h is on L, then also

$$\frac{p}{mq} = \gamma_1 = \frac{\alpha_j - \alpha_h}{h - j} = \frac{m_j - m_h}{m(h - j)}.$$

Hence

$$q(m_j - m_h) = p(h - j),$$

and since p and q have no common factors, q is a factor of $h - j$. Thus for every P_h on L we have $h = j + sq$, s being a non-negative integer. Therefore (3.4) has the form

$$c^j \phi(c^q) = 0,$$

where $\phi(z)$ is a polynomial, of degree $(k - j)/q$, such that $\phi(0) \neq 0$. If $c_1 \neq 0$ is an r-fold root, $r \geqslant 1$, of $\phi(z^q) = 0$, we have

$$\phi(z^q) = (z - c_1)^r \psi(z), \quad \psi(c_1) \neq 0.$$

Then

$$\begin{aligned}
f_1(x,y_1) &= x^{-\beta_1} f(x, x^{\gamma_1}(c_1 + y_1)) \\
&= x^{-\beta_1}[\bar{a}_0 + \bar{a}_1 x^{\gamma_1}(c_1 + y_1) + \cdots + \bar{a}_n x^{n\gamma_1}(c_1 + y_1)^n] \\
&= x^{-\beta_1}\Sigma \bar{a}_h x^{h\gamma_1}(c_1 + y_1)^h + x^{-\beta_1}\Sigma a_l x^{l\gamma_1}(c_1 + y_1)^l,
\end{aligned}$$

where h runs over the values of i for which P_i is on L, and l runs over the remaining values of i. Since $\bar{a}_h = a_h x^{\alpha_h} + \cdots$,

$$f_1(x,y_1) = x^{-\beta_1} \Sigma a_h x^{\alpha_h + h\gamma_1} (c_1 + y_1)^h$$
$$+ x^{-\beta_1} [\Sigma (\bar{a}_h - a_h) x^{h\gamma_1} (c_1 + y_1)^h + \Sigma \bar{a}_l x^{l\gamma_1} (c_1 + y_1)^l].$$

Since $\alpha_h + h\gamma_1 = \beta_1$, the first summation reduces to

$$x^{\beta_1} (c_1 + y_1)^i \phi((c_1 + y_1)^q) = x^{\beta_1} y_1^r (c_1 + y_1)^i \psi(c_1 + y_1).$$

Since $O(\bar{a}_h - a_h) > \alpha_h$, and $O(\bar{a}_l x^{l\alpha_l}) > \beta_1$, we obtain

$$f_1(x,y) = b_1 y_1^r + b_2 y_1^{r+1} + \cdots + g(x,y_1),$$

where $b_1 = c_1^j \psi(c_1) \neq 0$ and each power of y_1 in $g(x,y_1)$ has a coefficient of positive order. Hence if we write

$$f_1(x,y_1) = \bar{b}_0 + \bar{b}_1 y_1 + \cdots + \bar{b}_n y_1^n,$$

then

$$O(\bar{b}_i) \geqslant 0, \quad i = 0, \cdots, n,$$
$$O(\bar{b}_i) > 0, \quad i = 0, \cdots, r - 1,$$
$$O(\bar{b}_r) = 0.$$

In taking the next step, with $y_1 = x^{\gamma_2}(c_2 + y_2)$, we can use only positive values of γ_2. These are obtained from the arc $P_0 P_r$ of the Newton

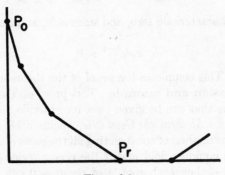

Figure 3.2

polygon of $f_1(x,y_1)$ (Fig. 3.2); in particular, there is at least one choice for γ_2, except in the case in which $\bar{b}_0 = \cdots = \bar{b}_{r-1} = 0$. In this exceptional case we have the root $\bar{y}_1 = 0$, or $y = c_1 x^{\gamma_1}$; in all other cases the process can be continued.

We have now only to show that the successive γ's have bounded denominators, that is, that after a certain number of steps the value of q is always 1. Since r is at most $k - j$, which is the horizontal length of the chosen segment of Newton's polygon, and since the segment to be chosen in the next step must have a horizontal length of at most r, r cannot increase from step to step. Hence after a finite number of steps

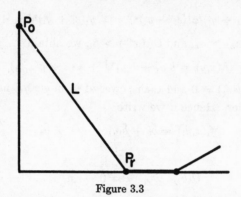

Figure 3.3

r has a constant value r_0. Newton's polygon then has the form shown in Fig. 3.3, and

$$\phi(z^q) = d(z - c)^{r_0}$$

$$= dz^{r_0} - \cdots \mp r_0 dc^{r_0 - 1} z \pm dc^{r_0}.$$

Since K is of characteristic zero, and since r_0, d, and c are each different from zero,

$$r_0 dc^{r_0 - 1} \neq 0,$$

and so $q = 1$. This completes the proof of the theorem.

3.3. Discussion and example. This proof of Theorem 3.1 is not the shortest one that can be given (see, for example, van der Waerden, *Einführung in die Algebraische Geometrie*, Theorem 14), but it yields the most convenient method of constructing all the roots of a given equation.

If K is the complex field and if the power series $\bar{a}_i$ converge in a domain $|x| < \epsilon$, then each root $\bar{y}$ of $f(x,y) = 0$ can be shown to be convergent in a similar domain. In this case a very quick proof of Theorem 3.1 can be obtained by using the method of analytic continuation. (See Picard, *Traité d'Analyse*, Vol. II, Chap. 13.) This proof, also, is not adaptable to actual construction of the power series.

Example. Consider

$$f(x,y) = (-x^3 + x^4) - 2x^2 y - xy^2 + 2xy^4 + y^5.$$

Newton's polygon (Fig. 3.4) consists of two segments. For the segment P_0P_2 we have

$$p = 1, \quad q = 1, \quad \gamma_1 = 1, \quad \beta_1 = 3.$$

Equation (3.4) becomes $-1 - 2c - c^2 = 0$, so that $\phi(c) = -(1 + c)^2$. Hence $c_1 = -1$. Then

$$f_1(x,y_1) = x^{-3}f(x,x(-1 + y_1))$$

$$= (x + x^2) - 3x^2y_1 + (-1 + 2x^2)y_1^2 + 2x^2y_1^3 - 3x^2y_1^4 + x^2y_1^5.$$

Note. The substitution of $x(-1 + y_1)$ for y in $f(x,y)$ can often be simplified by the following device. On the Newton diagram mark the points corresponding to every term of $f(x,y)$ and draw lines (dotted in

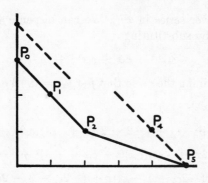

Figure 3.4

Figure 3.4) through them parallel to P_0P_2. If the terms of $f(x,y)$ are collected into groups according to the lines on which the corresponding points lie, it will be found that the algebraic work can be made somewhat easier. In our example, we have

$$f(x,y) = (-x^3 - 2x^2y - xy^2) + x^4 + (2xy^4 + y^5)$$

$$= -x(x + y)^2 + x^4 + y^4(2x + y).$$

Since $x + x(-1 + y_1) = xy_1$, we have

$$x^3f_1(x,y_1) = -x^3y_1^2 + x^4 + x^4(-1 + y_1)^4(x + xy_1).$$

Newton's polygon for f_1 is shown in Fig. 3.5. There is only one segment to the polygon, and for it $p = 1$, $q = 2$, $\gamma_2 = 1/2$, $\beta_2 = 1$, $\phi(c^2) = 1 - c^2$, and so $c_2 = \pm 1$. Let us take $c_2 = 1$. Then

$$f_2(x,y_2) = x^{-1}f_1(x,x^{1/2}(1 + y_2))$$
$$= (x - 3x^{3/2} + \cdots) + (-2 - 3x^{3/2} + \cdots)y_2$$
$$+ (-1 + 2x^3 + \cdots)y_2^2 + \cdots.$$

We have now reached the point where $r = r_0 = 1$, and so we know that

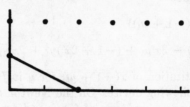

Figure 3.5

$\bar{y}_2$ must be a power series in $x^{1/2}$. We can dispense with the Newton polygon method by substituting

$$c_3x^{1/2} + c_4x + c_5x^{3/2} + \cdots$$

for $\bar{y}_2$ and determining the c's so that $f_2(x,\bar{y}_2) = 0$. We get

$$f_2(x,c_3x^{1/2} + c_4x + \cdots)$$
$$= (x - 3x^{3/2} + \cdots) + (-2 - 2x^{3/2} + \cdots)(c_3x^{1/2} + c_4x + \cdots)$$
$$+ (-1 + 2x^2 + \cdots)(c_3x^{1/2} + c_4x + \cdots)^2 + \cdots$$
$$= -2c_3x^{1/2} + (-2c_4 + 1 - c_3^2)x + (-2c_5 - 3 - 2c_3c_4)x^{3/2} + \cdots.$$

Hence we must have

$$c_3 = 0, \quad c_4 = \frac{1}{2}, \quad c_5 = -\frac{3}{2}, \quad \cdots.$$

A root of $f(x,y) = 0$ is therefore

$$x[-1 + x^{1/2}(1 + \frac{1}{2}x - \frac{3}{2}x^{3/2} + \cdots)]$$

$$= -x + x^{3/2} + \frac{1}{2}x^{5/2} - \frac{3}{2}x^3 + \cdots.$$

Similarly, by choosing $c_2 = -1$, we get the root

$$-x - x^{3/2} - \frac{1}{2}x^{5/2} + \frac{3}{2}x^3 + \cdots.$$

Now consider side P_2P_5 in Fig. 3.4. Here we have $p = 1$, $q = 3$, $\gamma_1 = 1/3$, $\beta_1 = 5/3$. Equation (5) is $-c^2 + c^5 = 0$, and so $\phi(c^3) =$

$-1 + c^3$. Hence $c = 1$, ω, or ω^2, where ω is a root of $\omega^2 + \omega + 1 = 0$. Taking $c_1 = \omega$, for example, we get

$$f_1(x,y_1) = x^{-5/3}f(x,x^{1/3}(\omega + y_1))$$

$$= (-x^{4/3} + x^{7/3}) + (3\omega + 6x^{2/3})y_1 + (9 + 12\omega^2 x^{2/3})y_1^2$$

$$+ (10\omega^2 + 8\omega x^{2/3})y_1^3 + (5\omega + 2x^{2/3})y_1^4 + y_1^5.$$

We have again arrived at the case $r = 1$, and so $\bar{y}$ can be expressed as a power series in $x^{1/3}$ and the coefficients determined by substitution.

The above example illustrates how the computation of a root can be simplified on reaching the stage after which r has the constant value r_0. If $r_0 = 1$ this stage is easily recognized, but if $r_0 > 1$ we have no means of telling whether or not there will eventually be a reduction in the value of r. However, *the case $r_0 > 1$ can arise only if $f(x,y) = 0$ has a multiple root.* To see this let $f(x,\bar{y}) = 0$, where

$$\bar{y} = c_1 x^{\gamma_1} + c_2 x^{\gamma_1 + \gamma_2} + \cdots,$$

with $\gamma_i = p_i/m$. The value of β is given by $\beta_i = v + u\gamma_i$, where (u,v) is any point on L. Since $(r_0,0)$ is on L, we have $\beta_i = r_0\gamma_i = r_0 p_i/m$. Putting $t = x^{1/m}$, we obtain

$$f(t^m,t^{p_1}(c_1 + y_1)) = t^{r_0 p_1}f_1(t^m,y_1),$$

$$f_1(t^m,t^{p_2}(c_2 + y_2)) = t^{r_0 p_2}f_2(t^m,y_2), \text{ etc.}$$

Hence

$$f(t^m,c_1 t^{p_1} + c_2 t^{p_1 + p_2} + \cdots + t^{p_1 + \cdots + p_s}y_s) = t^{r_0(p_1 + \cdots + p_s)}f_s(t^m,y_s).$$

Differentiating this with respect to y_s gives

$$f'(t^m,c_1 t^{p_1} + \cdots + t^{p_1 + \cdots + p_s}y_s) = t^{(r_0 - 1)(p_1 + \cdots + p_s)}f_s'(t^m,y_s).$$

where $f'(x,y)$ is the derivative of $f(x,y)$ with respect to y. Since $p_i \geqslant 1$, we have

$$f(t^m,c_1 t^{p_1} + \cdots + t^{p_1 + \cdots + p_s}y_s) \equiv 0 \pmod{t^s},$$

and if $r_0 > 0$, then also

$$f'(t^m,c_1 t^{p_1} + \cdots + t^{p_1 + \cdots + p_s}y_s) \equiv 0 \pmod{t^s}.$$

Now let $D(x)$ be the discriminant of $f(x,y)$ with respect to y. Then (Theorem I-9.6)

$$D(x) = A(x,y) f(x,y) + B(x,y) f'(x,y).$$

Replacing x by t^m and y by

$$c_1 t^{p_1} + \cdots + t^{p_1 + \cdots + p_s} y_s$$

gives, in virtue of the preceding observations,

$$D(t^m) \equiv 0 \pmod{t^s}.$$

Since this is true for each s we have $D(t^m) = 0$; that is, $D(x) = 0$ and $f(x,y)$ has a multiple root.

Since multiple roots can be detected by the vanishing of $D(x)$, and determined, when present, by finding the highest common factor of f and f', the case $r_0 > 1$ can always be avoided in computing roots.

3.4. Extensions of the basic theorem. The following four theorems are simple extensions of Theorem 3.1. We assume for all of them that

$$f(x,y) = \bar{a}_0 + \bar{a}_1 y + \cdots + \bar{a}_n y^n, \quad \bar{a}_i \in K(x)^*, \quad \bar{a}_n \neq 0.$$

THEOREM 3.2. *There exists a unique set of elements $\bar{y}_1, \cdots, \bar{y}_n$ of $K(x)^*$ such that*

$$f(x,y) = \bar{a}_n \Pi(y - \bar{y}_j).$$

This is just Theorem I-7.5 with $D = K(x)^*$.

THEOREM 3.3. *If $O(\bar{a}_n) \leqslant O(\bar{a}_i)$, $i = 0, \cdots, n - 1$, the $\bar{y}_j$ of Theorem 3.2 are elements of $K[x]^*$.*

THEOREM 3.4. *If $O(\bar{a}_n) = 0, O(\bar{a}_0) > 0, O(\bar{a}_i) \geqslant 0, i = 1, \cdots, n - 1$, then for at least one of the $\bar{y}_j$ of Theorem 3.2, $O(\bar{y}_j) > 0$.*

THEOREM 3.5. *If $f(x,y) \in K[x,y]$ and has no factor not involving y, then f has a multiple factor in $K[x,y]$ if and only if $f(x,y) = 0$ has a multiple root in $K(x)^*$.*

This follows from Theorem I-9.5.

3.5. Exercises. 1. Find the first four non-vanishing terms of each root of the following equations:

   (a) $x^4 - x^3 y + 3x^2 y^3 - 3xy^5 + y^7 = 0.$

   (b) $2x^5 - x^3 y + 2x^2 y^2 - xy^3 + 2y^5 = 0.$

   (c) $(x^2 + 4x^3 + 6x^4) - 4x^4 y + (-2x - 4x^2 - 2x^3)y^2 + y^4 = 0.$

2. In Theorem 3.4, if k is the least integer for which $O(\bar{a}_k) = 0$, then exactly k of the $\bar{y}_j$'s are of positive order.

§4. PLACES OF A CURVE

4.1. Place with given center. The relation between roots of $f(x,y) = 0$ and places of the curve f is given by the following theorem.

Theorem 4.1. *If* $f(x,y) \in K[x,y]$, *to each root* $\bar{y} \in K(x)^*$ *of* $f(x,y) = 0$ *for which* $O(\bar{y}) > 0$ *there corresponds a unique place of the curve* $f(x,y) = 0$ *with center at the origin. Conversely, to each place* $(\bar{x},\bar{y})$ *of* f *with center at the origin there correspond* $O(\bar{x})$ *roots of* $f(x,y) = 0$, *each of order greater than zero.*

Proof. Let $f(x,\bar{y}) = 0$, $O(\bar{y}) > 0$. Let n be the least integer for which $\bar{y} \in K(x^{1/n})'$. Then putting $x^{1/n} = t$, $(t^n,\bar{y})$ is a parametrization with center at the origin, and it is irreducible by Theorem 2.1. Conversely, let $(\bar{x},\bar{y})$ be an irreducible parametrization of f, with $O(\bar{x}) = n > 0$, $O(\bar{y}) > 0$. By Theorem 2.2 there is an equivalent parametrization,

$$(4.1) \qquad (t^n,\, a_1 t^{n_1} + a_2 t^{n_2} + \cdots), \quad a_i \neq 0.$$

Now two such parametrizations can differ only by the substitution of ϵt for t, where $\epsilon^n = 1$. There are n such values of ϵ, and we wish to show that each one gives a distinct root of $f(x,y) = 0$. The values of y corresponding to ϵ_1 and ϵ_2 are

$$a_1 \epsilon_1^{n_1} t^{n_1} + a_2 \epsilon_1^{n_2} t^{n_2} + \cdots$$

and

$$a_1 \epsilon_2^{n_1} t^{n_1} + a_2 \epsilon_2^{n_2} t^{n_2} + \cdots.$$

Suppose that these are identical; that is, that

$$(4.2) \qquad a_i \epsilon_1^{n_i} = a_i \epsilon_2^{n_i}, \quad i = 1,2,\cdots.$$

Since $n,n_1,\cdots$ have no common factor greater than 1, by Theorem 2.1, we can find an integer m and integers $\alpha,\alpha_1,\cdots,\alpha_m$, such that

$$\alpha_1 n_1 + \alpha_2 n_2 + \cdots + \alpha_m n_m + \alpha n = 1,$$

(§I-6.3. Exercise 1). Writing (4.2) in the form

$$\epsilon_1^{n_i} = \epsilon_2^{n_i}, \quad i = 1,2,\cdots,m,$$

and adding the relation

$$\epsilon_1^n = \epsilon_2^n = 1,$$

we obtain by raising to the appropriate powers and multiplying,

$$\epsilon_1^{\alpha_1 n_1 + \cdots + \alpha_m n_m + \alpha n} = \epsilon_2^{\alpha_1 n_1 + \cdots + \alpha_m n_m + \alpha n},$$

or $\epsilon_1 = \epsilon_2$. Hence there are n distinct parametrizations like (4.1), and each gives rise to a root of $f(x,y) = 0$ of the type

$$a_1 x^{n_1/n} + a_2 x^{n_2/n} + \cdots.$$

We are now ready to prove Theorem 2.3. Let P be any point of the curve C. We may assume the axes chosen so that P is the origin and the curve does not pass through the point at infinity on the y-axis. Then

$$f(x,y) = a_0(x) + a_1(x)y + \cdots + y^n, \quad a_0(0) = 0.$$

By Theorem 3.4 there is a root $\bar{y}$ of $f(x,y) = 0$ of positive order, and by Theorem 4.1 it determines a place with center at P.

Conversely, each place with center at P determines at least one root of $f(x,y) = 0$. Hence there are at most n such places.

4.2. Case of multiple components. For later purposes it will be convenient to make a convention regarding the places of a curve with a multiple component. We have seen (Theorem 3.5) that if C is such a curve then $f(x,y) = 0$ has multiple roots $\bar{y}$ and conversely. We shall extend the correspondence between roots and places described in Theorem 4.1 by counting any place of C to the multiplicity of its corresponding root. It is easily seen that then every place of an r-fold component of C counts as r places of C.

4.3. Exercises. 1. For each of the curves of §3.5, Exercise 1, determine the number of places with centers at the origin, and get a parametrization of each such place.

§5. INTERSECTION OF CURVES

5.1. Order of a polynomial at a place. In terms of places and their parametrizations it is possible to give a definition of the number of intersections of two curves at an arbitrary point in such a way that two curves of orders m and n with no common components have exactly mn intersections. The definition is a generalization of the one given in §III-2.1 for the number of intersections of a line with a curve. The equations (III-3.1) can be regarded as a parametrization of the line L with center at (a,b), and the multiplicity of the intersection at this point is merely $O(f(a + \lambda t, b + \mu t))$. Before proceeding to the more general situation we shall find it convenient to make a few preliminary remarks.

Let $(\bar{x},\bar{y})$ be a place P with a finite center, and let $g(x,y)$ be any polynomial. By the *order* of g at P we mean the order of the power series $g(\bar{x},\bar{y})$. From Theorem 1.5 (i) it follows that the order of g depends only on the place P and not on the particular parametrization. We shall denote the order of g at P by $O_P(g)$. Evidently

$$O_P(gh) = O_P(g) + O_P(h),$$
$$O_P(g \pm h) \geqslant \min(O_P(g), O_P(h)).$$

If we make a change of coordinates the order of g at P will remain unchanged provided we make the corresponding transformation of g to the new coordinates. That is, we are not interested in the particular polynomial g but rather in the relation between the curve $g = 0$ and the place P. From this it follows that any concept defined in terms of the orders of polynomials at places is a geometric one, being independent of the coordinate system.

Similarly, if $(\bar{x})$ is a parametrization of P in projective coordinates, with all $O(\bar{x}_i) \geqslant 0$ and at least one $O(\bar{x}_i) = 0$, and if $G(x)$ is any homogeneous polynomial in x_0, x_1, x_2, we define $O_P(G)$ to be the order of $G(\bar{x})$. Here again $O_P(G)$ is independent of the parametrization. Moreover, if P has a finite center in the affine plane, and if g and G are associated polynomials, then $O_P(g) = O_P(G)$.

5.2. Intersection of curves. Bezout's Theorem. The definition of the multiplicity of an intersection of two curves is based on the following theorem.

THEOREM 5.1. *If $f(x,y) = 0$ and $g(x,y) = 0$ are curves having a common point p, then the sum of the orders of f at the places of g with centers at p equals the sum of the orders of g at the places of f with centers at p.*

PROOF. We choose axes so that p is the origin and the infinite point on the y-axis lies on neither f nor g. Then the coefficients of the highest powers of y in f and g can be taken to be 1, and so from Theorem 3.2 we have

$$f(x,y) = \Pi_1^m(y - \bar{y}_i), \quad g(x,y) = \Pi_1^n(y - \bar{z}_j),$$

where for some M, $\bar{y}_i, \bar{z}_j \in K[x^{1/m}]'$. Let $\bar{y}_i$ correspond to a place $P = (t^r, \Sigma b_i t^i)$ whose center is the origin. Then

$$(5.1) \qquad g(t^r, \Sigma b_i t^i) = at^N + \cdots, \quad a \neq 0,$$

where $O_P(g) = N$. If $O_P(g) = \infty$ the series $at^N + \cdots$ is replaced by 0. Now P has the equivalent parametrizations $(t^r, \Sigma b_i \epsilon_\lambda^i t^i)$, where ϵ_λ is any r-th root of unity. Each such parametrization gives rise to a different root $\bar{y}_\lambda$ of $f(x,y) = 0$. From (5.1) we obtain

$$g(x, \bar{y}_1) = ax^{N/r} + \cdots,$$

and similarly

$$g(x, \bar{y}_\lambda) = a\epsilon_\lambda^N x^{N/r} + \cdots.$$

Hence

$$\Pi_1^r g(x, \bar{y}_\lambda) = bx^N + \cdots, \quad b \neq 0.$$

Applying the same reasoning to each place of f with center at the origin we find that

$$O(\Pi_\alpha g(x, \bar{y}_\alpha)) = \Sigma O_P(g),$$

the product being over all α for which the root $\bar{y}_\alpha$ of $f(x,y) = 0$ is of positive order (Theorem 4.1), and the sum over all places of f with centers at the origin.

Now let $\bar{z}_\beta$ be a root of $g(x,z) = 0$ of positive order and $\bar{z}_{\beta}'$ one of order zero. Then

$$\Pi_\alpha g(x,\bar{y}_\alpha) = \Pi_{\alpha,\beta}(\bar{y}_\alpha - \bar{z}_\beta)\Pi_{\alpha,\beta'}(\bar{y}_\alpha - \bar{z}_{\beta'})$$
$$= \Pi_{\alpha,\beta}(\bar{y}_\alpha - \bar{z}_\beta)h(x),$$

where $O(h) = 0$. Hence

$$\Sigma O_P(g) = O(\Pi_{\alpha,\beta}(\bar{y}_\alpha - \bar{z}_\beta))$$
$$= O(\Pi_{\beta,\alpha}(\bar{z}_\beta - \bar{y}_\alpha)) = \Sigma O_Q(f),$$

the last sum being over all places Q of g with centers at the origin. The last equality is obtained by reversing the roles of f and g in the above discussion. This completes the proof of the theorem.

We define $\Sigma O_P(g) = \Sigma O_Q(f)$ to be the *number of intersections*, or the multiplicity of the intersection, of f and g at the point p. As remarked in §5.1, this definition gives the same number in any coordinate system. Notice that the number of intersections at a point may be infinite.

The following lemma relates the number of intersections to the resultant.

THEOREM 5.2. *Let $f(x,y)$ and $g(x,y)$ have no intersections on the y-axis except possibly at the origin. If $R(x)$ is their resultant with respect to y, then $R(x) = 0$ has zero as a root of multiplicity equal to the number of intersections of f and g at the origin.*

PROOF. Let

$$f = \Pi_\alpha(y - \bar{y}_\alpha)\Pi_{\alpha'}(y - \bar{y}_{\alpha'}),$$
$$g = \Pi_\beta(y - \bar{z}_\beta)\Pi_{\beta'}(y - \bar{z}_{\beta'}),$$

where

$$O(\bar{y}_\alpha) > 0, \; O(\bar{z}_\beta) > 0, \; O(\bar{y}_{\alpha'}) = O(\bar{z}_{\beta'}) = 0.$$

By Theorem I-10.10 we have

$$R(x) = \Pi_{\alpha,\beta}(\bar{y}_\alpha - \bar{z}_\beta)\Pi_{\alpha',\beta}(\bar{y}_{\alpha'} - \bar{z}_\beta)\Pi_{\alpha,\beta'}(\bar{y}_\alpha - \bar{z}_{\beta'})\Pi_{\alpha',\beta'}(\bar{y}_{\alpha'} - \bar{z}_{\beta'}).$$

Evidently

$$O(\Pi_{\alpha',\beta}(\bar{y}_{\alpha'} - \bar{z}_\beta)) = O(\Pi_{\alpha,\beta'}(\bar{y}_\alpha - \bar{z}_{\beta'})) = 0.$$

Also

$$O(\Pi_{\alpha',\beta'}(\bar{y}_{\alpha'} - \bar{z}_{\beta'})) = 0,$$

for if $O(\bar{y}_{\alpha'} - \bar{z}_{\beta'}) > 0$ for some α', β', then $\bar{y}_{\alpha'}$ and $\bar{z}_{\beta'}$ would begin with the same constant $a \neq 0$. The corresponding places would then have the same center $(0,a)$ on the y-axis, contrary to the assumption that f and g have no intersections on the y-axis other than $(0,0)$. Hence

$$O(R(x)) = O(\Pi_{\alpha,\beta}(\bar{y}_\alpha - \bar{z}_\beta))$$

= number of intersections at the origin.

This proves the theorem.

We leave to the reader the task of making the changes in the above proof necessary to prove

THEOREM 5.3. *If the infinite point on the y-axis is on neither f nor g, the multiplicity of the root a of $R(x) = 0$ is equal to the number of intersections of f and g on the line $x = a$.*

We can now prove the strongest form of Bezout's Theorem for plane curves.

THEOREM 5.4. *Two plane curves of orders m and n with no common components have exactly mn intersections.*

PROOF. We already know (Theorem III-3.1) that they have at most mn distinct intersections. Choose projective coordinates so that none of these is on $x_0 = 0$, and so that $(0,0,1)$ is not on either curve. The curves then have the form

$$F = a_0 x_2^m + a_1 x_2^{m-1} + \cdots + a_m = 0,$$
$$G = b_0 x_2^n + b_1 x_2^{n-1} + \cdots + b_n = 0,$$

where a_i, b_i are homogeneous of degree i in x_0, x_1. Since F and G have no common factor their resultant $R(x_0, x_1)$ with respect to x_2 is not zero, and hence is homogeneous of degree mn (Theorem I-10.9). If $R(0,1) = 0$ there would be an a such that $(0,1,a)$ would be a common point of F and G; this is excluded by the choice of the line $x_0 = 0$. Hence $R(0,1) \neq 0$, and so $R(1,x)$ is of degree mn. Passing to affine coordinates and applying Theorem 5.3, we have the desired result.

Example. Let

$$f = x^3 + y^3 - 2xy,$$
$$g = 2x^3 - 4x^2 y + 3xy^2 + y^3 - 2y^2.$$

The resultant with respect to y is

$$R(x) = x^5 (x - 1)^3 (7x - 4),$$

and we find that the intersections are at $(0,0)$, $(1,1)$, and $(4/7, -8/7)$. (Fig. 5.1.) Consider first the intersections at $(0,0)$. g has only one place with this center, namely $P = (t^2, t^3 + \cdots)$. Then

$$f(t^2, t^3 + \cdots) = -2t^5 + \cdots,$$

and so $O_P(f) = 5$. On the other hand, f has two places with centers at (0,0), namely

$$P_1 = (t, \tfrac{1}{2}t^2 + \cdots) \quad \text{and} \quad P_2 = (\tfrac{1}{2}t^2 + \cdots, t).$$

We have

$$g(t, \tfrac{1}{2}t^2 + \cdots) = 2t^3 + \cdots,$$

$$g(\tfrac{1}{2}t^2 + \cdots, t) = 2t^2 + \cdots,$$

and so $O_P(f) = O_{P_1}(g) + O_{P_2}(g)$. At the point $(1,1)$ f and g each have a single place, and the order of each polynomial on the place of the other

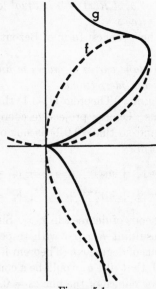

Figure 5.1

is 3. Similarly, at $(4/7, -8/7)$ the corresponding orders are each equal to 1.

The following two theorems are useful corollaries of Bezout's Theorem.

Theorem 5.5. *If $F(x)$ and $G(x)$, of degrees m and n, have no common factors, the sum of the orders of G at all the places of F is mn.*

Theorem 5.6. *If $G(x)$ is of infinite order at a place of $F(x) = 0$ then F and G have a common factor.*

5.3. Tangent, order, and class of a place. We shall conclude this investigation of the intersections of curves by relating it to the notions discussed in §III-2. We first prove the following lemma.

THEOREM 5.7. *If P is a place with center p, of all the lines $L = 0$ which pass through p there is one and only one, $L_0 = 0$, such that $O_P(L_0) > $ min $O_P(L)$.*

PROOF. Let

$$x = \Sigma a_i t^i, \quad y = \Sigma b_i t^i,$$

be a parametrization of P. Since $L = 0$ passes through p, we have $L = a(x - a_0) + b(y - b_0)$, and $L(\bar{x}, \bar{y}) = \Sigma_1^\infty (aa_i + bb_i)t^i$. Now if r is the least positive integer for which at least one of a_r, b_r is not zero, then $O_P(L) = r$ if and only if $aa_r + bb_r \neq 0$. On the other hand, if $aa_r + bb_r = 0$ then $O_P(L) > r$. Hence the condition $aa_r + bb_r = 0$ determines a unique L_0 whose order is greater than the minimum.

The positive integer $r = $ min $O_P(L)$, where L is a line on the center of P, is called the *order* of the place P. A place is said to be *linear* if it is of order one. The unique line L_0 for which $O_P(L_0) > r$ is called the *tangent* to P, and also the tangent to the curve at the place P. The positive integer $s = O_P(L_0) - r$ is the *class* of P. s may be ∞, but this is the case if and only if P is a place of a line.

Example. The place $(t^2, t^3 + \cdots)$ is of order 2 and class 1. This is the characteristic feature of a simple cusp. (See §III-2.4, Example 3, and §III-7.6, Example 4.) The ramphoid cusp $(t^2, t^4 + t^5 + \cdots)$, §III-2.4, Example 5, is of order 2 and class 2.

The relation between these concepts and the ones considered in §III-2 is shown in

THEOREM 5.8. (i). *If p is an r-fold point of F, the sum of the orders of the places of F with centers at p is r.*

(ii). *A point of F is non-singular if and only if it is the center of just one, linear, place.* (This criterion is sometimes used as the definition of a non-singular point.)

(iii). *The tangents to F at a point p coincide with the tangents to F at the places with centers at p.*

PROOF. (i). A line not tangent to F at any place with center p intersects F in Σr_i points at p, where the r_i are the orders of the places with centers at p. But all but a finite set of lines through the r-fold point p intersect F in r points at p. Hence $\Sigma r_i = r$.

(ii). This follows at once from (i).

(iii). A line is tangent to F at p if and only if it has more than r intersections with F at p. A line is tangent to F at a place with center at p if and only if it has more than Σr_i intersections with F at p. Since $r = \Sigma r_i$ the two types of tangents must coincide.

A useful application of these results is

THEOREM 5.9. *If P is a place of order r and if G has an s-fold point at* the center p of P, then $O_P(G) \geqslant rs$, the equality holding if and only if the tangent to P is not tangent to G at p.

PROOF. Choose affine coordinates with the origin at p, and with the y-axis not tangent to P or tangent to G at p. Then the place P and places Q_α of G whose centers are at p have parametrizations of the form

$$P, \quad \bar{x} = t^r, \bar{y} = at^r + \cdots,$$

$$Q_\alpha, \quad \bar{x}_\alpha = t^{r_\alpha}, \bar{y}_\alpha = a_\alpha t^{r_\alpha} + \cdots,$$

where $\Sigma r_\alpha = s$. The corresponding fractional power series are then

$$P, \quad \bar{y}_\lambda = ax + \cdots, \quad \lambda = 1, \cdots, r;$$

$$Q_\alpha, \quad \bar{z}_{\alpha\mu} = a_\alpha x + \cdots, \quad \mu = 1, \cdots, r_\alpha.$$

Hence, as in the proof of Theorem 5.2,

$$\Pi_\lambda g(x, \bar{y}_\lambda) = \Pi_{\lambda,\alpha,\mu}(\bar{y}_\lambda - \bar{z}_{\alpha\mu})(b + \cdots)$$

$$= \Pi_{\lambda,\alpha,\mu}((a - a_\alpha)x + \cdots)(b + \cdots)$$

$$= (\Pi_\alpha(a - a_\alpha)^{r r_\alpha} x^{rs} + \cdots)(b + \cdots),$$

where $b \neq 0$. Hence $O_P(G) \geqslant rs$, and the equality holds if and only if a is different from all the a_α, that is, if and only if the tangent to P is not tangent to G at p.

A corollary of this theorem has been mentioned earlier (§III-7.7);

THEOREM 5.10. *If p is a point of multiplicity r for F and s for G then F and G have at p at least rs intersections, and they have exactly rs intersections here if and only if no tangent to F at p is tangent to G at p.*

The following consequence of Theorem 5.9 will be needed later.

THEOREM 5.11. *If p is an ordinary r-fold point of F, the center of the places $P_1, \cdots, P_r$, and if, for some $s \leqslant r$, $O_{P_i}(G) \geqslant s$ for each i, then p is a point of G of multiplicity at least s.*

PROOF. If the multiplicity of G at p is $s' < s$, by Theorem 5.9 the tangent at P_i must be tangent to G at p. But there are r distinct such tangents, since p is an ordinary multiple point, and G can have at most $s' < s \leqslant r$ distinct tangents at p. This contradiction proves the theorem.

5.4. Exercises. 1. For each of the following pairs of curves, find the multiplicity of each of their distinct intersections and use Bezout's Theorem as a check. [Theorem 5.10 can often be used to advantage.]

$$\text{(a)} \quad (x^2 - y)^2 - x^5 = 0,$$

$$x^4 + x^3 y - y^2 = 0.$$

(Compare with §III-7.8, Exercise 4.)

(b) $y^4 - y^2 + x^4 = 0$,

$$y^4 - 2y^3 + (1 - x)y^2 - 2x^2y + x^4 = 0.$$

2. The number of intersections of two places $(a + t^r,\ b + a_1t + a_2t^2 + \cdots)$ and $(a + t^s,\ b + b_1t + b_2t^2 + \cdots)$ with the same center is defined to be the order of $\Pi_{\alpha,\beta}(\bar{y}_\alpha - \bar{z}_\beta)$, where

$$\bar{y}_\alpha = \Sigma a_i \epsilon_\alpha^i x^{i/r}, \quad \epsilon_\alpha^r = 1, \quad \alpha = 1, \cdots, r,$$

$$\bar{z}_\beta = \Sigma b_i \eta_\beta^i x^{i/s}, \quad \eta_\beta^s = 1, \quad \beta = 1, \cdots, s.$$

If two places have different centers we define their number of intersections to be zero. Prove the following:

(i). The number of intersections of two cocentral places of orders r and s is $\geqq rs$, the equality holding if the places have different tangents.

(ii). The order of a polynomial G at a place P is equal to the total number of intersections with P of all the places of the curve G.

(iii). The number of intersections of two curves at a point p is equal to the sum of the number of intersections of each place of one with each place of the other whose center is p.

(iv). If two curves of orders m and n have no common component the sum of the number of intersections of each place of one with each place of the other is mn.

3. Show that the tacnode of §III-2.4, Example 4, is the center of two linear places having two intersections.

4. Verify (iii) of Exercise 2 for the curves of Exercise 1.

5. Prove that two distinct irreducible curves cannot have a common place.

§6. PLÜCKER'S FORMULAS

6.1. Class of a curve. Let $F(x) = 0$ be a curve in the projective plane, of order n, with no multiple components, and let q be a point not on F. Suppose that q lies on m lines which are tangents to F, and suppose that each of these lines is tangent to F at just one point, which is neither a singular point nor a flex. Then m is called the *class* of F.

For this definition to have value it is necessary to show, first that such points as q exist, and second that two such points yield the same value of m. Although this can be done without great difficulty we shall find it easier and more instructive to alter the definition by removing the restrictions on the tangents through q, and introducing a notion of the multiplicity of a tangent from q to F.

Suppose that the point q, with coordinates (q_0, q_1, q_2), lies on the tangent to F at a non-singular point p. A necessary and sufficient condition for this is that $\Sigma q_i F_i(p) = 0$, where $F_i(x) = \dfrac{\partial F}{\partial x_i}$ (Theorem III-2.5). An alternative statement of this condition is that $\Sigma q_i F_i(x)$ have positive order at the place of F whose center is at p. This leads us to the general investigation of the order of $\Sigma q_i F_i$ at any place P of F.

We shall show first that $O_P(\Sigma q_i F_i)$ is independent of the coordinate system employed. Let $P = (\bar{x})$. If we make a change of coordinates by (II-1.1) the point q has the new coordinates (r) and P has new coordinates $(\bar{y})$, where

$$q_i = \Sigma A_i^j r_j, \quad \bar{x}_i = \Sigma A_i^j \bar{y}_j.$$

Also $F(x)$ becomes $G(y) = F(\Sigma_j A_i^j y_j)$. Hence

$$G_j(y) = \Sigma[F_i(\Sigma_j A_i^j y_j) \frac{\partial}{\partial y_j} \Sigma_j A_i^j y_j]$$

$$= \Sigma_i F_i(\Sigma_j A_i^j y_j) A_i^j$$

Therefore,

$$O_P(\Sigma_j r_j G_j) = O(\Sigma_j r_j G_j(\bar{y}))$$

$$= O(\Sigma_j r_j \Sigma_i F_i(\Sigma_j A_i^j \bar{y}_j) A_i^j)$$

$$= O(\Sigma_i (\Sigma_j A_i^j r_j) F_i(\Sigma_j A_i^j \bar{y}_j))$$

$$= O(\Sigma_i q_i F_i(\bar{x}))$$

$$= O_P(\Sigma_i q_i F_i).$$

Now let P be a place of F. By Theorem 2.2 we can choose coordinates and a parameter so that P has the parametrization

(6.1) $$\bar{x}_0 = 1, \quad \bar{x}_1 = t^r, \quad \bar{x}_2 = t^{r+s} + \cdots,$$

where $r, s \geqslant 1$, unless P is a place of a linear component of F. We shall exclude this exception by requiring that F have no linear components. r and s are respectively the order and the class of P, and $x_2 = 0$ is the tangent at P. By Euler's Theorem (Theorem I-10.2),

$$\Sigma \bar{x}_i F_i(\bar{x}) = nF(\bar{x}) = 0.$$

Differentiating $F(\bar{x}) = 0$, we get

$$\Sigma \bar{x}_i' F_i(\bar{x}) = 0.$$

Substituting the values of $\bar{x}_i$ and $\bar{x}_i'$ from (6.1) into these equations, we obtain

$$F_0(\bar{x}) = F_2(\bar{x})[(s/r)t^{s+r} + \cdots],$$

$$F_1(\bar{x}) = F_2(\bar{x})[-(1 + s/r)t^s + \cdots].$$

Designating $O(F_2(\bar{x}))$ by $\delta(P)$, we have

$$O_P(\Sigma q_i F_i) = \delta(P) + \epsilon(P),$$

where

$\epsilon(P) = 0$ if q is not on the tangent at P,

$\epsilon(P) = s$ if q is on this tangent but is not at p,

$\epsilon(P) = s + r$ if q is at p.

Define $\epsilon(P)$ to be the *number of tangents*, or the *multiplicity of the tangent*, from q to P. The total number m of tangents from q to F is therefore $\Sigma_P \epsilon(P)$, the sum being over all places P of F. Now

$$\Sigma_P O_P(\Sigma q_i F_i) = n(n-1),$$

and so we have

$$\Sigma_P \delta(P) + \Sigma_P \epsilon(P) = n(n-1),$$

or

(6.2) $m = n(n-1) - \Sigma_P \delta(P).$

Now $\delta(P)$, which was defined in a particular coordinate system, is independent of the system used, for it can also be defined as the minimum value of $O_P(\Sigma q_i F_i)$ for all choices of the q's. This expression has been shown to be independent of the coordinate system, and it agrees with the other definition for the particular system used in (6.1). Also, $\Sigma_P \delta(P)$ depends only on the curve F and not at all on the point q. Hence (6.2) tells us that the total number of tangents from q to F, counted with their proper multiplicities, is independent of the position of q. Moreover, if the conditions mentioned at the beginning of this section are satisfied each tangent will have multiplicity one. Hence m is the class of F.

6.2. Flexes of a curve. In §III-6.3 we found that the flexes of F were its non-singular intersections with

$$H(x) = |F_{ij}| = \left| \frac{\partial^2 F}{\partial x_i \partial x_j} \right|.$$

Let P be a place of F whose center is a non-singular point; in the parametrization (6.1) we then have $r = 1$. We pass to affine coordinates, (6.1) becoming

(6.3) $$\bar{x} = t, \; \bar{y} = t^{s+1} + \cdots,$$

with center at the origin. Now $f(\bar{x},\bar{y}) = 0$, and at least one of $f_x(0,0)$, $f_y(0,0)$ is not zero. It is readily shown that these conditions require $f(x,y)$ to have the form

(6.4) $$f(x,y) = y - x^{s+1} + g(x,y),$$

where g contains no term of the form ay.

By Euler's Theorem,

$$x_0 F_{0i} = (n - 1)F_i - x_1 F_{1i} - x_2 F_{2i},$$
$$x_0 F_0 = nF - x_1 F_1 - x_2 F_2.$$

Substituting in H, the expression reduces to

$$H(x) = \begin{vmatrix} \dfrac{n}{n-1}F & F_1 & F_2 \\ \\ F_1 & F_{11} & F_{12} \\ \\ F_2 & F_{21} & F_{22} \end{vmatrix} \cdot \frac{(n-1)^2}{x_0^2}.$$

Hence in affine coordinates

$$h(x,y) = \begin{vmatrix} \dfrac{n}{n-1}f & f_x & f_y \\ \\ f_x & f_{xx} & f_{xy} \\ \\ f_y & f_{yx} & f_{yy} \end{vmatrix}$$

to within a constant factor. Using the expression for f given in (6.4) we find from (6.3) that

$$h(\bar{x},\bar{y}) = \begin{vmatrix} 0 & -(s+1)t^s + \bar{g}_x & 1 + \bar{g}_y \\ -(s+1)t^s + \bar{g}_x & -s(s+1)t^{s-1} + \bar{g}_{xx} & \bar{g}_{xy} \\ 1 + \bar{g}_y & \bar{g}_{xy} & \bar{g}_{yy} \end{vmatrix}$$

where we have written $\bar{g}_x$ for $g_x(\bar{x},\bar{y})$, etc.

From (6.4) we have $t^{s+1} + \cdots - t^{s+1} + g(\bar{x},\bar{y}) = 0$, so that $Og(\bar{x},\bar{y}) \geqslant s + 2$. Differentiating twice with respect to t gives

$$O[\bar{g}_x + \bar{g}_y((s+1)t^s + \cdots)] \geqslant s + 1,$$
$$O[\bar{g}_{xx} + 2\bar{g}_{xy}((s+1)t^s + \cdots) + \bar{g}_{yy}((s+1)t^s + \cdots) + \bar{g}_y(s(s+1)t^{s-1}$$
$$+ \cdots)] \geqslant s.$$

From the condition on g it follows that $O\bar{g}_y \geqslant 1$. The above relations then give $O\bar{g}_x \geqslant s + 1$, $O\bar{g}_{xx} \geqslant s$. It follows that $h(\bar{x},\bar{y}) = s(s+1)t^{s-1} + \cdots$ is of order $s - 1$.

One consequence of this result is that any common irreducible component of f and h is a line. For if P is a non-singular place of such a component then $O_P(h) = \infty$. But $O_P(h) = s - 1$, and so $s = \infty$; that is, P is a place of a line. As in §6.1 we consider only curves with no line components, and so f and h will have no common components.

Now P is a flex if and only if $s \geqslant 2$, that is, if and only if $O_P(h) > 0$. This gives us an independent proof of Theorem III-6.3. However, we can do more than this. We define $s - 1$ to be the multiplicity of the flex at P. Let i be the total number of flexes, counted according to their multiplicities. Then since H is of degree $3(n - 2)$, we have

$$(6.5) \qquad i = 3n(n - 2) - \Sigma_\alpha O_{P_\alpha}(H),$$

where P_α are the places of F with singular centers.

6.3. Plücker's formulas. Equations (6.2) and (6.5) are generalized forms of the first two Plücker formulas. The other two formulas will be obtained after the notion of dual curves has been discussed (§V-8). The usual form of Plücker's formulas relate to curves which have no singularities except simple nodes and cusps. A simple node is the center of exactly two places of F, both places being of order one and class one and having distinct tangents. A cusp is the center of a single place of order two and class one. To obtain Plücker's formulas we need merely evaluate $\delta(P)$, and $O_P(H)$ at these types of places. (Obviously $\delta(P) = 0$ if p is non-singular.)

(i). Let P be one place of a simple node. Choosing proper coordinates and parameters, we get the parametrization

$$\bar{x} = t, \quad \bar{y} = t^2 + \cdots,$$

with $f = xy + g$, each term of g being of degree 3 or more. By direct computation we find that

$$\delta(P) = 1, \quad O_P(h) = 3.$$

(ii). Similarly, for a cusp we have

$$\bar{x} = t^2, \quad \bar{y} = t^3 + \cdots,$$

$$f = y^2 - x^3 + yg + k,$$

where g is homogeneous of degree two and each term of k is of degree 4 or more. Then

$$\delta(P) = 3, \quad O_P(h) = 8.$$

Denoting the number of simple nodes by δ and of cusps by κ, we get,

$$(6.6) \qquad m = n(n - 1) - 2\delta - 3\kappa.$$

$$i = 3n(n - 2) - 6\delta - 8\kappa.$$

These are Plücker's formulas.

Similar expressions could obviously be obtained by investigating more general singularities.

6.4. Exercises. 1. An irreducible cubic can have no more singularities than one simple node or one cusp, and all its flexes are of multiplicity one. Hence there are just three types of irreducible cubics, with $m = 6, 4, 3$ and $i = 9, 3, 1$ respectively.

2. There are ten types of irreducible quartics having no singularities but cusps and simple nodes. Calculate the class and the number of flexes for each of these types.

3. The six points of contact of the tangents to a non-singular cubic from an external point lie on a conic.

4. If we define a flex of multiplicity $s - 1$ as a *place* of order 1 and class s, Plücker's formulas still hold if we admit double points having two linear branches with distinct tangents.

5. With the above definition of flex, Plücker's formulas apply to curves having no singularities except cusps and multiple points with distinct tangents if we count such a point of multiplicity r as $r(r - 1)/2$ double points.

§7. Nöther's Theorem

7.1. Nöther's theorem. A very useful theorem concerning intersections of curves was proved by Max Nöther. The theorem states that if three curves F, G, H satisfy certain conditions, then there exist homogeneous polynomials A, B such that $H = AG + BF$. The theorem has various forms, depending on the restrictions one puts on the singularities of F and G. We shall prove the form of the theorem which will be most useful in our later investigations.

We first prove a lemma.

Theorem 7.1. *Let F have no factor involving only x_0 and x_1, and let $R(x_0, x_1) = UG + VF$ be the resultant of F and G with respect to x_2. Then H can be expressed in the form $AG + BF$ if there exists a homogeneous polynomial Q such that $T = UH - QF$ is a homogeneous polynomial which has R as a factor.*

Proof. Let $T = AR$. We have

$$RH = UHG + VHF$$
$$= QGF + TG + VHF$$
$$= ARG + (QG + VH)F.$$

Hence $R \mid (QG + VH)F$, and since F has no factor involving only x_0 and x_1, we must have $QG + VH = BR$. Then $H = AG + BF$.

We can now prove the following form of Nöther's Theorem.

THEOREM 7.2. *Let F and G have no common factor, and let each place P_i of F for which $O_{P_i}(G) > 0$ have as its center an ordinary r_i-fold point of Γ, $r_i \geqslant 1$. If for each such P_i,*

$$O_{P_i}(H) \geqslant O_{P_i}(G) + r_i - 1,$$

then $H = AG + BF$.

PROOF. Since both the hypotheses and the conclusion of this theorem are independent of coordinates, we can choose our coordinate system at will. Take $(0,0,1)$ not on F and not on any line of the following finite sets: (i) the lines joining all pairs of intersections of F and G, (ii) the tangents to F at its intersections with G, (iii) the further tangents to F from these intersections, (iv) the lines joining these intersections to multiple points of F. Since the coefficient of the highest power of x_2 in F is then a constant, we can carry out the division transformation of UH by F, obtaining $UH = QF + T$, where T is of degree at most $n - 1$ in x_2, n being the degree of F.

Let (a) be an r-fold point of F, the center of the places $P_1, \cdots, P_r$, and let

$$O_{P_i}(G) = \sigma_i > 0, \quad i = 1, \cdots, r.$$

Let $\sigma = \Sigma \sigma_i$. Since no other intersection of F and G is on the line $L = a_1 x_0 - a_0 x_1$, by (i) R will be divisible by L exactly to the power σ. If we can show that T is divisible by L^σ our theorem will be proved, for the same argument will be applicable to each factor of R. Suppose then that $T = L^\rho T_1$, where $\rho < \sigma$ and $L \dagger T_1$. From $T = UH - QF$ we have

$$O_{P_i}(T) = O_{P_i}(U) + O_{P_i}(H)$$
$$\geqslant O_{P_i}(U) + O_{P_i}(G) + r - 1,$$

and from $R = UG + VF$ it follows that

$$O_{P_i}(U) + O_{P_i}(G) = O_{P_i}(R) = \sigma,$$

since $O_{P_i}(L) = 1$ by (ii). Hence

$$O_{P_i}(T_1) = O_{P_i}(T) - \rho \geqslant \sigma - \rho + r - 1 \geqslant r.$$

From Theorem 5.11 it then follows that (a) is a point of multiplicity at least r for the curve $T_1 = 0$, and hence that $T_1(a_0,a_1,x_2) = 0$ has $x_2 = a_2$ as a root of multiplicity at least r.

Now let (a_0,a_1,b_j) be another intersection of L with F. By (ii), (iii), and (iv) there are $n - r$ such intersections, each at a place P_j of F of order one, and we have

$$O_{P_j}(L) = 1, \quad O_{P_j}(G) = 0, \quad O_{P_j}(R) = \sigma.$$

Then, as above,

$$O_{P_j}(U) = O_{P_j}(R) = \sigma,$$

$$O_{P_j}(T_1) = O_{P_j}(T) - \rho = \sigma + O_{P_j}(H) - \rho \geqslant 1.$$

Therefore $T_1 = 0$ passes through each of these points; that is, $T_1(a_0,a_1,x_2) = 0$ has roots $b_1,\cdots,b_{n-r}$. With the r-fold root a_2 this gives n roots of $T_1(a_0,a_1,x_2) = 0$, and since this equation is of degree $n - 1$ it must be identically satisfied. This implies that L is a factor of T_1, contrary to assumption, and so the theorem is proved.

From the consideration of the degrees of the polynomials involved we see that

$$\deg A = \deg H - \deg G,$$

$$\deg B = \deg H - \deg F.$$

We also have

$$O_{P_i}(A) + O_{P_i}(G) = O_{P_i}(H)$$

$$\geqslant O_{P_i}(G) + r_i - 1,$$

so that

$$O_{P_i}(A) \geqslant r_i - 1.$$

From Theorem 5.11 it then follows that the curve $A = 0$ has the center of P_i as a point of multiplicity at least $r_i - 1$.

7.2. Applications. One simple and interesting application of Nöther's Theorem is a generalization of Theorem III-6.2.

THEOREM 7.3. *If the nine points of intersection of two cubics F and G are simple points of F, then every cubic on eight of these points is on the ninth.*

This statement is to be interpreted as follows. Let P_i be the places of F at which $O_{P_i}(G) = n_i > 0$. Then if H is any cubic for which it is known that $O_{P_i}(H) \geqslant n_i$ for each P_i but one, say P_1, and if $O_{P_1}(H) \geqslant n_1 - 1$, then $O_{P_1}(H) \geqslant n_1$.

PROOF. Let L be a line on the center of P_1 intersecting F in two other distinct points a and b not on G. Then $O_{P_i}(LH) \geqslant n_i$ for each i, and hence Theorem 7.2 can be applied to F, G, LH to give

$$LH = AG + BF.$$

Now L and F both vanish at a and b, and since G does not, A must also vanish at these points. Since A is linear it must, therefore, differ from L only by a constant factor. Hence

$$LH = cLG + BF.$$

and so $L \mid BF$. Since $L \nmid F$, we must have $B = dL$. We thus obtain

$$H = cG + dF,$$

and the required conclusion follows at once.

Several interesting corollaries follow by specializing G.

THEOREM 7.4. *If a line cuts a cubic in three distinct points, the residual intersections of the tangents at these points are collinear.*

PROOF. Take F to be the cubic, G the product of the three tangents, and H the square of the original line times the line joining two of the residual intersections.

The line of the residual intersections is called the *satellite* of the original line.

In case the line of Theorem 7.4 passes through two flexes, we have

THEOREM 7.5. *A line joining two flexes of a cubic passes through a third flex.*

A more general form of Theorem 7.4 is

THEOREM 7.6. *If a conic is tangent to a cubic at three distinct points the residual intersections of the tangents at these points are collinear.*

The following generalization of Theorem III-4.1 is easily proved by the use of Nöther's Theorem.

THEOREM 7.7. *If the mn intersections of G_m and F_n are simple points of F, and if G_r, $r < m$, intersects F in rn of these points, then there is a G_{m-r} intersecting F in the remaining $(m - r) n$ points.*

PROOF. Since all the intersections are at simple points of F, Theorem 7.2 will apply to F, G_r, G_m. Then

$$G_m = A_{m-r}G_r + BF.$$

It follows at once that $G_{m-r} = A_{m-r}$ has the required property.

Theorems 7.4, 7.5, and 7.6, as well as various generalizations of these, follow from this theorem.

None of these consequences of Theorem 7.2 uses the full force of this theorem, for the singularities of F are always avoided. The real importance of Theorem 7.2 lies in its application to the theory of linear series (Chapter VI).

7.3. Exercises. 1. Extend Theorem 7.4 to any line.

2. If a conic is tangent to a cubic at three distinct points, the residual intersections with the cubic of the lines joining these points in pairs are collinear.

3. Given two non-singular points of an irreducible cubic show how to construct a conic tangent to the cubic at these points and also at a third point. Discuss the various special cases and the number of solutions in each case.

4. A *sextatic* point of an irreducible cubic is a non-singular point, not a flex, at which a conic can have six intersections with the cubic. Show that the sextatic points are the points of contact of the tangents from the flexes, and that there are 27, 3, or 0 according as the cubic is non-singular or has a node or a cusp.

5. The tangents at the six intersections of a cubic and a conic meet the cubic again in six points on a conic. Generalize.

6. A line cutting a cubic of class m in three distinct points none of which is a flex is the satellite of $(m - 2)^2$ distinct lines. When $m = 6$ the 16 lines are concurrent by fours in 12 points, three points lying on each line. (See *Journal für die reine und angewandte Mathematik*, Vol. 108 (1891), p. 269, for a discussion of this configuration.) Investigate the configuration obtained when the given line is tangent to the cubic.

(For other applications of Theorems 7.3 and 7.7 see H. Hilton, *Plane Algebraic Curves*, Oxford, 1920, Chapter XII.)

V. Transformations of Curves

The notion of a *transformation* is important in all branches of geometry. In this chapter we shall consider three types of transformations of curves, the birational, rational, and algebraic transformations, in increasing order of generality. These give us a means of extending the definition of algebraic curve to include loci in spaces of dimension greater than two.

Before proceeding to the investigation of transformations we shall find it useful to develop some further properties of rings and fields.

§1. IDEALS

1.1. Ideals in a ring. In any commutative ring R certain subrings play an important role. A subring I of R is said to be an *ideal* of R if for every $a \in I$ and every $b \in R$ the product $ab \in I$.

The following examples illustrate this definition:

1. R = set of integers; I = set of even integers.
2. $R = D[x,y]$; I = set of all $f(x,y) \in R$ for which $f(0,0) = 0$.
3. $R = D[x]'$; I = set of all $f(x) \in R$ for which $O(f) \geqslant m$.
4. R = any domain; I = set of all multiples by elements of R of a fixed element a of R.
5. R = any commutative ring; $I = R$.
6. R = any commutative ring; I contains only one element, the zero element of R.

In Example 4 the ideal I is called a *principal* ideal, and is said to be generated by the element a. That not all ideals are principal is shown by Example 2.

The importance of ideals is due largely to the following property.

THEOREM 1.1. *If I is an ideal in a commutative ring R, the relation $a \sim b$, defined by $a - b \in I$, is an equivalence relation which is preserved under addition and multiplication.*

PROOF. That the relation is an equivalence follows from the fact that I is a ring, for if $a - b \in I$ then $b - a = -(a - b) \in I$, and if also $b - c \in I$ then $a - c = (a - b) + (b - c) \in I$. Let $a_1 \sim a_2$, $b_1 \sim b_2$. Then

$$(a_1 \pm b_1) - (a_2 \pm b_2) = (a_1 - a_2) \pm (b_1 - b_2) \in I,$$

and so $a_1 \pm b_1 \sim a_2 \pm b_2$. Also

$$a_1b_1 - a_2b_2 = a_1(b_1 - b_2) + b_2(a_1 - a_2) \in I,$$

since $b_1 - b_2$ and $a_1 - a_2 \in I$. Hence $a_1b_1 \sim a_2b_2$.

Let I_a denote the equivalence class containing a. We define the sum and the product of two equivalence classes by

$$I_a + I_b = I_{a+b}, \quad I_aI_b = I_{ab}.$$

Because equivalence is preserved under addition and multiplication the sum and the product of classes are uniquely defined. It is easy to verify that the set of classes forms a commutative ring with $I_0 = I$ as the zero element. This ring is indicated by R/I and is called the *residue-class* ring of I in R.

Example. Let R be the set of integers and let I be the principal ideal generated by the integer m. Then we can use the common notation of number theory and write $a \equiv b \pmod{m}$ instead of $a \sim b$. We see then that the properties of integers reduced modulo m are just the properties of the ring R/I.

The relation between R and R/I is expressed in

THEOREM 1.2. *The correspondence between a and I_a is a homomorphism of R into R/I in which I consists of the elements of R which map into the zero of R/I. Conversely, if we have a homomorphism of R into a ring R', each element of R' being the image of some element of R, then the set of elements of R mapping into the zero of R' is an ideal I in R and R/I is isomorphic to R'.*

PROOF. The first part of the theorem follows at once from the definition of R/I. Suppose then that $a \to a'$ is a homomorphism of R into R' and let I be the set of elements of R mapping into the zero $0'$ of R'. We see at once that $a \to 0'$, $b \to 0'$ implies $a \pm b \to 0'$, and so I is closed under addition and subtraction. Also for any c in R we have $ac \to 0'c' = 0'$ and so I is an ideal. If I_a and I_b are two elements of R/I, we have $I_a = I_b$ if and only if $a - b \in I$, which in turn is true if and only if $a' = b'$. Hence there is a one-to-one correspondence between the elements of R/I and those of R'. Since $I_a + I_b = I_{a+b}$ and $I_aI_b = I_{ab}$, while $a' + b' = (a + b)'$ and $a'b' = (ab)'$, this correspondence is preserved under addition and multiplication, and so is an isomorphism.

1.2. Exercises. 1. If R is a commutative ring with a unity element, any set, finite or infinite, of elements $a_1, a_2, \cdots$ determines an ideal consisting of all finite sums Σb_ia_i, where $b_i \in R$.

2. Every ideal in the ring of integers is a principal ideal.

3. If R is the ring of integers and I the principal ideal generated by a positive prime p, then R/I is a field of characteristic p containing just p elements.

4. (a) The only ideals in a field are the field itself and the ideal consisting of the zero element.

(b) A homomorphism of a field K into any ring R either maps every element of K into the zero of R or is an isomorphism between K and a subset of R.

5. If R is a commutative ring with a unity element, R/I is a domain if and only if I has the property that if $a,b \in R$, $a \notin I$, $ab \in I$, then $b \in I$. In this case I is called a *prime* ideal.

§2. EXTENSIONS OF A FIELD

2.1. Transcendental extensions. We shall be concerned here with the process of extending a field; that is, of passing from a given field K to a field $\Sigma \supset K$. We have already had examples of this process in the construction of the fields $K(x)$, $K(x)'$, $K(x)^*$.

Let Σ be a field containing K, and let $\theta_1, \cdots, \theta_r$ be elements of Σ. By the notation $K(\theta_1, \cdots, \theta_r)$ we indicate the smallest subfield of Σ containing K and the elements $\theta_1, \cdots, \theta_r$. Evidently every element of $K(\theta_1, \cdots, \theta_r)$ is expressible in the form $g(\theta_1, \cdots, \theta_r)/h(\theta_1, \cdots, \theta_r)$, where g and h are polynomials and $h(\theta_1, \cdots, \theta_r) \neq 0$; for this set of elements of Σ forms a field which is contained in every field containing K and $\theta_1, \cdots, \theta_r$. We say that $K(\theta_1, \cdots, \theta_r)$ is obtained from K by the *adjunction* of elements $\theta_1, \cdots, \theta_r$, and that $\theta_1, \cdots, \theta_r$ is a *basis* of $K(\theta_1, \cdots, \theta_r)$ over K.

We shall find it convenient to designate by $K[\theta_1, \cdots, \theta_r]$ the set of all elements of $K(\theta_1, \cdots, \theta_r)$ of the form $f(\theta_1, \cdots, \theta_r)$, where $f(x_1, \cdots, x_r) \in K[x_1, \cdots, x_r]$. $K(\theta_1, \cdots, \theta_r)$ is evidently the quotient field of $K[\theta_1, \cdots, \theta_r]$.

If $r = 1$ the adjunction is said to be *simple*. Simple adjunctions are divided into two classes. If θ satisfies an equation of the type $f(\theta) = 0$, where $f(x) \in K[x]$, the adjunction of θ is said to be *algebraic*, and θ is *algebraic over* K. If θ satisfies no such equation the adjunction is *transcendental*.

The following theorem gives a complete analysis of simple transcendental adjunctions.

THEOREM 2.1. *If θ is transcendental over K then $K(\theta)$ is isomorphic to the field $K(x)$ of rational functions of an indeterminate x.*

PROOF. We have seen that every element of $K(\theta)$ is expressible in the form $g(\theta)/h(\theta)$, $g,h \in K[x]$. If two such expressions are equal, say $g_1(\theta)/h_1(\theta) = g_2(\theta)/h_2(\theta)$, we would have $g_1(\theta)h_2(\theta) - g_2(\theta)h_1(\theta) = 0$. Since θ is transcendental this implies that $g_1(x)h_2(x) - g_2(x)h_1(x) = 0$; that is, that $g_1(x)/h_1(x) = g_2(x)/h_2(x)$. Conversely, $g_1(x)/h_1(x) = g_2(x)/h_2(x)$ obviously implies $g_1(\theta)/h_1(\theta) = g_2(\theta)/h_2(\theta)$. Hence the correspondence between $g(\theta)/h(\theta)$ and $g(x)/h(x)$ is one-to-one, and as it is preserved under addition and multiplication it is an isomorphism.

This result can easily be generalized to non-simple adjunctions. We define $\theta_1, \cdots, \theta_r$ to be *algebraically independent* over K if they satisfy no equation $f(\theta_1, \cdots, \theta_r) = 0$, f being a polynomial over K. We then have

THEOREM 2.2. *If $\theta_1, \cdots, \theta_r$ are algebraically independent over K, then $K(\theta_1, \cdots, \theta_r)$ is isomorphic to the field $K(x_1, \cdots, x_r)$ of rational functions of indeterminates $x_1, \cdots, x_r$.*

The proof is the same as for Theorem 2.1.

2.2. Simple algebraic extensions. Algebraic adjunctions are not quite so easy to handle. We first prove

THEOREM 2.3. *If θ is algebraic over K there is an irreducible polynomial $f(x) \in K[x]$, unique to within a constant factor, such that for any polynomial $k(x)$, $k(\theta) = 0$ if and only if $f(x) \mid k(x)$.*

PROOF. Since θ is algebraic there is a polynomial $g(x) \neq 0$ such that $g(\theta) = 0$. Let $g(x) = g_1(x)g_2(x) \cdots g_r(x)$ be an irreducible factorization of $g(x)$. Then $g_1(\theta)g_2(\theta) \cdots g_r(\theta) = 0$, and hence at least one $g_i(\theta) = 0$. Denote one such $g_i(x)$ by $f(x)$. If $f(x) \mid k(x)$ then obviously $k(\theta) = 0$, since $f(\theta) = 0$. On the other hand, if $f(x) \nmid k(x)$ then f and k have no common factor, since f is irreducible, and so by Theorem I-6.7 there exist polynomials $a(x)$, $b(x)$ such that $af + bk = 1$. Hence $a(\theta)f(\theta) + b(\theta)k(\theta) = 1$, and since $f(\theta) = 0$ this implies that $k(\theta) \neq 0$. Finally if $f_1(x)$ is another irreducible polynomial such that $f_1 \mid k$ if and only if $k(\theta) = 0$, we have $f \mid f_1$ and $f_1 \mid f$. Hence $f_1 = af$, $a \in K$.

To prove a theorem for algebraic adjunctions analogous to Theorem 2.1 we must first show how to construct an algebraic extension. This is done in

THEOREM 2.4. *If I is the principal ideal in $K[x]$ generated by the irreducible polynomial $f(x)$, then $K[x]/I$ is a field $K(\xi)$, where $f(\xi) = 0$.*

PROOF. To prove that $\Lambda = K[x]/I$ is a field we need merely to show that for any $I_a, I_b \in \Lambda, I_a \neq I$, there is an I_g such that $I_a I_g = I_b$. For by taking $I_b = I_a$ we have the existence of a unity element, and by taking I_b to be unity we have the existence of an inverse. In terms of elements of $K[x]$, $I_a I_g = I_b$ says that there exists a $c \in K[x]$ such that $ag = b + cf$. Now $f \nmid a$, since $I_a \neq I$, and since f is irreducible there exist $d, e \in K[x]$ such that $da + ef = 1$ (Theorem I-6.7). Taking $g = bd$, $c = -be$, we have the required relation. Now let $\xi = I_x$. Since every element of $K[x]$ is a polynomial in x, it follows from the homomorphism between $K[x]$ and Λ that every element of Λ is a polynomial in ξ; that is, $\Lambda = K[\xi]$, and hence also $\Lambda = K(\xi)$ since Λ is a field. Finally, $f(x)$ maps into zero in the homomorphism, and so $f(\xi) = 0$.

We have thus established the existence of an algebraic extension corresponding to any irreducible polynomial $f(x)$. The next theorem tells us that such an extension is unique.

THEOREM 2.5. *If θ satisfies the irreducible equation $f(\theta) = 0$ over K, then $K(\theta)$ is isomorphic to the field $K(\xi)$ defined in Theorem 2.4.*

PROOF. The mapping of $K[x]$ into $K[\theta]$ defined by $g(x) \to g(\theta)$ is a homomorphism, and by Theorem 2.3 $g(x) \to 0$ if and only if $f \mid g$. Hence the ideal I of elements mapping into zero is the principal ideal generated by $f(x)$. By Theorem 1.2 we then have that $K(\xi) = K[x]/I$ is isomorphic to $K[\theta]$. Hence $K[\theta]$ is a field containing K and θ and contained in $K(\theta)$. Therefore $K[\theta] = K(\theta)$, and the theorem is proved.

An important by-product of the above proof is

THEOREM 2.6. *If $f(x)$ is of degree r then every element of $K(\theta)$ is expressible as a polynomial in θ of degree less than r.*

PROOF. That every element ϕ of $K(\theta)$ is expressible as a polynomial $g(\theta)$ follows from the remark above that $K(\theta) = K[\theta]$. If $g(x)$ is of degree greater than or equal to r, divide $g(x)$ by $f(x)$, obtaining

$$g(x) = q(x)f(x) + h(x),$$

with $h = 0$ or $\deg h < r$. Then obviously $\phi = g(\theta) = h(\theta)$, as was to be proved.

The integer r is called the *degree* of the extension. The next theorem shows that this degree depends only on the two fields involved, and not on the particular element θ used to get the extension.

THEOREM 2.7. *If θ satisfies an irreducible equation over K of degree r then every element ϕ of $K(\theta)$ satisfies an equation over K of degree at most r, and if $K(\phi) = K(\theta)$ this equation is irreducible and of degree r.*

PROOF. Since $1, \phi, \phi^2, \cdots, \phi^r$ are elements of $K(\theta)$ we have from Theorem 2.6

$$1 = 1,$$
$$\phi = b_0^{(1)} + b_1^{(1)}\theta + \cdots + b_{r-1}^{(1)}\theta^{r-1},$$
$$\phi^2 = b_0^{(2)} + b_1^{(2)}\theta + \cdots + b_{r-1}^{(2)}\theta^{r-1},$$
$$\cdots \cdots \cdots \cdots \cdots \cdots \cdots$$
$$\phi^r = b_0^{(r)} + b_1^{(r)}\theta + \cdots + b_{r-1}^{(r)}\theta^{r-1}.$$

Since the $r + 1$ quantities $1, \phi, \cdots, \phi^r$ are expressible as linear combinations over K of the r quantities $1, \theta, \cdots, \theta^{r-1}$, they are linearly dependent over K. That is, there exist $c_0, c_1, \cdots, c_r \in K$, not all zero, such that $c_0 + c_1\phi + \cdots + c_r\phi^r = 0$. If $K(\phi) = K(\theta)$, and ϕ satisfies an irreducible equation of degree s, then by the above result $s \leqslant r$. Similarly $r \leqslant s$, and so $r = s$.

The method of proving this theorem makes it evident that the degree of $K(\theta)$ over K can be defined as the maximum number of elements of $K(\theta)$ linearly independent over K.

2.3. Algebraic extensions. The theorems in §2.2 determine the structure of a simple algebraic extension. We wish now to consider more general extensions. An extension Σ of K is said to be algebraic if *every* element of Σ is algebraic over K. We first prove

THEOREM 2.8. *The result of a finite sequence of simple algebraic adjunctions is an algebraic extension.*

PROOF. Let $\theta_1, \theta_2, \cdots, \theta_m$ be elements such that θ_1 is algebraic over K and θ_i is algebraic over $K(\theta_1, \cdots, \theta_{i-1})$, $i = 2, \cdots, m$. We have to show that every element of $\Sigma = K(\theta_1, \cdots, \theta_m)$ is algebraic over K. Let r_i be the degree of the adjunction θ_i. Then any element of Σ is expressible as a linear combination, with coefficients in $K(\theta_1, \cdots, \theta_{m-1})$ of $1, \theta_m, \cdots, \theta_m^{r_m-1}$. Each of these coefficients is expressible as a linear combination, with coefficients in $K(\theta_1, \cdots, \theta_{m-2})$ of $1, \theta_{m-1}, \cdots, \theta_{m-1}^{r_{m-1}-1}$. By continuing this process we see that any element of Σ is a linear combination over K of the $r_1 r_2 \cdots r_m = R$ elements of the form $\theta^{p_1} \theta^{p_2} \cdots \theta_m^{p_m}$ where $0 \leqslant p_t \leqslant r_i - 1$. Hence if ϕ is any element of Σ the $R + 1$ elements $1, \phi, \phi^2, \cdots, \phi^R$ are linearly dependent over K and hence ϕ is algebraic over K.

In the case of fields of characteristic zero we can prove the much stronger theorem that the result of a finite sequence of algebraic extensions can be obtained by a *simple* algebraic extension. For later applications it will be useful to prove this result in the following more specific form.

THEOREM 2.9. *If $\theta_1, \theta_2, \cdots, \theta_m$ are each algebraic over a field K of characteristic zero and if S is any infinite subset of K, there exist $a_i \in S$, $i = 1, \cdots, m$, such that if $\phi = \Sigma a_i \theta_i$ then $K(\theta_1, \cdots, \theta_m) = K(\phi)$.*

PROOF. Let $L = K(x_1, \cdots, x_m)$ be the field of rational functions of the indeterminates $x_1, \cdots, x_m$. Then $L(\theta_1, \cdots, \theta_m)$ is an algebraic extension of L. Let $y = \Sigma x_i \theta_i$. We may assume that $y \neq 0$, since the only alternative is $\theta_1 = \cdots = \theta_m = 0$, a trivial case. Since $y \in L(\theta_1, \cdots, \theta_m)$ y is algebraic over L, by Theorem 2.8, and so there is a polynomial

$$f(x,z) = b_0(x) + b_1(x)z + \cdots + b_n(x)z^n,$$

irreducible over L, for which $f(x,y) = 0$. The $b_i(x)$ are elements of L, and by multiplying by a common denominator we may assume that they are elements of $K[x_1, \cdots, x_m]$. Then

$$f(x_1, \cdots, x_m, \ x_1\theta_1 + \cdots + x_m\theta_m) = 0$$

as an element of $K(\theta_1, \cdots, \theta_m)[x_1, \cdots, x_m]$, and so

$$(2.1) \qquad \left(\frac{\partial f}{\partial x_i}\right)_{z=y} + \theta_i \left(\frac{\partial f}{\partial z}\right)_{z=y} = 0, \quad i = 1, \cdots, m,$$

where $y = x_1\theta_1 + \cdots + x_m\theta_m$ has been substituted for z in $\dfrac{\partial f}{\partial x_i}$ and $\dfrac{\partial f}{\partial z}$.

If $\left(\dfrac{\partial f}{\partial z}\right)_{z=y}$ were zero then $f(x,z)$ and $\dfrac{\partial f}{\partial z}$ would have a common factor $z - y$ in $K(\theta_1, \cdots, \theta_m)[x_1, \cdots, x_m]$ and hence, by Theorem I-9.5, a common factor in $K[x_1, \cdots, x_m]$, contrary to the assumption that f is irreducible over L. Therefore $\left(\dfrac{\partial f}{\partial z}\right)_{z=y} \neq 0$, and by Theorem I-6.3 there exist constants $a_i \in S$ such that $\dfrac{\partial f}{\partial z} \neq 0$ for $x_i = a_i$, $z = \phi = a_1\theta_1 + \cdots + a_m\theta_m$. From (2.1) we obtain

$$\theta_i = -\left[\frac{\partial f}{\partial x_i} \Big/ \frac{\partial f}{\partial y}\right]_{x_i = a_i,\, z = \phi},$$

and so the θ_i are expressed as rational functions of ϕ over K. It follows that $\theta_i \in K(\phi)$, so that $K(\theta_1, \cdots, \theta_m) \subset K(\phi)$. Since obviously $K(\phi) \subset K(\theta_1, \cdots, \theta_m)$ we have the desired result.

2.4. Exercises. 1. Any field obtained from a field K of characteristic zero by a finite number of simple adjunctions is isomorphic to a simple algebraic extension of a field $K(x_1, \cdots, x_r)$ of rational functions over K.

2. If L is an extension of K the maximum number of elements of L algebraically independent over K is called the *dimension* of L over K and is denoted by $\dim_K L$. Prove that if L is obtained from K, and M is obtained from L, each by a finite number of simple adjunctions, then $\dim_K M = \dim_K L + \dim_L M$.

§3. RATIONAL FUNCTIONS ON A CURVE

3.1. The field of rational functions on a curve. Associated with an irreducible curve $f(x,y) = 0$ is an important concept known as the *field of rational functions on the curve*. This field, which we designate by Σ, is defined to be $K(\xi, \eta)$, where ξ is transcendental over K, and η is algebraic over $K(\xi)$, satisfying the irreducible equation $f(\xi, \eta) = 0$. This construction is impossible if f is a polynomial in x alone. But then we must have $f = ax + b$, a trivial case which we shall exclude from consideration.

This definition of Σ, while it is easy to formulate and to use, is slightly unsatisfactory in that it treats the variables x and y in an unsymmetric way. We leave it to the reader to prove the following statement: Σ is the quotient field of the domain $K[x,y]/I$, where I is the principal ideal generated by $f(x,y)$.

Since $\Sigma = K(\xi,\eta)$, every element of Σ is expressible as a rational function of ξ and η, that is, in a form $g(\xi,\eta)/h(\xi,\eta)$, where $g(x,y),h(x,y) \in K[x,y]$, and $h(\xi,\eta) \neq 0$. Such an expression of an element of Σ is, of course, not unique.

The reason for calling Σ the field of rational functions on f is easily seen. If $g_1(x,y)/h_1(x,y)$ and $g_2(x,y)/h_2(x,y)$ are rational functions over K, and if (a,b) is any point of f at which these functions have values, then these values will be equal if $g_1(\xi,\eta)/h_1(\xi,\eta) = g_2(\xi,\eta)/h_2(\xi,\eta)$. Conversely, if this last equality does not hold, then $f(x,y) \nmid g_1(x,y)h_2(x,y) - g_2(x,y)h_1(x,y)$, and there are points of f at which the two rational functions assume distinct values. In other words, as far as points of f are concerned the rational functions behave like elements of Σ.

For brevity we shall usually refer to Σ as "the field of f." Elements of Σ will usually be designated by small Greek letters.

By definition Σ contains at least one element which is algebraically independent over K. The next theorem limits the number of such elements.

THEOREM 3.1. *Any two elements of Σ are algebraically dependent over K.*

PROOF. Since Σ is algebraic over $K(\xi)$ any element ϕ of Σ satisfies an equation

$$g(\xi,\phi) = a_0 + \cdots + a_r\phi^r = 0, \quad a_i \in K(\xi).$$

By multiplying by the least common denominator of the a_i and dividing by their common factor we may assume that $a_i \in K[\xi]$, and that $g(\xi,z)$, now an element of $K[\xi,z]$, has no non-constant factor involving ξ alone. Similarly for the element ψ of Σ we have

$$h(\xi,\psi) = 0,$$

with $h(\xi,w)$ satisfying the same condition. Then $g(x,z)$ and $h(x,w)$ can have no non-constant factor, and so their resultant $R(z,w)$ is not zero. However $g(x,\phi)$ and $h(x,\psi)$ have the common factor $x - \xi$, and so $R(\phi,\psi) = 0$, as was to be proved.

The following theorem is an extension of Theorem 3.1, and gives us an intrinsic characterization of Σ.

THEOREM 3.2. *A field Σ over an algebraically closed field K of characteristic zero is the field of rational functions on a curve if and only if*

(i)   *Σ contains an element, but no pair of elements, algebraically independent over K, and*

(ii)   *Σ has a finite basis over K.*

PROOF. The necessity of (i) and (ii) follow from the definition of a field of rational functions and Theorem 3.1. Suppose then that Σ is a field with properties (i) and (ii). By (i), Σ contains an element ξ transcendental over K. If $\theta_1, \cdots, \theta_n$ is a basis for Σ over K, by (i) each θ_i is algebraic over $K(\xi)$, and so by Theorem 2.9 there is an η algebraic over $K(\xi)$ such that $\Sigma = K(\xi, \eta)$. If $f(\xi, \eta)$ is the irreducible equation satisfied by η, then Σ is the field of $f(x, y) = 0$.

We shall call a field satisfying (i) and (ii) an *admissible* field.

3.2. Invariance of the field. If we pass from affine to projective coordinates by putting $x = x_1/x_0$, $y = x_2/x_0$, it is convenient to make a similar change in the representation of elements of Σ. We replace ξ and η by ξ_1/ξ_0 and ξ_2/ξ_0. Then the elements of Σ can be expressed as rational functions of ξ_0, ξ_1, ξ_2 in which the numerator and denominator are homogeneous polynomials of the same degree. It must be remembered that ξ_0, ξ_1, ξ_2 are not themselves elements of Σ, but that their ratios are.

If by a change in coordinates the variables x, y are replaced by

$$(3.1) \quad \begin{aligned} x' &= a_1 x + b_1 y + c_1, \\ y' &= a_2 x + b_2 y + c_2, \quad a_1 b_2 - a_2 b_1 \neq 0, \end{aligned}$$

then ξ', η', defined from ξ, η by the corresponding transformation, are elements of Σ. Conversely, if Σ' is the field $K(\xi', \eta')$ defined by the new equation $f'(x', y') = 0$ of the curve, then $\xi, \eta \in \Sigma'$. Hence $\Sigma' = \Sigma$. As a change in projective coordinates can be treated similarly we see that *the field Σ is uniquely determined by the curve.*

3.3. Order of a rational function at a place. Let $(\bar{x}, \bar{y})$ be a parametrization of the place P of f. Since we are assuming that f is not of the form $ax + b$, $\bar{x}$ must be transcendental over K, and so $K(\bar{x})$ is isomorphic to $K(x)$ by Theorem 2.1. It follows that $f(\bar{x}, y)$ is irreducible when considered as a polynomial in y with coefficients in $K(\bar{x})$. Since $f(\bar{x}, \bar{y}) = 0$, it follows from Theorem 2.5 that the field $K(\bar{x}, \bar{y})$ is isomorphic to Σ in such a way that $\bar{x}$ and $\bar{y}$ correspond to ξ and η.

Since each element $\bar{g}$ of $K(\bar{x}, \bar{y})$ is a power series with a definite order, we can associate this order with the corresponding element ϕ of Σ. We call this the order of ϕ at the place P, and designate it by $O_P(\phi)$. $O_P(\phi)$ has the same properties as $O(\bar{g})$, namely

$$O_P(\phi \psi) = O_P(\phi) + O_P(\psi),$$

$$O_P(\phi + \psi) \geqslant \min[O_P(\phi), O_P(\psi)],$$

$$O_P(\phi) = 0 \text{ if } \phi \in K, \phi \neq 0,$$

$$O_P(\phi) = \infty \text{ if and only if } \phi = 0.$$

Evidently $O_P(\phi)$ does not depend on the particular parametrization used to represent P, since $O(\bar{g})$ does not. That $O_P(\phi)$ is also independent of the coordinate system follows from §3.2. For if $\phi = \phi(\xi, \eta)$, $\phi(x,y) \in K(x,y)$, then $O_P(\phi) = O(\phi(\bar{x}, \bar{y}))$. If we pass to a new coordinate system by (3.1), we obtain $\phi = \phi'(\xi', \eta')$, where $\phi'(a_1x + b_1y + c_1, a_2x + b_2y + c_2) = \phi(x,y)$. Since the new coordinates $(\bar{x}', \bar{y}')$ of P are obtained from the old ones by (3.1), we evidently have $\phi'(\bar{x}', \bar{y}') = \phi(\bar{x}, \bar{y})$, and so $O_P(\phi) = O(\phi'(\bar{x}', \bar{y}'))$ remains unchanged.

Thus to each place P of F there is associated a function $O_P(\phi)$ whose argument ranges over Σ and whose values include the integers and ∞. We shall see later (§10) that the place P is completely determined by this function.

If $(\bar{x}_0, \bar{x}_1, \bar{x}_2)$ are projective coordinates of a parametrization of P, and if $\phi = G(\xi)/H(\xi)$ in projective form, we obviously have $O_P(\phi) = O_P(G) - O_P(H)$, where $O_P(G)$ and $O_P(H)$ are defined as in §IV-5.1. Since G and H are of the same degree an application of Theorem IV-5.5 gives us the following important result.

THEOREM 3.3. *The sum of the orders of any non-zero element of Σ on all the places of F is zero.*

3.4. Exercises. 1. Is the mapping $g(x,y) \to g(\xi, \eta)$ a homomorphism of $K[x,y]$ into $K[\xi, \eta]$? Is it a homomorphism of $K[x,y]$ into Σ? Is it a homomorphism of $K(x,y)$ into Σ?

2. Associated with an irreducible hypersurface $f(x_1, \cdots, x_r) = 0$ is a field Σ which is the quotient field of the domain $K[x_1, \cdots, x_r]/I$, I being the principal ideal generated by f. A necessary and sufficient condition that an extension Σ of K be the field of a hypersurface in S_r is that Σ have a finite basis over K and be of dimension $r - 1$ over K. (See §2.4, Exercise 2.)

§4. BIRATIONAL CORRESPONDENCE

4.1. Birational correspondence between curves. The elements ξ, η form a basis for the field Σ of the curve $f(x,y) = 0$, but there may exist other bases. Suppose that we also have $\Sigma = K(\xi', \eta')$. Then by Theorem 3.1 there is a relation $f'(\xi', \eta') = 0$, $f'(x', y') \in K[x', y']$, and we may assume that f' is irreducible. Since at least one of ξ', η' is transcendental over K—for otherwise we would have $K(\xi', \eta') = K \neq \Sigma$— we see that Σ is also the field of the curve $f' = 0$. This relationship between f and f' is called a *birational correspondence*, and the two curves are said to be birationally equivalent.

Since $\xi', \eta' \in K(\xi, \eta)$, we have

$$\xi' = \phi(\xi, \eta), \quad \eta' = \psi(\xi, \eta),$$

where $\phi(x,y)$, $\psi(x,y) \in K(x,y)$. Consider the transformation defined by

(4.1) $x' = \phi(x,y), \quad y' = \psi(x,y)$.

Let $(\bar{x},\bar{y})$ be a parametrization of a place P of f. Then its transform $(\bar{x}',\bar{y}')$ defined by (4.1) is a parametrization of a place P' of f'. For since $0 = f'(\xi',\eta') = f'(\phi(\xi,\eta),\psi(\xi,\eta))$, we have by the isomorphism between $K(\xi,\eta)$ and $K(\bar{x},\bar{y})$ that $f'(\bar{x}',\bar{y}') = 0$; and since one of $\xi',\eta' \notin K$, one of $\bar{x}',\bar{y}' \notin K$.

Similarly we have an inverse transformation

$$x = \phi'(x',y'), \quad y = \psi'(x',y').$$

where

$$\xi = \phi'(\xi',\eta'), \quad \eta = \psi'(\xi',\eta'),$$

which transforms P' back into P. Hence *a birational correspondence between two curves induces a one-to-one correspondence between their places.*

If P has a finite center (a,b), and if $a' = \phi(a,b)$, $b' = \psi(a,b)$ exist, then (a',b') is the center of P', and conversely. Hence we also have that *a birational correspondence between two curves induces a one-to-one correspondence between the points of the curves not in a certain finite set.*

It should be noticed that the transformation (4.1) can be written in many different forms, for a given element ξ' of Σ is expressible in many ways as a rational function of ξ,η. Because of the isomorphism between $K(\xi,\eta)$ and $K(\bar{x},\bar{y})$, for any place $(\bar{x},\bar{y})$ the transform $(\bar{x}',\bar{y}')$ depends only on the elements ξ' and η' and not on the particular forms of the rational functions ϕ and ψ.

In projective coordinates the transformation (4.1) can be given a more convenient form. We have first of all,

$$\frac{x_1'}{x_0'} = \frac{G_1(x)}{G_0(x)}, \quad \frac{x_2'}{x_0'} = \frac{G_2(x)}{G_0(x)},$$

as we may evidently reduce the rational functions to a common denominator. Here the $G_i(x)$ are homogeneous polynomials in x_0,x_1,x_2 of the same degree. These equations can now be written in the form

(4.2) $x_i' = G_i(x), \quad i = 0,1,2.$

Example. Let

$$f(x,y) = y^2 - x^3 - x^2,$$

$$\phi(x,y) = \frac{x^2}{x^2 + y^2}, \quad \psi(x,y) = \frac{xy}{x^2 + y^2}$$

We then have

$$\eta^2 - \xi^3 - \xi^2 = 0.$$

$$\xi' = \frac{\xi^2}{\xi^2 + \eta^2} = \frac{\xi^2}{2\xi^2 + \xi^3} = \frac{1}{2 + \xi}.$$

$$\eta' = \frac{\xi\eta}{\xi^2 + \eta^2} = \frac{\eta}{\xi}\frac{1}{2 + \xi}.$$

Hence

$$\xi = \frac{1 - 2\xi'}{\xi'}, \quad \eta = \frac{\eta'}{\xi'}\frac{1 - 2\xi'}{\xi'},$$

so that $K(\xi',\eta') \supset K(\xi,\eta) = \Sigma$.

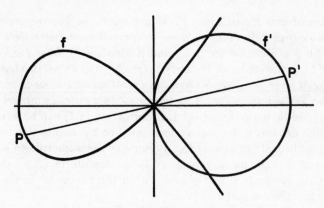

Figure 4.1

Thus

$$x' = \frac{x^2}{x^2 + y^2}, \quad y' = \frac{xy}{x^2 + y^2},$$

$$x = \frac{1 - 2x'}{x'}, \quad y = \frac{y'(1 - 2x')}{x'^2},$$

define a birational correspondence between f and some curve f'. The equation of f' is easily obtained. We have

$$0 = f(\xi,\eta) = f\left(\frac{1 - 2\xi'}{\xi'}, \frac{\eta'(1 - 2\xi')}{\xi'^2}\right)$$

$$= \frac{(1 - 2\xi')^2}{\xi'^4}(\xi'^2 + \eta'^2 - \xi').$$

Hence $\xi'^2 + \eta'^2 - \xi' = 0$, and so the equation of f' is $x'^2 + y'^2 - x' = 0$. (See Figure 4.1 for the geometric interpretation.) The effect of the transformation on the places and the points of the two curves is now easily obtained. It will be found that the two places of f with centers at the origin are transformed into places of f' with distinct centers.

4.2. Quadratic transformation as birational correspondence. An important type of birational transformation arises from the quadratic transformation (§III-7). In affine coordinates this transformation is defined by the equations

$$(4.3) \qquad\qquad x' = 1/x, \quad y' = 1/y.$$

If neither ξ nor η is zero, $\xi' = 1/\xi$ and $\eta' = 1/\eta$ are obviously a basis for $K(\xi,\eta)$. Hence *the quadratic transformation* (4.3) *induces a birational transformation on any irreducible curve not an irregular line of* (4.3). We see at once that the definition given in §III-7.3 of the transform of a curve agrees with the one given above.

The essential part of Theorem III-7.4 can now be stated in the following form: *Any irreducible curve is birationally equivalent to a curve with no singularities but ordinary multiple points.* This fact will be used to a considerable extent in the next chapter.

4.3. Exercise. 1. Extend the concept of birational transformation to irreducible hypersurfaces.

§5. SPACE CURVES

5.1. Definition of space curve. Birational correspondences give us an easy way of generalizing the concept of an irreducible algebraic curve. In considering a basis of Σ there is no real reason why we must restrict ourselves to one consisting of only two elements. Let $\Sigma = K(\xi_1, \cdots, \xi_n)$, where

$$\xi_i = \phi_i(\xi,\eta), \quad i = 1, \cdots, n,$$

and

$$\xi = \phi(\xi_1, \cdots, \xi_n), \quad \eta = \psi(\xi_1, \cdots, \xi_n),$$

with $\phi_i(x,y) \in K(x,y)$, $\phi(x) = \phi(x_1, \cdots, x_n) \in K(x_1, \cdots, x_n)$, $\psi(x) \in K(x_1, \cdots, x_n)$. Then, as in §4.1, a parametrization $(\bar{x}, \bar{y})$ of a place P of f corresponds to a set $(\bar{x}_1, \cdots, \bar{x}_n) = (\bar{x})$ of power series not all of which are constants. We regard $(\bar{x})$ as the affine coordinates of a parametrization of an *irreducible algebraic curve C in S_n*, and a set of equivalent parametrizations as a place P of C. Corresponding projective coordinates of P are then $(\bar{y}_0, \bar{y}_1, \cdots, \bar{y}_n)$, where $\bar{y}_i/\bar{y}_0 = \bar{x}_i$. As in §IV-2.1 we can choose $\bar{y}$'s so that $\min O(\bar{y}_i) = 0$; then $(\bar{y}_i(0))$ is a point of S_n and is called the center of P. The points of S_n which are the centers of places of C will be called points of C, and by the curve C itself we shall mean the set of all its points. The term "space curve" is usually applied to C if we wish to emphasize that it is not necessarily a plane curve.

This terminology will be justified if the set of points of C determines the set of places of C. That this is the case will be shown later (§9), when more properties of C have been developed. At present we may regard C as being the set of all its places rather than its points. In fact we can get along very well without ever mentioning the points of C, but this is rather unsatisfying from the geometric point of view.

It is now apparent that everything that was said about plane curves in §3 and §4 can be extended, with suitable changes, to space curves. In particular we can consider birational correspondences between any two curves with the same field. These are defined by equations of the type

$$\xi'_j = \phi_j(\xi_1, \cdots, \xi_n), \quad j = 1, \cdots, n,$$

or in projective coordinates by

$$\xi'_j = G_j(\xi_0, \cdots, \xi_n), \quad j = 0, \cdots, n.$$

Each admissible field Σ therefore determines a class of birationally equivalent curves. There is one curve corresponding to each basis of Σ over K, and conversely each curve corresponds to at least one such basis.

5.2. Places of a space curve. The places of a space curve C are defined as transforms of places of a plane curve. It is often useful to have a characterization of these places involving no curve other than C. One such is provided by the following theorem.

THEOREM 5.1. *A set of power series* $(\bar{x}_1, \cdots, \bar{x}_n)$ *is a parametrization of C if and only if there is an isomorphism between Σ and $K(\bar{x}_1, \cdots, \bar{x}_n)$ in which ξ_i corresponds to $\bar{x}_i$.*

PROOF. If $(\bar{x})$ is a parametrization of C it is the transform of some parametrization $(\bar{x}, \bar{y})$ of a plane curve f. The isomorphism between Σ and $K(\bar{x}_1, \cdots, \bar{x}_n)$ then follows from that between Σ and $K(\bar{x}, \bar{y})$. Conversely, suppose that we have an isomorphism between Σ and $K(\bar{x}_1, \cdots, \bar{x}_n)$ in which ξ_i and $\bar{x}_i$ correspond. We have

$$\xi = \phi(\xi_1, \cdots, \xi_n), \quad \eta = \psi(\xi_1, \cdots, \xi_n),$$

and we define $\bar{x}$ and $\bar{y}$ by

$$\bar{x} = \phi(\bar{x}_1, \cdots, \bar{x}_n), \quad \bar{y} = \psi(\bar{x}_1, \cdots, \bar{x}_n).$$

We see at once that $(\bar{x}, \bar{y})$ is a parametrization of f whose transform is $(\bar{x})$; that is $(\bar{x})$ is a parametrization of C.

5.3. Geometry of space curves. Bezout's Theorem. We shall now extend to space curves a few of the less obvious definitions relating to plane curves and derive corresponding properties.

Let C be curve in S_r, and let

$$\bar{x}_i = a_i + a_{i1}t + \cdots, \quad i = 0,\cdots,r,$$

with not all $a_i = 0$, be a parametrization of a place P of C. If $G(x)$ is any homogeneous polynomial in the x_i, by the order of G at P we mean the order of $G(\bar{x})$ as an element of $K[t]'$. (See §IV-5.1.)

Obviously $O_P(G) \neq 0$ if and only if G vanishes at the center (a) of P.

Let $\pi(x) = \Sigma b_i x_i = 0$ be a hyperplane of S_r. Then $O_P(\pi) > 0$ if and only if π contains (a). If π does contain (a), then

$$\pi(\bar{x}) = \Sigma b_i a_{i1}t + \Sigma b_i a_{i2}t^2 + \cdots,$$

and $O_P(\pi)$ is equal to the least value of s for which $\Sigma b_i a_{is} \neq 0$. Now suppose $a_{ij} = k_j a_i$ for $j < p$ but that no such relation holds for $j = p$. Then $\Sigma b_i a_i = 0$ implies $\Sigma b_i a_{ij} = 0$ for $j < p$ but not for $j = p$. That is, every hyperplane on (a) has order at least p and some hyperplanes have order p. We say that p is the *order* of the place P. (Compare with Theorem IV-5.7.)

If $O_P(\pi) > p$, π must satisfy the two independent conditions

$$\Sigma b_i a_i = 0, \quad \Sigma b_i a_{ip} = 0.$$

The hyperplanes satisfying these equations have a common line, given parametrically by

$$x_i = a_i + \lambda a_{ip},$$

which is said to be the *tangent* line to C at P.

The next step in this process would be to consider the hyperplanes through the tangent line whose order is higher than the minimum possible. They satisfy one more condition, and so contain a plane, the *osculating* plane to C at P. Successively higher osculating spaces can be similarly defined until one is obtained that contains the whole curve C.

The following theorem is the space equivalent of Bezout's Theorem.

THEOREM 5.2. *If a hyperplane π does not contain C the sum of the orders of π at the places of C is a constant n independent of π. If G is a homogeneous polynomial of degree m which is not of infinite order at each place of C, the sum of the orders of G at the places of C is mn.*

PROOF. Let $F(y_0,y_1,y_2) = 0$ be a plane curve birationally equivalent to C under the transformation

$$x_i = H_i(y), \quad i = 0,\cdots,r.$$

To any place $P = (\bar{x})$ of C, with not all $\bar{x}_i(0) = 0$, there corresponds a place $Q = (\bar{y})$ of F such that $t^q \bar{x}_i = H_i(\bar{y})$, $q \geqslant 0$. If we define $G_1(y)$ to be $G(H_i(y))$, then $G_1(\bar{y}) = t^{qm}G(\bar{x})$, so that $O_Q(G_1) \geqslant O_P(G)$. Now by Bezout's Theorem for plane curves, if $\Sigma_Q O_Q(G_1) = \infty$, then $F \mid G$ and $O_Q(G_1) = \infty$ for each Q. This implies that $O_P(G) = \infty$ for each P. If this does not happen $\Sigma_Q O_Q(G_1)$ is finite and hence so is $\Sigma_P O_P(G)$. If G' is any other homogeneous polynomial of degree m not of infinite order at each place of C, then $G(\xi)/G'(\xi) \in \Sigma$, and by Theorem 3.3 $\Sigma_P O_P(G/G') = 0$; that is, $\Sigma_P O_P(G) = \Sigma_P O_P(G')$. Taking $m = 1$, we obtain the first part of the theorem. Then the last part follows by taking $G' = \pi^m$.

The integer n thus associated with C is known as its *order;* if C is a plane curve this definition obviously agrees with the one previously given.

In accordance with Theorem IV-5.8 (ii) we define a point of a space curve to be *singular* if it is the center of a place of order greater than one or if it is the center of more than one place. A curve is called non-singular if it has no singular points.

A more detailed discussion of space curves and their singularities is reserved for the next chapter.

5.4. Exercises. 1. The basis x, x^2, x^3 of the admissible field $\Sigma = K(x)$ defines a curve C in S_3.

(i) C is non-singular.

(ii) C is of order 3.

(iii)   The tangent line to C at the point (a, a^2, a^3) is given by the parametric equations,

$$x_1 = a + t,$$

$$x_2 = a^2 + 2at,$$

$$x_3 = a^3 + 3a^2t,$$

(iv)   The osculating plane to C at the point (a, a^2, a^3) is

$$a^3 - 3a^2x_1 + 3ax_2 - x_3 = 0.$$

2. If C is a curve in S_n defined by the basis $\xi_1, \cdots, \xi_n$ of Σ, then the points of C span a subspace S_r of S_n if and only if $r + 1$ is the maximal number of 1, $\xi_1, \cdots, \xi_n$ linearly independent over K.

3. Any curve C of order r in S_n spans a subspace of S_n of dimension at most r.

§6. RATIONAL TRANSFORMATIONS

6.1. Rational transformations of a curve. Let C be a curve in S_n associated with the basis $\xi_1, \cdots, \xi_n$ of its field Σ, and let

$$\eta_j = \phi_j(\xi_1, \cdots, \xi_n) = \phi_j(\xi), \quad j = 1, \cdots, m,$$

be *arbitrary* elements of Σ. Then the field $\Sigma' = K(\eta_1, \cdots, \eta_m)$ is a subfield of Σ. There are two cases to consider.

(i) $\Sigma' = K$. Here each $\phi_j(\xi) \in K$, and so we may assume that $\phi_j(x) = a_j \in K$.

(ii) Σ' is transcendental over K. In this case Σ' is an admissible field, and so the basis $\eta_1, \cdots, \eta_m$ determines a curve C' in S_m.

We say that the equations

$$(6.1) \qquad\qquad y_j = \phi_j(x), \quad j = 1, \cdots, m,$$

determine a *rational transformation* of C into the point (a) in case (i) and into the curve C' in case (ii). We shall be mainly interested in the second case.

In projective coordinates we can, as in the case of a birational transformation, reduce equations (6.1) to the form

$$y_j = G_j(x_0, \cdots, x_n), \quad j = 0, \cdots, m,$$

where the G_j are homogeneous polynomials of the same degree. Conversely, every set of equations of this form determines a rational transformation of C unless each G_j is of infinite order at every place of C. For if G_0, say, has finite order at $(\bar{x})$, then $G_i(\bar{x})/G_0(\bar{x}) \in K(\bar{x}_1/\bar{x}_0, \cdots, \bar{x}_n/\bar{x}_0)$, and so

$$\phi_i = G_i(\xi)/G_0(\xi) \in K(\xi_1/\xi_0, \cdots, \xi_n/\xi_0) = \Sigma.$$

6.2. Rational transformation of a place. We now consider the relation between the places of a curve C and those of its rational transform C'. (We assume here, of course, that C' is a curve and not a point.) In one direction a correspondence is easily established.

THEOREM 6.1. *Equations* (6.1) *transform each place of C into a place of C'.*

PROOF. Let $(\bar{x})$ be a place of C and let

$$\bar{y}_j = \phi_j(\bar{x}), \quad j = 1, \cdots, m.$$

Since $K(\xi)$ and $K(\bar{x})$ are isomorphic, with ξ_i corresponding to $\bar{x}_i$, it follows that $K(\eta)$ and $K(\bar{y})$ are isomorphic, with η_j corresponding to $\bar{y}_j$. Hence by Theorem 5.1 $(\bar{y})$ is a parametrization of C'. Equivalent parametrizations $(\bar{x})$ obviously give equivalent parametrizations $(\bar{y})$. $(\bar{y})$ might be reducible, but even so it determines a unique place of C' which we call the transform of the place $(\bar{x})$.

The correspondence in the other direction is not so easy to establish. Before attempting this we must investigate the relation between Σ and Σ'. We know of course that $\Sigma \supset \Sigma'$. Since $\Sigma = K(\xi_1, \cdots, \xi_n)$ we also have $\Sigma = \Sigma'(\xi_1, \cdots, \xi_n)$. Now Σ' contains an element transcendental over K, and Σ contains no pair of elements algebraically independent over K. Hence each ξ_i must be algebraic over Σ', and so, by Theorem 2.9, Σ is a simple algebraic extension of Σ'. Let ν be the degree of this extension. We then have

THEOREM 6.2. *A place of C' is the transform of μ places of C, where $1 \leqslant \mu \leqslant \nu$; and there is only a finite set of places of C' for which $\mu < \nu$.*

PROOF. Let $(\bar{y})$ be a place of C'. We then have an isomorphism between Σ' and $K(\bar{y})$, and we shall seek to extend this isomorphism to Σ. Since Σ is algebraic of degree ν over Σ' we have $\Sigma = \Sigma'(\zeta)$, where $a_0 + a_1\zeta + \cdots + a_\nu\zeta^\nu = 0$, $a_i \in \Sigma'$, $a_\nu \neq 0$. By expressing the a_i as rational functions over K of $\eta_1, \cdots, \eta_m$, clearing fractions, and removing any common factor, we may assume that $a_i = a_i(\eta)$, where $a_i(y) \in K[y_1, \cdots, y_m]$ and the $a_i(y)$ have no common factor. We then have $g(\eta, \zeta) = 0$, where

$$g(y,z) = a_0(y) + a_1(y)z + \cdots + a_\nu(y)z^\nu$$

is an irreducible element of $K[y_1, \cdots, y_m, z]$. Since $a_\nu(\eta) \neq 0$, we have $a_\nu(\bar{y}) \neq 0$. Hence the equation

(6.2) $g(\bar{y}, z) = 0$

has a root $\bar{z} \in K(s)'$, where $s = t^{1/N}$ for some N (Theorem IV-3.1). We now replace the parameter t in each $\bar{y}_j$ by s^N. This has no effect on the isomorphism between Σ' and $K(\bar{y})$. Since $g(\eta, z)$ is irreducible, so is $g(\bar{y}, z)$, and hence $\Sigma = \Sigma'(\zeta)$ is isomorphic to $K(\bar{y}, \bar{z})$. In this isomorphism let ξ_i correspond to $\bar{x}_i$. Then $(\bar{x})$ is a parametrization of C, and $(\bar{y})$ is its transform. We have thus proved that $\mu \geqslant 1$.

To see that $\mu \leqslant \nu$ we merely notice that to each $(\bar{x})$ which transforms into $(\bar{y})$ there corresponds a root $\bar{z}$ of (6.2), namely the $\bar{z}$ corresponding to ζ in the isomorphism between Σ and $K(\bar{x})$. Since $(\bar{x})$ in turn is a rational function of $(\bar{y})$ and $\bar{z}$, different $(\bar{x})$'s must give rise to different $\bar{z}$'s. Since (6.2) has at most ν distinct roots, we have the desired inequality.

Let $D(y)$ be the discriminant of $g(y,z)$ with respect to z. Since $g(\eta, z)$ is irreducible we have $D(\eta) \neq 0$, and so $D(\eta)$ is of order zero at all but a finite set of places of C' (Theorem 3.3). Let $(\bar{y})$ be a place of C' at which $D(\eta)$ is of order zero. $(\bar{y})$ necessarily has a finite center (b), and $D(b) \neq 0$. Then the equation $g(b,z) = 0$ has ν distinct roots $b^{(1)}, \cdots, b^{(\nu)}$, and by Theorem IV-3.2 $G(\bar{y}, z) = 0$ has roots $\bar{z}^{(\alpha)} = b^{(\alpha)} + \cdots \in K[t]'$, $\alpha = 1, \cdots, \nu$. Since the $b^{(\alpha)}$ are all different, not two $\bar{z}^{(\alpha)}$ are equivalent. Hence the places $(\bar{x}^{(\alpha)})$ of C which they determine are all different, since, as was remarked above, $\bar{z}^{(\alpha)}$ is a rational function of the $x_i^{(\alpha)}$. This completes the proof of the theorem.

An important corollary of Theorem 6.2 is

THEOREM 6.3. *If C' is a rational transform of C and if there is an infinite set of places of C' each of which is the transform of just one place of C, then the transformation from C to C' is birational.*

PROOF. In virtue of Theorem 6.2, the hypotheses of this theorem imply that $\nu = 1$. Hence $\Sigma' = \Sigma$, which gives the desired conclusion.

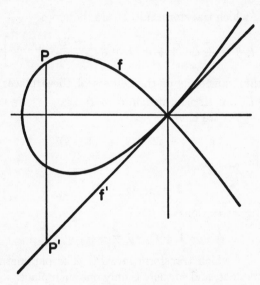

Figure 6.1

6.3. Example. We consider the transformation of the curve $f = x^2 + x^3 - y^2 = 0$ defined by

$$x' = x, \quad y' = x.$$

Geometrically this is a projection of f from the infinite point on the y-axis into the line $y = x$ (Figure 6.1). Obviously $f' = x' - y'$, and $\Sigma' = K(\xi)$. For the element ζ we may use η. Then $g(\xi',\eta',\zeta) = \xi'^2 + \xi'^3 - \zeta^2$, and we have $\nu = 2$, $\xi = \xi'$, $\eta = \zeta$. Any place P' of f' has a parametrization $(a + t, a + t)$. Hence $\bar{z}$ is to be a root of

$$(a + t)^2 + (a + t)^3 - \bar{z}^2 = 0.$$

This reduces to

$$\bar{z}^2 = (a^2 + a^3) + (2a + 3a^2)t + (1 + 3a)t^2 + t^3.$$

There are now three possibilities.

(i) If $a \neq 0, -1$, then

$$\bar{z} = \pm \sqrt{(a^2 + a^3) + (2a + 3a^2)t + (1 + 3a)t^2 + t^3}$$

$$= \pm a \sqrt{1 + a} \sqrt{1 + \frac{2 + 3a}{a + a^2} t + \frac{1 + 3a}{a^2 + a^3} t^2 + \frac{1}{a^2 + a^3} t^3}$$

$$= \pm a \sqrt{1 + a} \left[1 + \frac{1}{2} \frac{2 + 3a}{a + a^2} t + \frac{1}{8} \frac{4a + 3a^2}{(a + a^2)^2} t^2 + \cdots \right].$$

The places of f which transform into P' are therefore

$$\bar{x} = a + t, \quad \bar{y} = \pm a \sqrt{1 + a} \left[1 + \frac{1}{2} \frac{2 + 3a}{a + a^2} t + \cdots \right].$$

Considering the transforms of the centers of these places, the points $(a, \pm a\sqrt{1 + a})$ are transformed into (a, a).

(ii) If $a = -1$ we have

$$\bar{z}^2 = t - 2t^2 + t^3 = t(1 - t)^2$$

Putting $s = t^{1/2}$, we have

$$\bar{z} = \pm s(1 - s^2).$$

Hence the parametrizations

$$\bar{x} = -1 + s^2, \quad \bar{y} = \pm s(1 - s^2)$$

define places of f which transform into P'. The parametrizations are obviously equivalent, and so there is only one such place.

(iii) If $a = 0$,

$$\bar{z}^2 = t^2 + t^3,$$

so that

$$\bar{z} = \pm t \sqrt{1 + t}$$

$$= \pm t \left[1 + \frac{1}{2} t - \frac{1}{8} t^2 + \cdots \right].$$

In this case the two parametrizations

$$\bar{x} = t, \quad \bar{y} = \pm t \left[1 + \frac{1}{2} t + \cdots \right]$$

are not equivalent, and hence define distinct places transforming into P'. The two places have the same center, however, so that the center of P' is the transform of only one point of f.

(iv) f' has one infinite point, with homogeneous coordinates $(0,1,1)$. A parametrization of the place with this center is $(1/t, 1/t)$. Then

$$\bar{z}^2 = \frac{1}{t^2} + \frac{1}{t^3} = \frac{1}{t^3}(1 + t).$$

Putting $t = s^2$ again, we get

$$\bar{z} = \pm \, s^{-3} \left[1 + \frac{1}{2} s^2 - \frac{1}{8} s^4 + \cdots \right],$$

and

$$\bar{x} = s^{-2}, \; \bar{y} = \pm \, s^{-3} \left[1 + \frac{1}{2} s^2 + \cdots \right].$$

Here again we have a single place transforming into P'.

In this example the discriminant of g is $x'^2 + x'^3$, and so case (i) covers all the possibilities that were provided for by Theorem 6.2. From case (iii) we see, however, that in certain cases P' may be the transform of ν distinct places even though the discriminant is of positive order at P'.

6.4. Projection as a rational transformation. An important type of rational transformation is generated by projection. Let a point $(x_0, \cdots, x_n)$ of S_n be projected from an S_{n-m-1} into the point $(y_0, \cdots, y_m)$ of an S_m. By properly choosing coordinates (see §II-5) the relation between the points has the form

$$(6.3) \qquad\qquad y_j = x_j, \quad j = 0, \cdots, m.$$

Now let C be a curve in S_n with field Σ. Since we have already fixed our coordinate system we cannot assume that $\Sigma = K(\xi_1/\xi_0, \cdots, \xi_n/\xi_0)$, but we can assume that for some p, $\Sigma = K(\xi_0/\xi_p, \cdots, \xi_n/\xi_p)$. We now consider several cases.

(i) If $\xi_j/\xi_p = 0$, $j = 0, \cdots, m$, then for any parametrization $(\bar{x}_0, \cdots, \bar{x}_n)$ of C we have $\bar{x}_j = 0$. Since $x_j = 0$, are the defining equations of S_{n-m-1}, C spans a subspace of S_{n-m-1}. In this case the projection of C into S_m is not defined.

(ii) If not all $\xi_j/\xi_p = 0$, say $\xi_q/\xi_p \neq 0$, then p may be replaced by q, or, what is the same, we may assume $0 \geqslant p \geqslant m$. If $\xi_j/\xi_p = b_j \in K$ for all $j = 0, \cdots, m$, then C spans a subspace of the S_{n-m} which is the join of S_{n-m-1} and the point (b), and the rational transformation (6.3) transforms C into (b).

(iii) If ξ_j/ξ_p, for some $0 \leqslant p \leqslant m$, do not all belong to K, then $K(\xi_0/\xi_p, \cdots, \xi_m/\xi_p)$ is the field of a curve C' in S_m, and C' is the rational transform of C by (6.3).

The relation between the rational transformation and the projection of the points of C is contained in the following theorem.

THEOREM 6.4. *In case* (iii) *above, a point of C' is either the projection of a point of C not in S_{n-m-1} or the intersection of S_m with an S_{n-m} which is the join of S_{n-m-1} and a space osculating C at a place with center in S_{n-m-1}.*

PROOF. A point of C' is the center of a place of C', and by Theorem 6.2 every place of C' is the transform of a place of C. Hence we have merely to investigate the centers of the transforms of the places of C. If a place P of C does not have its center on S_{n-m-1} then obviously the center of the transform is the projection of the center of P, and so we need prove only the last part of the theorem. Let $(\bar{x})$ be a place of C having its center on S_{n-m-1}, and let $(\bar{y})$ be its transform, where

$$\bar{y}_j = t^{-q}\bar{x}_j = b_j + \cdots, \quad j = 0, \cdots, m,$$

and not all b_j are zero. Let S_{r-1} be the largest osculating space at P which is contained in S_{n-m-1}; then the next osculating space S_r is not. We see from Theorem II-2.8 that the join of S_r and S_{n-m-1} is then an S_{n-m}, and we have to show that this S_{n-m} intersects S_n in the point (b). To do this it is sufficient to show that every hyperplane π of S_n which contains both S_r and S_{n-m-1} necessarily contains (b). If $\pi \supset S_{n-m-1}$ we must have $\pi = \Sigma c_j x_j$; and so $O_P(\pi) \geqq q$ and there exist such π's of order q. Since S_r is defined as the intersection of hyperplanes having an order at P greater than or equal to some n_r, and since $S_r \not\subset S_{n-m-1}$, we must have $n_r > q$. Hence for $\Sigma c_j x_j = 0$ to contain S_r it is necessary that $\Sigma c_j b_j = 0$. That is, every such hyperplane contains (b).

The most important case of this theorem is the one for which $m = n - 1$. Then the points of C' are the projections of the points of C plus the intersections of the hyperplane of projection with the tangent lines to C at the center of projection.

A useful application of projections is indicated in the following theorem.

THEOREM 6.5. *Any space curve can be birationally projected into a plane curve.*

PROOF. Let C be defined by the basis $\xi_1, \cdots, \xi_n$ of Σ. At least one of the ξ_i is transcendental over K, and we may assume that ξ_1 is. Then $\xi_2, \cdots, \xi_n$ are algebraic over $K(\xi_1)$. By Theorem 2.9 there exist constants a_i, $i = 2, \cdots, n$, such that if $\xi_2' = \Sigma a_i \xi_i$, then $\Sigma = K(\xi_1)(\xi_2, \cdots, \xi_n) = K(\xi_1, \xi_2')$. We now make a change of coordinates in S_n,

$$x_1' = x_1,$$
$$x_2' = a_2 x_2 + \cdots + a_n x_n,$$
$$x_k' = x_{j_k}, \qquad k = 3, \cdots, n,$$

where $j_3, \cdots, j_n$ is some selection from $2, \cdots, n$, omitting some i for which $a_i \neq 0$; this makes the determinant of the transformation different from zero. In the new coordinates we have

$$\Sigma = K(\xi_1', \cdots, \xi_n') = K(\xi_1', \xi_2').$$

Hence the projection defined by

$$x = x_1', \; y = x_2'$$

sends C birationally into a plane curve.

As an important consequence of this theorem we have

THEOREM 6.6 *A space curve has at most a finite number of singular points.*

PROOF. Let F be a birational projection of a space curve C. By Theorem 6.4 every point of F is the projection of a point of C, with the exception of the centers of places of F which correspond to places of C having their centers in the center of projection S_{n-3}. Since C does not lie entirely in S_{n-3} there is only a finite number of these exceptional places, and so they may be ignored. Now if a point A of C projects into a point A' of F then every place of C with center at A projects into a place of F with center at A'. Moreover, a place of order r obviously projects into a place of order $\geq r$. It follows that every singular point of C not on S_{n-3} projects into a singular point of F. Since F has only a finite number of singular points, C can have only a finite number.

As another rather obvious deduction from Theorem 6.6 we see that a curve in S_n cannot completely fill S_n if $n > 1$.

6.5. Algebraic transformation of a curve. Theorem 6.2 can be used to define a type of transformation of an irreducible curve which is more general than the rational transformation. Consider two rational transformations of a curve C into curves C' and C''. To each place P' of C' there correspond distinct places $P_1, \cdots, P_\mu$ on C, and to these there correspond places $P_1'', \cdots, P_\mu''$, not necessarily distinct, on C''. The transformation associating with P' each of the P_μ'' will be called an *algebraic transformation*. The general study of such transformations will not be undertaken here, but we shall prove one theorem concerning them.

A rational transformation is obviously a special type of algebraic transformation. A rational transformation is single-valued, that is, each place has a unique transform. The following theorem states the converse of this.

THEOREM 6.7. *An algebraic transformation which is single-valued at an infinite set of places is rational.*

PROOF. Let the transformations $C \to C'$ and $C \to C''$ be defined by

$$\xi_j' = \phi_j'(\xi), \quad \xi_k'' = \phi_k''(\xi),$$

and let $\Sigma = \Sigma'(\zeta)$, where

$$g(\xi',\zeta) = a_0 + a_1\zeta + \cdots + a_\nu\zeta^\nu = 0,$$

as before. We have

$$\xi_i = \phi_i(\xi',\zeta).$$

Hence

$$\xi_k'' = \phi_k''(\phi(\xi',\zeta)) = b_{k0} + b_{k1}\zeta + \cdots + b_{k,\nu-1}\zeta^{\nu-1},$$

where $b_{ki} \in \Sigma'$. Now let $(\bar{x}')$ be a place P' of C' with center (b'). There is only a finite number of places of C' at which $g(b',z) = 0$ has a multiple root or $b_{ki}(\bar{x}')$ is of negative order. If P' is not one of these places, then $g(\bar{x}',z) = 0$ has roots $\bar{z}_\alpha = c_\alpha + \cdots$, where the c_α are distinct, and

$$\bar{x}_{k,\alpha}'' = b_{k0}(\bar{x}') + b_{k1}(\bar{x}')\bar{z}_\alpha + \cdots + b_{k,\nu-1}(\bar{x}')\bar{z}_\alpha^{\nu-1}$$

is a place P'' of C'', which is a transform of P', and which has a finite center (b_α''). Now by assumption there is an infinite set of P' for which there is only one P'', and hence there is an infinite subset of this set satisfying the above conditions. Hence for an infinite number of points (b') of C' we have

$$0 = -b_k'' + b_{k0}(b') + b_{k1}(b')c_\alpha + \cdots + b_{k,\nu-1}(b')c_\alpha^{\nu-1}$$

for ν distinct c_α. Regarding these ν equations as homogeneous equations in the ν unknowns $-b_k'', b_{k0}(b'), \cdots, b_{k,\nu-1}(b')$, we see that their only solution is the trivial one, since the determinant of their coefficients is the Vandermonde determinant (see §I-7.4, Exercise 2).

$$| 1, c_\alpha, \cdots, c_\alpha^{\nu-1} | = \Pi_{\alpha<\beta}(c_\beta - c_\alpha) \neq 0.$$

Hence $b_{ki}(b') = 0$, $i = 1, \cdots, \nu - 1$, at an infinite set of points of C'; that is, $b_{ki}(\xi')$ is of order greater than zero at an infinite set of places of C', and so $b_{ki}(\xi') = 0$. Hence

$$\xi_k'' = b_{k0}(\xi'),$$

and so the transformation from C' to C'' is rational.

This theorem is often useful in showing that certain transformations are rational. We shall make an application of it in Theorem VI-8.4.

6.6. Exercises. 1. Investigate the effect of the rational transformation

$$x' = 1, \quad y' = y/x,$$

on the curve $x^2 - x^3 - y^2 = 0$. On the curve $x^2 - x^4 - y^2 = 0$.

2. Let C' be the transform of C by (6.1), and let $P^{(\alpha)}$, $\alpha = 1, \cdots, \mu$, be the places of C transforming into the place P' of C'. Let $(\bar{x}^{(\alpha)})$ be a parametrization of $P^{(\alpha)}$ and define $\bar{y}_j^{(\alpha)} = \phi_j(\bar{x}^{(\alpha)})$. As the parametrization $(\bar{y}^{(\alpha)})$ may be reducible let $\bar{y}^{(\alpha)} \in K(t^{n_\alpha})'$ be suitable choice of the parameter t, where n_α has its greatest possible value. Then $\Sigma_1^\mu n_\alpha = \nu$.

n_α may be regarded as the multiplicity with which $P^{(\alpha)}$ is transformed into P'. We thus have an extension of Theorem 6.2: Any place of C' is the transform of exactly ν places, properly counted, of C.

§7. RATIONAL CURVES

7.1. Rational transform of a rational curve.
We have seen that if $\Sigma' \supset \Sigma$ any curve with field Σ' can be rationally transformed into any curve with field Σ. Now the field $K(\lambda)$, where λ is transcendental over K, is isomorphic to a subfield of any admissible field, and so its curves are rational transforms of any curve. A curve whose field is $K(\lambda)$ is said to be *rational*. Since the line $y = 0$ has $K(\lambda)$ as its field, *a curve is rational if and only if it is birationally equivalent to a line.*

An important property of rational curves is stated in the following theorem:

THEOREM 7.1. *Every rational transform of a rational curve is a rational curve.*

This follows at once from

THEOREM 7.2. *If λ is transcendental over K and if $K \subset \Sigma \subset K(\lambda)$, $\Sigma \neq K$, then there is a μ, transcendental over K, such that $\Sigma = K(\mu)$.*

PROOF. Let $\phi = g(\lambda)/h(\lambda)$ be a non-constant element of Σ. Then $g(\lambda) - \phi h(\lambda) = 0$, that is, λ is a root of the equation $g(x) - \phi h(x) = 0$ with coefficients in Σ, and so λ is algebraic over Σ. Let

$$f(x) = a_0 + a_1 x + \cdots + a_r x^r, \quad a_i \in \Sigma, \quad a_r \neq 0,$$

be an irreducible polynomial over Σ for which $f(\lambda) = 0$. Since the $a_i \in K(\lambda)$ they are rational functions of λ. Let $h(\lambda)$ be the lowest common multiple of their denominators, and $k(\lambda)$ the highest common factor of their numerators. Then

$$b_i = a_i h/k \in K[\lambda],$$

and

$$f_1(\lambda, x) = b_0 + b_1 x + \cdots + b_r x^r$$

is a polynomial in λ and x having no factor in λ only. At least one of b_i/b_r, say b_s/b_r, is not in K. For brevity put $p(\lambda) = b_s$, $q(\lambda) = b_r$, $\mu = b_s/b_r = a_s/a_r \in \Sigma$. Then $p(x) - \mu q(x) \in \Sigma[x]$, and since $p(\lambda) - \mu q(\lambda) = 0$ we have by Theorem 2.3,

$$p(x) - \mu q(x) = g(x)f(x), \quad g(x) \in \Sigma[x].$$

This is reducible to

$$q(\lambda)p(x) - p(\lambda)q(x) = g_1(\lambda,x)f_1(\lambda,x),$$

where

$$g_1(\lambda,x) = g(x)q(\lambda)k(\lambda)/h(\lambda) \in K(\lambda)[x].$$

But since f_1 is not divisible by any polynomial in λ we must have $g_1 \in K[\lambda,x]$. Now the degree of $p(\lambda)$ or $q(\lambda)$ in λ cannot exceed the degree of f_1 in λ, and so g_1 cannot involve λ. But if $q(\lambda)p(x) - p(\lambda)q(x)$ had a factor involving x only it would, by symmetry, have a factor involving λ only. Hence g_1 is a constant, and so the degree of each of p and q is at most r, the degree of f in x. Thus $p(x) - \mu q(x) = 0$ is an equation of degree r over the field $K(\mu)$ satisfied by λ. Since $K(\mu) \subset \Sigma$, if $K(\mu) \neq \Sigma$ there is a $\psi \in \Sigma$, $\psi \notin K(\mu)$. Since $\psi \in K(\lambda)$ and since λ is of degree at most r over $K(\mu)$ we have

$$\psi = c_0 + c_1\lambda + \cdots + c_{r-1}\lambda^{r-1}, \quad c_i \in K(\mu).$$

But this would imply that λ is of degree less than r over Σ, contradicting the definition of r. Hence $K(\mu) = \Sigma$.

7.2. Lüroth's Theorem. We shall now show that the above definition of rational curve agrees with the one given in Theorem III-5.1. Suppose that $f(x,y) = 0$ is rational as previously defined; that is, that there exist $\phi, \psi \in K(\lambda)$ such that

    (i)   For all but a finite set of $\lambda_0 \in K$, $f(\phi(\lambda_0), \psi(\lambda_0)) = 0$.

    (ii)   With a finite number of exceptions, for every x_0, y_0 for which $f(x_0,y_0) = 0$ there is a unique $\lambda_0 \in K$ such that $x_0 = \phi(\lambda_0)$, $y_0 = \psi(\lambda_0)$.

(ii) implies that ϕ and ψ are not both constants, and so we may assume that ϕ is transcendental over K. As $f(\phi,\psi) = 0$, from (i), we see that $K(\phi,\psi)$ is isomorphic to $K(\xi,\eta)$ in such a way that ϕ and ψ correspond respectively to ξ and η. But $K(\phi,\psi) \subset K(\lambda)$, and so Σ is isomorphic to a subfield of $K(\lambda)$. Hence by Theorem 7.2 there is a $\mu \in K(\lambda)$ such that Σ is isomorphic to $K(\mu)$; that is, f is rational in the sense of Theorem 7.1.

Conversely, if $K(\lambda)$ is the field of f, then f is birationally equivalent to the line $y' = 0$ in the $x'y'$-plane. If

$$x = \phi(x'), \quad y = \psi(x')$$

are the equations of the transformation, then (i) and (ii) follow from the one-to-one correspondence between all but a finite number of points of f and y'.

Notice that the only use we made of (ii) was to insure that the rational functions ϕ and ψ were not both constants. We can therefore combine the above results into the following Theorem of Lüroth:

THEOREM 7.3. *If a curve* $f(x,y) = 0$ *satisfies* (i) *for rational functions* $\phi(\lambda)$, $\psi(\lambda)$ *which are not both constants, then there exist rational functions* $\phi'(\mu)$, $\psi'(\mu)$ *for which both* (i) *and* (ii) *are satisfied, and the curve is rational.*

Theorems 7.1, 7.2, and 7.3 are all equivalent, and are often indiscriminantly called Lüroth's Theorem.

7.3. Exercises. 1. A curve C in S_r is rational if and only if there exist homogeneous polynomials $G_i(s,t)$, $i = 0, \cdots, r$, of the same degree such that

(i)   For all but a finite set of ratios $s_0 : t_0$, $(G_i(s_0,t_0))$ is a point of C;

(ii)   With a finite number of exceptions, for every point (a_i) of C there is a unique ratio $s_0 : t_0$ such that $\rho a_i = G_i(s_0,t_0)$, $\rho \neq 0$.

2. If C is a rational curve in S_r with the associated polynomials $G_i(s,t)$ as in Exercise 1, then for each ratio $s_0 : t_0$, $\bar{x}_i = G_i(s_0,t_0 + t)$ is a parametrization of a place of C. Conversely, for each place P of C there is a unique ratio $s_0 : t_0$ such that $\bar{x}_i = G_i(s_0,t_0 + t)$ is a parametrization of P.

3. If the polynomials G_i in Exercise 1 are of degree n then the curve C is of order n.

4. A curve C of order n spanning S_n is rational. [Consider the intersection with C of the hyperplanes of a pencil containing $n - 1$ points of C.] Such a curve is known as a rational *normal* curve.

5. By proper choice of the coordinate system a rational normal curve can be represented by the polynomials $G_i = s^i t^{n-i}$.

6. A rational normal curve is non-singular.

§8. DUAL CURVES

8.1. Dual of a plane curve. Let C be an irreducible plane curve with field Σ. We have seen that to every place of C there corresponds a point, the center of the place, whose coordinates in a given projective coordinate system satisfy an irreducible homogeneous equation $F(x_0,x_1,x_2) = 0$, that every point whose coordinates satisfy this equation is the center of at least one place of C, and that Σ is determined by the equation. Now to each place of C there also corresponds a *line*, namely the tangent to C at the place. We shall show that if C is not itself a line there is an irreducible homogeneous equation $G(u_0,u_1,u_2) = 0$ satisfied by the coordinates, in a given projective line coordinate system, of all the tangents to the places of C, that every line whose coordinates satisfy this equation is tangent to C at at least one place, and that the equation determines the same field Σ as C.

Writing $F_i(x)$ for the derivative of $F(x)$ with respect to x_i, $i = 0,1,2$, the equations

$$u_i = F_i(x)$$

define a rational transformation of C. The transform of C is a curve provided $F_1(\xi)/F_0(\xi)$, $F_2(\xi)/F_0(\xi)$ are not both constants. If they were we would have $F_1(x) - aF_0(x)$, $F_2(x) - bF_0(x)$ both divisible by $F(x)$, and hence both zero since their degrees are less than the degree of F. Then from Euler's Theorem would follow

$$nF = x_0F_0 + x_1F_1 + x_2F_2$$

$$= (x_0 + ax_1 + bx_2)F_0.$$

Since F is irreducible this would imply that $n = 1$ and $F_0 \in K$, contrary to the assumption that F is not a line. Hence the transform of F is an irreducible curve $G(u) = 0$.

Let $(\bar{x})$ be any parametrization of F. As in Theorem IV-6.1, we obtain

$$\Sigma\bar{x}_i'F_i(\bar{x}) = 0, \quad \Sigma\bar{x}_iF_i(\bar{x}) = 0.$$

Now the transform $(\bar{u})$ of $(\bar{x})$ is

$$\bar{u}_i = F_i(\bar{x}),$$

and so the above relations become

(8.1) $$\Sigma\bar{x}_i'\bar{u}_i = 0,$$

(8.2) $$\Sigma\bar{x}_i\bar{u}_i = 0.$$

Differentiating (8.2) and subtracting (8.1) from the result, we have

$$\Sigma\bar{x}_i\bar{u}_i' = 0.$$

Now consider the transformation of G defined by

$$y_i = G_i(u).$$

Exactly as above we see that it transforms G into a curve $H(y) = 0$, and the parametrization $(\bar{u})$ into $(\bar{y})$, with

$$\Sigma\bar{y}_i\bar{u}_i = 0, \quad \Sigma y_i\bar{u}_i' = 0.$$

Hence $\bar{x}_i$ and $\bar{y}_i$ are both solutions of the equations

$$\Sigma z_i\bar{u}_i = 0, \quad \Sigma z_i\bar{u}_i' = 0,$$

and so are proportional unless the $\bar{u}_i'$ are proportional to the $\bar{u}_i$. That this is not the case is shown by (8.3) below. Hence $(\bar{x})$ and $(\bar{y})$ are the same parametrization, and the curves H and F are identical. From this it follows not only that F and G are birationally equivalent, but that the relation between them, when the proper coordinates are used, is completely symmetrical.

To investigate the transformation more carefully, let

$$\bar{x}_0 = a_0,$$

$$\bar{x}_1 = a_1 + t^r,$$

$$\bar{x}_2 = a_2 + at^r + bt^{r+s} + \cdots, \quad a_0 b \neq 0,$$

be a parametrization of a place P of F of order r and class s. The tangent at P is the line

$$(a_1 a - a_2)x_0 - a_0 a x_1 + a_0 x_2 = 0.$$

Solving (8.1) and (8.2) we find that

$$\bar{u}_0 = (a_1 a - a_2) + \left(1 + \frac{s}{r}\right)a_1 b t^s + \cdots,$$

(8.3) $$\qquad \bar{u}_1 = -a_0 a - a_0\left(1 + \frac{s}{r}\right)bt^s + \cdots,$$

$$\bar{u}_2 = a_0.$$

Hence

(i)   The coordinates of the center of the transform P' of P are the line coordinates of the tangent at P.

(ii)   The order of P' is the class of P.

Because of the symmetry between G and F we also obtain

(iii)   The coordinates of the center of P are the line coordinates of the tangent at P'.

(iv)   The class of P' is the order of P.

The curves F and G are said to be *dual* to each other. If we follow the usual practice and regard the projective spaces with coordinates (x) and (u) as dual spaces (§II-3.2) with corresponding coordinate systems, then G is the locus of tangents to F, and F is the locus of points of contact of G.

8.2. Plücker's formulas. Referring to the definition of the class of a curve given in §IV-6.1, we see at once that *the class of an irreducible curve is the order of its dual*.

We obtain the remaining two Plücker formulas by applying the two already known (IV-5.2) to the dual curve. We assume, then, that the dual curve G has no singularities but simple nodes and cusps. Now a cusp is a point which is the center of a single place of order two and class one. Its dual is therefore a line tangent to F at a single place of order one and class two; that is, at a simple flex. Similarly, the dual of a simple node is a line tangent to F at two places of order one and class one with distinct centers; such a line is called a double tangent and the number of double tangents is denoted by τ. We then have

$$n = m(m - 1) - 2\tau - 3i,$$

$$\kappa = 3m(m - 2) - 6\tau - 8i,$$

as the other two Plücker formulas. The four formulas are not independent, any three implying the fourth, but examples can be given to show that any three are independent.

The integers n, m, δ, τ, κ, i attached to an algebraic curve are known as its *Plücker characteristics*. They have been the subject of a large number of investigations, but there are still some unsolved problems concerning them. Probably the most interesting of these is the determination of a criterion for telling when six given integers can be the Plücker characteristics for an irreducible curve. A necessary condition is of course that the numbers satisfy Plücker's formulas and the inequality

$$(n - 1)(n - 2)/2 - \delta - \kappa \geqslant 0$$

obtained from Theorem III-4.3. It is known that this condition is not sufficient (for example, there is no irreducible curve for which $n = m = 7$, $\kappa = i = 11$, $\delta = \tau = 1$), but just what further conditions are necessary is still an open question. For a discussion of questions related to this the reader is referred to Coolidge, *Algebraic Plane Curves*, Book I, Chap. VII, Theorem 2.

8.3. Exercises. 1. Express τ in terms of κ, δ, n. Compute τ for the ten types of irreducible quartics. (See §IV-6.4, Exercise 2.)

2. Show that

$$(n - 1)(n - 2)/2 - \delta - \kappa = (m - 1)(m - 2)/2 - \tau - i.$$

3. Show that

$$i - \kappa = 3(m - n),$$

$$2(\tau - \delta) = (m - n)(m + n - 9);$$

and from these prove the theorem:

If any two dual Plücker characteristics are equal then each characteristic is equal to its dual, except in four cases when the sum of the order and the class of the curve is 9.

§9. THE IDEAL OF A CURVE

9.1. The ideal of a space curve. The properties of the points of a curve C in S_n are best investigated by means of a certain ideal I in the ring $K[x] = K[x_1, \cdots, x_n]$. The elements of I are the polynomials $f(x) = f(x_1, \cdots, x_n)$ for which $f(\xi) = 0$; that these form an ideal is obvious.

The most important property of I is given in

THEOREM 9.1. *$K[x]/I$ is a domain whose quotient field is Σ.*

PROOF. The mapping of $K[x]$ into $K[\xi]$ defined by $x_i \rightarrow \xi_i$ is a homomorphism. The elements of $K[x]$ which map into zero constitute the ideal I. Hence, by Theorem 1.2, $K[x]/I$ is isomorphic to $K[\xi]$. Since $\Sigma = K(\xi)$ is the quotient field of $K[\xi]$ we have the desired result.

It follows that the ideal I determines the curve C uniquely, as it determines the field Σ of C and the basis $\xi_1, \cdots, \xi_n$. The relation between I and the points of C is expressed in the next two theorems.

THEOREM 9.2. *$f(x) \in I$ if and only if $f(a) = 0$ for every finite point (a) of C.*

PROOF. If $f(x) \in I$ then $f(\bar{x}) = 0$ for every parametrization $(\bar{x})$ of C, by the isomorphism between Σ and $K(\bar{x})$. Considering only the parametrizations with finite centers, we have $f(x(0)) = 0$, and so $f(a) = 0$ for every (a) of C, since by definition every such (a) is the center of some such parametrization. Conversely, if $f(a) = 0$ for every finite point (a) of C then $f(\xi)$ is of positive order at an infinite set of places of C, and hence $f(\xi) = 0$, so that $f(x) \in I$.

THEOREM 9.3. *If $f(a) = 0$ for every $f \in I$, then (a) is a point of C.*

PROOF. Suppose that there is a point (a) not on C such that $f(a) = 0$ for every $f \in I$. By a series of projections we shall reduce the given situation to a similar one in S_2; hence we assume at present that $n \geqslant 3$. We first project C from (a) into an S'_{n-1}. By Theorem 6.4, the projection C_0 is a curve and so does not contain all points of S'_{n-1}, since $n - 1 > 1$. Let O be a point in S'_{n-1} not on C_0, and project from O into S_{n-1}. Let C' be the projection of C and (a') the projection of (a). By Theorem 6.4, C' is a curve which does not contain (a') since the line $O(a)$ contains no point of C. To see that (a') has the other property assumed for (a), let O have projective coordinates $(0,0,\cdots,0,1)$, so that the projection takes the affine form

$$y_j = x_j, \quad j = 1, \cdots, n - 1.$$

If $f(y)$ is a polynomial for which $f(\eta) = 0$, then $f(x)$ is a polynomial in $x_1, \cdots, x_n$ (x_n does not appear) for which $f(\xi) = 0$; that is, $f(x) \in I$. Hence $f(a) = 0$. But as $b_j = a_j$ and as a_n does not appear in $f(a)$, we have $f(a') = 0$. We thus have the same relation between (a') and C' in S_{n-1} as between (a) and C in S_n. The process can therefore be continued until we come to the case $n = 2$. In this case, if $f(x_1, x_2) = 0$ is the equation of the curve then $f \in I$, and so (a) is a point of the curve, a contradiction. Thus our theorem is proved.

From these theorems, and others proved previously, we see that a curve is uniquely determined by any one of the following:

(i)   The set of its places,

(ii)   The set of its points,

(iii)   A basis of its field Σ,

(iv)   Its ideal I.

The first two of these can be strengthened to

(i')   Any one of its places,

(ii')   Any infinite set of its points.

(i') follows from (iii) and Theorem 5.1, and (ii') from (iv) and Theorem 5.2.

9.2. Definition of a curve in terms of its ideal. We have defined the ideal I in terms of the curve C. This process can be reversed, so that C is defined in terms of an ideal I in $K[x_1, \cdots, x_n]$. However not every ideal I in this domain can serve to define a curve, but the ideal must satisfy certain conditions. To specify these conditions we first define the *dimension* of an ideal I in $K[x_1, \cdots, x_n]$. I is of dimension r if there exist elements $f_1, \cdots, f_r$ of $K[x_1, \cdots, x_n]$ such that for any non-zero polynomial $g(z_1, \cdots, z_r)$ over K, $g(f_1, \cdots, f_r) \notin I$, and if there exist no $r + 1$ such elements. We also recall the definition of a prime ideal (§1.2, Exercise 5).

THEOREM 9.4. *An ideal I of $K[x_1, \cdots, x_n]$ is the ideal of an irreducible algebraic curve in S_n if and only if I is prime and of dimension one.*

PROOF. We first prove the necessity of the conditions. That I must be prime follows from Theorem 9.1. We also have that Σ is the quotient field of $K[x_1, \cdots, x_n]/I$. Hence if $f_\alpha(x_1, \cdots, x_n) \in K[x_1, \cdots, x_n]$ and $g(z_1, \cdots, z_r) \in K[z_1, \cdots, z_r]$, then $g(f_\alpha(x)) \in I$ if and only if $g(f_\alpha(\xi)) = 0$. The one-dimensionality of I then follows immediately from Theorem 3.2 (i). Conversely, if I is prime then $K[x_1, \cdots, x_n]/I$ is a domain D and has a quotient field Σ. Σ is generated by the elements $\xi_1, \cdots, \xi_n$ into which $x_1, \cdots, x_n$ map in the homomorphism $K[x_1, \cdots, x_n] \to D$. Reversing the argument above we see that the one-dimensionality of I implies condition (i) of Theorem 3.2. Hence Σ is an admissible field generated by the ξ_i, and I is obviously the ideal of the associated curve.

9.3. Exercises. If I is an ideal of dimension r in $K[x_1, \cdots, x_n]$ the points (a) of A_n such that $F(a) = 0$ for every $F(x) \in I$ are said to constitute an *r-dimensional variety* V in A_n. If I is prime V is said to be irreducible, and the quotient field Σ of $K[x_1, \cdots, x_n]/I$ is called the field of V. Two irreducible varieties are said to be birationally equivalent if their fields are isomorphic.

1. An irreducible r-dimensional variety is birationally equivalent to an irreducible hypersurface in A_{r+1}.

2. Define rational transformation of an irreducible r-dimensional variety. Show that as a point transformation it is defined and single valued with the possible exception of points on an $(r - 1)$-dimensional subvariety, and the transformed points lie on an irreducible variety of dimension $\leqslant r$.

§10. VALUATIONS

From the remarks of Theorem 5.1 we see that all the places of all the curves having a given field Σ can be divided into classes, each class having just one place on each of the curves and all the places of a class being birational transforms of each other. Furthermore, if ϕ is any element of Σ and if P and Q are two places in the same class, then $O_P(\phi) = O_Q(\phi)$. That is, to each class of places there corresponds a function $V(\phi)$, whose argument is in Σ and whose values are in the set I consisting of all integers and ∞, which satisfies the following conditions:

(i) $V(\phi\psi) = V(\phi) + V(\psi)$,

(ii) $V(\phi \pm \psi) \geqslant \min[V(\phi), V(\psi)]$,

(iii) $V(\phi) = 0$ if $\phi \in K$, $\phi \neq 0$,

(iv) $V(\phi) = \infty$ if and only if $\phi = 0$.

Such a function is called a *valuation** of Σ over K.

We shall now show, conversely, that with one exception each valuation of Σ over K is obtained from a unique class of birationally equivalent places of the curves associated with Σ. The exception is the trivial valuation which maps each non-zero element of Σ onto the zero of I. We shall exclude this case from further consideration.

Let $V(\phi)$ be any non-trivial valuation of Σ over K. We first prove two lemmas.

THEOREM 10.1. *If $V(\phi) \geqslant 0$ there is a unique $a \in K$ such that $V(\phi - a) > 0$.*

PROOF. If $\phi \in K$, we take $a = \phi$. Suppose then that $\phi \notin K$. Let ξ be a non-zero element of Σ for which $V(\xi) \neq 0$. Either $V(\xi) > 0$ or $V(\xi^{-1}) > 0$, and we may assume that $V(\xi) > 0$. ϕ and ξ satisfy a polynomial equation

$$a_0(\phi) + a_1(\phi)\xi + \cdots + a_n(\phi)\xi^n = 0,$$

with $a_0(\phi) \neq 0$, $a_n(\phi) \neq 0$, $n > 0$. Hence

---

* More accurately, this is a discrete valuation of rank one. For the general definition of a valuation see W. Krull, *Idealtheorie*, Springer, Berlin, 1935, pp. 101, 109.

$$V(a_0(\phi)) = V(a_1(\phi)\xi + \cdots + a_n(\phi)\xi^n)$$

$$\geqslant \min[V(a_1) + V(\xi),\ V(a_2) + 2V(\xi), \cdots, V(a_n) + nV(\xi)].$$

Since each a_i is a polynomial in ϕ, and since $V(\phi) \geqslant 0$, it follows from repeated application of (i) and (ii) that $V(a_i) \geqslant 0$. From the assumption that $V(\xi) > 0$ it therefore follows that $V(a_0(\phi)) > 0$. Now K is algebraically closed, and so

$$a_0(\phi) = b_0(\phi - b_1) \cdots (\phi - b_r), \quad b_i \in K.$$

Hence

$$V(b_0) + V(\phi - b_1) + \cdots + V(\phi - b_r) > 0.$$

Since $V(b_0) = 0$, at least one $V(\phi - b_i) > 0$, as was to be proved. The uniqueness follows at once, for if $V(\phi - a) > 0$, $V(\phi - b) > 0$, then

$$V(b - a) = V[(\psi - a) - (\psi - b)] > 0,$$

and so $b = a$.

THEOREM 10.2. *If r is the least positive value assumed by any element of Σ, then the value of any element of Σ is a multiple of r.*

PROOF. Let $V(\xi) = r$, and let $V(\phi) = s$. Dividing s by r we obtain $s = qr + t$, where q is an integer and t is a non-negative integer smaller than r. Then $V(\phi\xi^{-q}) = t$, and since by assumption r is the smallest positive value of any element of Σ, we must have $t = 0$. Hence r is a factor of s, as was to be proved.

If $V(\phi)$ is a valuation for which the minimum positive value r is greater than 1 then $V(\phi)/r$ is a valuation for which the minimum positive value is 1. As these two valuations have the same essential properties we need consider only the latter type, which we shall call an *irreducible* valuation.

We can now prove our main theorem.

THEOREM 10.3. *If $V(\phi)$ is an irreducible valuation of Σ over K then there is a place P of a curve associated with Σ, unique to within birational transformations, such that $V(\phi) = O_P(\phi)$.*

PROOF. Let ξ be an element of Σ of value 1. Then $\xi \notin K$, and so is transcendental over K. There is therefore an η such that $\Sigma = K(\xi,\eta)$. Since we also have $K(\xi,\eta^{-1}) = \Sigma$, and since $V(\eta^{-1}) = -V(\eta)$, we may assume that $V(\eta) \geqslant 0$. By Theorem 10.1 there is an $a_0 \in K$ such that $V(\eta - a_0) > 0$. Hence $V((\eta - a_0)/\xi) \geqslant 0$, and so there is an $a_1 \in K$ such that

$$V\left(\frac{\eta - a_0}{\xi} - a_1\right) = V\left(\frac{\eta - a_0 - a_1\xi}{\xi}\right) > 0.$$

Continuing in this way we obtain a sequence of constants $a_0, a_1, \cdots,$ such that if we put

$$\eta_n = a_0 + a_1\xi + \cdots + a_n\xi^n$$

we have

$$V\left(\frac{\eta - \eta_n}{\xi^n}\right) > 0,$$

or

$$V(\eta - \eta_n) > n.$$

Now let $g(\xi,\eta) \in K[\xi,\eta]$, and suppose first that $g(\xi,\eta) \neq 0$. Then $V(g(\xi,\eta)) = N < \infty$. We have by Theorem I-7.2

$$g(\xi,\eta) - g(\xi,\eta_n) = (\eta - \eta_n)h(\xi,\eta_n),$$

and so $V(g(\xi,\eta) - g(\xi,\eta_n)) > N$ for all $n > N$. Hence for all such n we must have

$$V(g(\xi,\eta_n)) = V(g(\xi,\eta)).$$

But $g(\xi,\eta_n)$ is a polynomial in ξ, and its value is just the maximum power of ξ which can be factored out of it. If $g(\xi,\eta) = 0$ a similar argument shows that for any N, $g(\xi,\eta_n)$ is divisible by ξ^N if $n > N$.

Now consider the parametrization $(t,\bar{y})$, where $\bar{y} = a_0 + a_1t + \cdots$. Put

$$\bar{y}_n = a_0 + a_1t + \cdots + a_nt^n.$$

Then for any polynomial $g(x,y)$ we have from Theorem IV-1.3 (ii),

$$O(g(t,\bar{y})) = \max O(g(t,\bar{y}_n)),$$

or

$$O(g(t,\bar{y})) = \infty$$

if $O(g(t,\bar{y}_n))$ increases without bound as n increases. Comparing this situation with the one in the preceding paragraph we see that

$$O(g(t,\bar{y})) = V(g(\xi,\eta)).$$

The same relation will then obviously hold if $g(\xi,\eta)$ is any element of the quotient field Σ of $K[\xi,\eta]$. If $f(x,y) = 0$ is the irreducible equation satisfied by ξ,η, then

$$O(f(t,\bar{y})) = V(f(\xi,\eta)) = V(0) = \infty,$$

and so $f(t,\bar{y}) = 0$. Hence $(t,\bar{y})$ is a parametrization of a place P of f.

We have only to show that the place P of f is uniquely determined. Suppose Q is a place of f for which $O_Q(\phi) = O_P(\phi) = V(\phi)$ for every $\phi \in \Sigma$. Then since $O_Q(\xi) = 1$, and $O_Q(\eta) \geqslant 0$, Q has a parametrization $(t, \bar{z})$. Proceeding with the process by which $\bar{y}$ was constructed, and using the fact that the constant obtained at each step is unique, we see that we must have $\bar{z} = \bar{y}$. Hence $Q = P$, and the theorem is proved.

VI. Linear Series

Among the most interesting properties of an irreducible curve are those which are unaffected by any birational transformation of the curve. In the investigation of such properties a central role is played by the theory of the so-called "linear series" of sets of places on the curve. The present chapter will be devoted to the study of these linear series and some of their applications.

§1. LINEAR SERIES

1.1. Introduction. Let F be an irreducible plane curve of order m. We have seen that a curve G of order n that does not contain F intersects F in precisely mn points, properly counted. Suppose we ask the following question, "Given mn points on F, is there a curve G which intersects F in precisely these points?" If $m = 1$ or 2 it is fairly obvious that the answer to this question is "yes." However, for larger values of m the answer depends, at least for some values of n, on the position of the points. Thus for $m = 3$ and $n = 1$ the answer is "yes" if the points are collinear and "no" otherwise. For larger values of n the answer is not at all obvious.

A more general form of this question is, "Given $k \leqslant mn$ points of F, how many independent curves of order n intersect F in these points, plus any $mn - k$ others?" We say "independent" curves because if a number of curves contain the given set of points any linear combination of them will also contain the points. We are therefore led to consider the intersections of F with linear systems of curves.

1.2. Cycles and series. For convenience in discussing the intersections of F with other curves we introduce the notion of a *cycle** on F. A cycle is a symbolic sum $n_1 P_1 + n_2 P_2 + \cdots + n_k P_k$, or $\Sigma n_i P_i$, the P's being places of F and the n's non-negative integers. It will often be useful to designate a cycle by $\Sigma n_P P$, where the summation includes all places P of F but $n_P = 0$ for all but a finite set of places P. In this notation, two cycles $\Sigma n_P P$ and $\Sigma m_P P$ are defined to be equal if and only if $n_P = m_P$ for all P. As usual, we define $\Sigma n_P P + \Sigma m_P P = \Sigma (n_P + m_P) P$, $r \Sigma n_P P = \Sigma (r n_P) P$, and $\Sigma n_P P - \Sigma m_P P = \Sigma (n_P - m_P) P$, provided $n_P - m_P \geqslant 0$ for all P. If $n_P = 0$ for all P the cycle $\Sigma n_P P$ has the usual

---

* The term "cycle" has been introduced by A. Weil (*Foundations of Algebraic Geometry*, American Mathematical Society, 1946). The classical geometric term was "point group." In the arithmetic treatment of algebraic functions the analogous concept is called a "divisor."

properties of a zero element and will be designated by 0. For any cycle $\Sigma n_P P$ the non-negative integer $n = \Sigma n_P$ is called the *order* of the cycle.

If $A = \Sigma n_P P$ and $B = \Sigma m_P P$ are two cycles we shall say that A *contains B* if $n_P \geqslant m_P$ for each P. Another way of expressing this condition is to say that $A - B$ is a cycle.

If $G = 0$ is any curve not having F as a component, the curve G (or the polynomial G) is said to *intersect F* in the cycle $\Sigma n_P P$ if $O_P(G) = n_P$.

One immediate consequence of this definition is that a curve of order m' intersects F in a cycle of order mm'. Another is that the cycle in which GH intersects F is the sum of the cycles in which G and H separately intersect F.

If G intersects F in a cycle B that contains a cycle A we shall say that G *cuts out A*. That is, G cuts out $\Sigma n_P P$ if $O_P(G) \geqslant n_P$.

Let

$$(1.1) \qquad \Sigma_0^r \lambda_i G_i = 0$$

be a linear system of curves of order m'. For brevity we shall let G_λ stand for $\Sigma \lambda_i G_i$. We consider only those values of the λ's for which G_λ does not have F as a component, and let A_λ designate the cycle in which G_λ intersects F. The set of cycles A_λ is called a *linear series* on F, and we say that the system (1.1) intersects F in this linear series.

Examples. 1. Let F be an irreducible conic, and let the set G_λ consist of all the lines through a point p not on F. If G_λ is not tangent to F it intersects F in two points which are the centers of places P_λ and Q_λ, and $A_\lambda = P_\lambda + Q_\lambda$. The two tangents to F from p are of order two at the respective places P and Q of F. Here the linear series consists of all the cycles $P_\lambda + Q_\lambda$ together with $2P$ and $2Q$.

2. If in the above example the point p is on the conic, then G_λ intersects F in $P_0 + P_\lambda$, where P_0 is the place of F with center at p. For the particular G_λ which is tangent to F at p, $P_\lambda = P_0$. The series thus consists of all cycles $P_0 + Q$, where Q is an arbitrary place of F. P_0 is called a *fixed place* (and p a *fixed point*) of the series.

The occurrence of fixed places—or, more generally, of fixed cycles—enables us to extend the definition of a linear series. As before, let G_λ intersect F in A_λ, and suppose that A_λ is expressible in the form $B_\lambda + C$, where C is a cycle independent of the λ's. Then the set of cycles B_λ is also called a linear series, and is said to be cut out on F by the system $G_\lambda = 0$. By allowing C to be zero this includes the original definition of linear series. In Example 2 above we can therefore take C to be P_0, and so the pencil of lines G_λ cuts out the series whose cycles are the individual places Q of F.

It should be noticed that C need not be taken to contain *all* the fixed places of the A_λ's. Thus the series of the B_λ's may contain some fixed places. In most cases, however, we find it most useful to choose C as large as possible, so as to eliminate the fixed places from the B_λ's.

3. The irreducible cubic $F = x^3 + y^3 - 2xy = 0$ has a double point at the origin, the tangents being the axes. The curve

$$\lambda_0(y - y^2) + \lambda_1(x^2 - y^2) + \lambda_2(xy - y^2) = 0$$

intersects F in $A_\lambda = 2P_1 + P_2 + P_3 + P_\lambda + Q_\lambda$, where P_1 and P_2 are the places at the origin and P_3 is the place at $(1,1)$ (Figure 1.1). Here we may choose C to be $2P_1 + P_2 + P_3$ or any cycle contained in this.

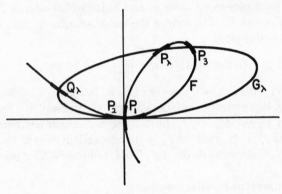

Figure 1.1

If $A_\lambda = B_\lambda + C$ then the order of B_λ is equal to the order of A_λ minus the order of C. But A_λ, being the intersection of curves of orders m and m', is of order mm', which is independent of the λ's. Hence the order of B_λ is a constant independent of the λ's, and so we may speak of the order of a linear series, meaning thereby the order of any one of its cycles.

1.3. Dimension of a series. Consider the series in which the conics $G_\lambda = \lambda_0 x^2 + \lambda_1 xy + \lambda_2 y^2 + \lambda_3 x + \lambda_4 y + \lambda_5 = 0$ intersect the line $y = 0$. The situation here differs in two respects from the examples considered above. In the first place, G_λ contains y as a factor whenever $\lambda_0 = \lambda_3 = \lambda_5 = 0$, hence in forming the series we must exclude such G_λ's from consideration. In the second place we notice that two different G_λ's may intersect the line in the same cycle. In fact, it is evident that A_λ is independent of λ_1, λ_2, and λ_4. It follows that if we replace the above system of curves by

$$\lambda_0 x^2 + \lambda_1 x + \lambda_2 = 0,$$

we obtain the same series but without these two disadvantages. We shall show that this process can be carried out in all cases.

Consider the system of curves (1.1). As shown in §III-4.1, we may assume that r is the dimension of this system, so that the G_i are linearly independent polynomials. We then have the following theorem.

THEOREM 1.1. *If $q + 1$, $0 \leqslant q \leqslant r$, independent curves of (1.1) intersect F in the same cycle, then q independent curves of (1.1) contain F as a component, and conversely.*

PROOF. Let $s = r - q$. We may assume that the $q + 1$ independent curves that intersect F in the cycle A are $G_s, G_{s+1}, \cdots, G_r$. Consider the curves $\alpha G_s + \beta G_{s+k} = 0$, $k = 1, \cdots, q$. If P is any place of F not in A then there exist non-zero values α_k and β_k for which $\alpha_k G_s + \beta_k G_{s+k}$ is of positive order ν at P. The sum of the orders of $\alpha_k G_s + \beta_k G_{s+k}$ at all the places of F is therefore

$$(\text{order of } A) + \nu = mm' + \nu > mm',$$

and so $\alpha_k G_s + \beta_k G_{s+k} = 0$ has F for a component. Since $\beta_k \neq 0$, $k = 1, \cdots, q$, these curves are independent. Conversely, if q independent curves of (1.1), say $G_1, \cdots, G_q$, have F for a common component and if G_λ intersects F in A_λ, then the $q + 1$ independent curves G_λ, $G_\lambda + G_1$, $\cdots, G_\lambda + G_q$ intersect F in A_λ. This completes the proof of the theorem.

As an important corollary we have

THEOREM 1.2. *Any linear series can be cut out by a system (1.1) in which there are no curves containing F as a component. In this case each curve cuts out a cycle of the series and each cycle of the series is cut out by a unique curve.*

PROOF. Let $\Sigma_0^{r'} \lambda_i G_i = 0$ cut out a series B_λ. Let q be the maximum number of independent curves having F as a component, and let $G_{r+1}, \cdots, G_{r'}$, where $r = r' - q$, be a set of such curves. Then $\Sigma_0^r \lambda_i G_i = 0$ cuts out B and satisfies the conditions stated.

When (1.1) has the property stated in Theorem 1.2, the integer r, which is the dimension of the system of curves, is called the *dimension* of the linear series. A series of order n and dimension r is designated by g_n^r.

1.4. Exercises. 1. $F = x^4 + y^4 - 4xy^2 = 0$ has the following places at the origin:

$$P_1 : (t^2, \, 2t - t^5/16 - 5t^9/1024 + \cdots),$$

$$P_2 : (t^2, \, t^3/2 + t^7/64 + 7t^9/4096 + \cdots).$$

Show that

$$\lambda_0 x^2 + \lambda_1 xy + \lambda_2 (y^2 - 4x) = 0$$

cuts out a g_3^2 with no fixed points. Find the condition on the λ's in order that B_λ contain P_1, and interpret geometrically. Do the same for P_2. Note that if B_λ contains P_2 it automatically contains $2P_2$.

2. Find the order and the dimension of the series with no fixed points cut out on $y - x^2 = 0$ by $\lambda_0 x^3 + \lambda_1 y^3 + \lambda_2 xy = 0$.

3. Let a, p, q be three collinear points of an irreducible cubic F. Let b, c, d, e be points of F such that p, q, b, c, d, e are on a conic. Show that the pencil of lines on a and the pencil of conics on b, c, d, e cut out on F the same series g_2^1 with no fixed points.

§2. COMPLETE SERIES

2.1. Virtual cycles. In the above definition of the dimension of a linear series we used the dimension of the system of curves cutting out the series. Now the same series may be cut out by different systems (see Exercise 3 above), and this gives rise to the question whether the dimension of the series is uniquely defined. To settle this question, as well as for other reasons, we find it convenient to consider cycles cut out not by polynomials but by rational functions.

We first extend the definition of a cycle to allow arbitrary integer coefficients. It is then evident that the set of all cycles forms a commutative group with respect to addition. A cycle of the previously considered type (one with no negative coefficients) will be said to be *effective;* a cycle with one or more negative coefficients is said to be *virtual.*

If ϕ is any non-zero element of Σ we define, as before, the cycle in which ϕ intersects F to be the cycle $\Sigma n_P P$, where $O_P(\phi) = n_P$. Then a restatement of Theorem V-3.3 is that every non-zero element of Σ intersects F in a cycle of order zero. The following lemma will prove to be useful.

THEOREM 2.1. *The only elements of Σ that intersect F in the cycle 0 are the constants.*

PROOF. That ϕ intersects F in 0 means that $O_P(\phi) = 0$ for every P. Let P_0 be any place of F and let $a \neq 0$ be the constant term in the expansion of ϕ at P_0. Then $O_{P_0}(\phi - a) > 0$, while still $O_P(\phi - a) \geqslant 0$ for every P. Hence $\Sigma_P O_P(\phi - a) > 0$, and so $\phi - a = 0$ (Theorem V-3.3), or $\phi = a$.

As a corollary we have

THEOREM 2.2. *If ϕ and ψ intersect F in the same cycle then $\phi = a\psi$,* $a \in K$.

2.2. Effective and virtual series. Let $\phi_0, \phi_1, \cdots, \phi_r$ be elements of Σ linearly independent over K. Then $\Sigma \lambda_i \phi_i \neq 0$ for any set of constants λ_i not all zero, and so $\Sigma \lambda_i \phi_i$ intersects F in a cycle A_λ. As before let $A_\lambda = B_\lambda + C$, where now C can be any cycle. The set of all cycles B_λ will again be called a linear series of dimension r, *effective* if all B_λ are effective, and otherwise *virtual*. We shall first of all justify this extension of the term "linear series" by showing that the series as originally defined coincide with effective series in the new definition and have the same dimensions. Let $G_\lambda = \Sigma_0^r \lambda_i G_i$ intersect F in A_λ, and let g_n^r consist of B_λ, where $A_\lambda = B_\lambda + C$. Let $\phi_i = G_i(\xi)/G_0(\xi)$. Then $\Sigma \lambda_i \phi_i$ intersects F in $A_\lambda - A_0$, where A_0 is the intersection of F with G_0, and so $\Sigma \lambda_i \phi_i$ intersects F in $B_\lambda + C'$, where $C' = C - A_0$. Conversely, let $\Sigma \lambda_i \phi_i$ intersect F in $B_\lambda + C$, all the B_λ being effective. The ϕ_i can all be expressed in the form $G_i(\xi)/G(\xi)$, the G's being homogeneous polynomials of the same degree, and we may further assume that, if A is the cycle in which G intersects F, the order of G is so high at all the places appearing in C that $C + A$ is effective. Then $\Sigma \lambda_i G_i$ intersects F in $B_\lambda + (C + A)$. We have therefore only to show that the definitions of the dimensions agree; that is, to show that if $\phi_i = G_i(\xi)/G(\xi)$, $i = 0$, $\cdots, r$, a linear combination of the ϕ_i is zero if and only if a linear combination of the $G_i(x)$ is divisible by F. But this follows at once from the definition of Σ, (§V-3.1).

The dependence of the dimension of a series only on the cycles constituting the series now follows from the following theorem.

THEOREM 2.3. *If $\Sigma_0^r \lambda_i \phi_i$ intersects F in $B_\lambda + C_1$, and $\Sigma_0^s \mu_j \psi_j$ intersects F in $B_\mu + C_2$, where the set of cycles B_λ is the same as the set B_μ, then $r = s$.*

PROOF. Let ϕ be a member of the first set of functions intersecting F in $B + C_1$, and ψ the member of the second set intersecting F in $B + C_2$. Then if $\psi_j' = \psi_j \phi/\psi$, $\Sigma_0^s \mu_j \psi_j'$ intersects F in $B_\mu + C_1$. For each j, ψ_j' intersects F in a cycle which is identical with that in which F is intersected by some member ϕ_j' of $\Sigma \lambda_i \phi_i$, and so by Theorem 2.2, $\psi_j' = a_j \phi_j'$. The ψ_j' are therefore linearly dependent on the ϕ_j, and so $s \leqslant r$, for obviously the ψ_j are independent if and only if the ψ_j' are. Similarly, $r \leqslant s$, and the theorem is proved.

From the method of proving the above theorem we can obtain further insight into the nature of a linear series. To each cycle of the series there correspond sets of λ's, and of μ's, each such set being unique to within a constant multiple, by Theorem 2.2. If we put $\psi_j' = \Sigma_i a_i^j \phi_i$, then the λ's and μ's corresponding to the same cycle are related by $\rho \lambda_i = \Sigma_j a_i^j \mu_j$, $\rho \neq 0$, and since the relation is reversible, $| a_i^j | \neq 0$. That is, the coefficients of combination of the rational functions cutting out a series act as projective coordinates in a uniquely defined S_r whose points are the cycles of the series. For an effective series we can of course replace the rational functions by polynomials.

2.3. Complete series. Since a linear series of dimension r can be thought of as an S_r, we can of course construct various subspaces of this S_r, which will also be linear series. More interesting is the converse problem: "Is it possible to construct an S_s, with $s > r$, of which S_r is a subspace?" Another closely related question is: "When can two cycles be considered as points of the same S_r?" The answer to the first question will be given later, but we can easily answer the second.

THEOREM 2.4. *Two cycles B_1 and B_2 can be considered as elements of the same series if and only if there is a $\phi \in \Sigma$ intersecting F in $B_1 - B_2$.*

PROOF. If ϕ intersects F in $B_1 - B_2$ let the rational functions $\lambda_0\phi + \lambda_1 1$ intersect F in $B_\lambda + C$, where $C = -B_2$. Then for $\lambda_0 = 1, \lambda_1 = 0$ we have $B_\lambda = B_1$, and for $\lambda_0 = 0, \lambda_1 = 1$ we have $B_\lambda = B_2$, and so B_1 and B_2 are in the series composed of the B_λ. Conversely, if $\Sigma\lambda_i\phi_i$ intersects F in $B_\lambda + C$, where B_1 and B_2 are among the B_λ, we may assume that ϕ_0 intersects F in $B_1 + C$ and ϕ_1 in $B_2 + C$. Then $\phi = \phi_0/\phi_1$ intersects F in $B_1 - B_2$.

This theorem has some interesting consequences. We shall say that B_1 and B_2 are equivalent, writing $B_1 \equiv B_2$, if they are members of the same series. Since any non-zero constant intersects F in $0 = B - B$, we have $B \equiv B$. If ϕ intersects F in $B_1 - B_2$ then ϕ^{-1} intersects F in $B_2 - B_1$, and so $B_1 \equiv B_2$ implies $B_2 \equiv B_1$. And finally, if ϕ intersects F in $B_1 - B_2$ and ψ in $B_2 - B_3$, then $\phi\psi$ intersects F in $B_1 - B_3$; that is, $B_1 \equiv B_2, B_2 \equiv B_3$, imply $B_1 \equiv B_3$. Hence this equivalence is reflexive, symmetric and transitive, and the cycles on F fall into equivalence classes.

If ϕ_1 intersects F in $A_1 - B_1$ and ϕ_2 in $A_2 - B_2$ then $\phi_1\phi_2$ intersects F in $(A_1 + A_2) - (B_1 + B_2)$. Hence $A_1 \equiv B_1$, $A_2 \equiv B_2$, imply $A_1 + A_2 \equiv B_1 + B_2$. It follows that if we designate the equivalence class containing A by $\{A\}$, then $\{A + B\}$ is uniquely determined by $\{A\}$ and $\{B\}$. If we define $\{A\} + \{B\}$ to be $\{A + B\}$ the set of classes forms a commutative group with respect to addition. This group is the difference group (or quotient group) of the group of cycles with respect to the subgroup $\{0\}$ consisting of all cycles which are the intersections of F with rational functions.

Cycles of the same equivalence class have the same order, and so we can associate the order with the class. The cycles of a linear series all belong to the same class. Conversely, if $B_0, \cdots, B_r$ are equivalent cycles, let ϕ_i intersect F in $B_i - B_0$, $i = 0, \cdots, r$. Then $\Sigma\lambda_i\phi_i$ intersects F in $B_\lambda - B_0$, and so the B_i are all members of the linear series composed of the B_λ. Since there exist arbitrarily large sets of linearly independent ϕ_i's, for example $1, \xi, \xi^2, \cdots, \xi^r$, we see that an equivalence class contains linear series of arbitrarily high dimensions. However if we restrict ourselves to effective series the situation is quite different, as the following theorems show.

THEOREM 2.5. *If g_n^r is effective, then $r \leqslant n$.*

PROOF. Let g_n^r be cut out by $G_\lambda = \Sigma_0^r \lambda_i G_i$ and suppose that $r > n$. If P is a place of F at which not all the G_i are of positive order, the set of G_λ which are of positive order at P forms a linear system of dimension $r - 1$ which cuts out on F a subseries of g_n^r having P as a fixed place. Removing this fixed place, we are left with a g_{n-1}^{r-1}. Continuing in this manner, we eventually obtain a $g_0^{r'}$, with $r' = r - n > 0$. But this is impossible, since the only effective cycle of order 0 is the zero cycle, and a projective space with only one element is necessarily of dimension zero. Hence $r \leqslant n$.

THEOREM 2.6. *The set of all effective cycles in an equivalence class $\{A\}$ is a linear series.*

PROOF. If $B_0, \cdots, B_r$ are effective cycles of $\{A\}$ let ϕ_i intersect F in $B_i - B_0$. If $B_0 = \Sigma n_P P$ then the effectiveness of B_i is equivalent to the condition that $0_P(\phi_i) \geqslant -n_P$. But if this condition is satisfied by each ϕ_i it is also satisfied by any linear combination of the ϕ_i. Hence if $\Sigma \lambda_i \phi_i$ intersects F in $B_\lambda - B_0$, the B_λ constitute an effective series. We now pick out a finite set of effective cycles of $\{A\}$ and form the effective series determined by the above process. This series will have a certain dimension r (if there are no effective cycles in $\{A\}$ we follow the usual convention of putting $r = -1$), and we may assume the series to be the set of B_λ's, where $\Sigma \lambda_i \phi_i$ intersects F in $B_\lambda - B_0$, the ϕ's being linearly independent over K. If the set of B_λ's contains all the effective cycles of $\{A\}$ the theorem is proved. If not, let ϕ_{r+1} intersect F in $B_{r+1} - B_0$, where B_{r+1} is not a B_λ. Then ϕ_{r+1} cannot be dependent on $\phi_0, \cdots, \phi_r$, and so $\Sigma_0^{r+1} \lambda_i \phi_i$ cuts out an effective series of dimension $r + 1$. Because of Theorem 2.5 this process cannot be continued indefinitely and so the theorem is proved.

Associated with each class of equivalent cycles there is therefore a unique maximal effective series (perhaps empty). Such a series is called a *complete* series. Since any cycle A belongs to a unique class it determines a unique complete series, designated by $|A|$. If A is effective it is an element of $|A|$.

$A \equiv B$ implies $|A| = |B|$. Conversely, however, $|A| = |B|$ does not always imply $A \equiv B$. If C is a cycle of $|A|$, and hence of $|B|$, we have $A \equiv C$, $B \equiv C$, and so $A \equiv B$. But if $|A|$, and $|B|$, is the empty set there exists no such C, and so nothing can be concluded. For example, if P is a place of F, then $| - P | = | -2P | = $ the empty set, but $-P \not\equiv -2P$ since the cycles are of different orders.

The complete series are the important entities in the study of linear series, and for the rest of this chapter we shall be concerned with them almost exclusively. Some of their properties which follow immediately from the definition are given in

THEOREM 2.7. (i) *An effective linear series g_n^r is contained in a unique complete series g_n^R, with $R \geqslant r$; in the sense of projective spaces, g_n^r is a subspace of g_n^R.*

(ii) *If two effective series g_n^r and g_n^s have a common cycle they are contained in the same complete series.*

(iii) *If $| A |$ and $| B |$ are any non-empty complete series, the complete series $| A + B |$ is uniquely determined by $| A |$ and $| B |$ and contains all the sums of a cycle of $| A |$ with a cycle of $| B |$.*

The following property of a complete series is important enough to deserve special mention.

THEOREM 2.8. *Let g_n^r be any effective series and A any effective cycle. If g is the set of all effective cycles B such that $A + B$ is a cycle of g_n^r, then g is a linear series and is complete if g_n^r is complete.*

PROOF. Let G_λ intersect F in $B'_\lambda + C$, where the B'_λ are the cycles of g_n^r. The G_μ which intersect F in cycles of the form $B_\mu + A + C$ obviously form a linear system, and so the set of B_μ is a linear series, g'. Evidently $g' \subset g$. On the other hand, if B is any element of g then there is a G_λ intersecting F in $B + A + C$, and so this G_λ is one of the G_μ and B is an element of g'. Hence $g = g'$. Finally, if g is not complete there is a $B_1 \equiv B \in g$, but $B_1 \not\subset g$. This implies $B'_1 = B_1 + A \equiv B + A \in g_n^r$, but $B'_1 \not\subset g_n^r$ and so g_n^r is not complete.

The series g is designated by $g_n^r - A$, and is called the *residue* of g_n^r with respect to A. It will be empty if no cycle of g_n^r contains A. If $g_n^r = | D |$, and $A \equiv A'$, then $g_n^r - A = g_n^r - A' = | D - A |$. Hence we can speak of the residue of $| D |$ with respect to $| A |$.

2.4. Exercises. 1. Let $\Sigma_0^r \lambda_i G_i$ cut out g_n^r and $\Sigma_0^s \mu_j H_j$ cut out g_n^s, and let g_n^r and g_n^s have a common cycle A which we may assume to correspond to the values $\lambda_0 = 1$, $\lambda_1 = \cdots = \lambda_r = 0$, $\mu_0 = 1$, $\mu_1 = \cdots = \mu_s = 0$. Then $\nu_0 G_0 H_0 + \Sigma_1^r \nu_i G_i H_0 + \Sigma_1^s \nu_{r+j} G_0 H_j$ cuts out a g_n^q which contains both g_n^r and g_n^s.

2. By actual computation verify the conclusion of Exercise 1 for the series of order 2 cut out by

$$\lambda_0(xy - y) + \lambda_1(x_t^2 + y^2 - 2x) = 0$$

and

$$\mu_0(x + 1) + \mu_1 y = 0,$$

on the curve $2y^2 - x^3 - x^2 = 0$.

3. (a) On an irreducible cubic with a double point a linear series is cut out by the system of conics passing through three simple points of the cubic. What are the dimension and the order of this series, and is it complete?

(b) How can one cut out a g_4^4 on a quartic with a triple point?

4. Show that the proof of Theorem III-5.1 depended essentially on the construction of a g_1^1 on the curve. Prove that every curve containing a g_1^1 is rational. Prove the same thing for a g_n^n.

§3. INVARIANCE OF LINEAR SERIES

In the above discussion, the basic curve F played no essential role whatever. Cycles are defined in terms of orders of rational functions at places, and these are properties of Σ rather than of F. And the remaining concepts, linear series, effective series, order, dimension, equivalence, and complete series, are all defined directly in terms of Σ. It follows that any cycle or series on F has an exact analogue on any birational transform of F. There are three important consequences of this observation.

In the first place, we can consider linear series on space curves as well as on plane curves. This is a relatively simple extension of the concept, and as a matter of fact could easily have been introduced at the very beginning of our discussion. The argument of §2.2 can be altered to show that every effective g_n^r on a curve C in S_k can be cut out by a system of homogeneous polynomials $\Sigma_0^r \lambda_i G_i(x_0, \cdots, x_k)$ none of which vanishes at all points of C.

Secondly, any entity related to a curve F and defined entirely in terms of linear series on F will be the same for any curve birationally equivalent to F. The discovery and investigation of such *birational invariants* is the most important application of linear series.

Finally, in investigating these birational invariants it is immaterial which of the class of birationally equivalent curves we use. Naturally, then, we shall choose to work with one of the simplest possible type. This freedom will be utilized in our further investigations.

§4. RATIONAL TRANSFORMATIONS ASSOCIATED WITH LINEAR SERIES

4.1. Correspondence between transformations and linear series. There is a simple connection between the linear series on a curve and the rational transformations of that curve. We shall proceed to develop this connection, and use it to throw some light on both concepts.

Let C be an irreducible curve in S_m, Σ being its field of rational functions. Let $G_\lambda = \Sigma_0^R \lambda_j G_j(x)$ intersect C in the cycle $A_\lambda + B$, where the A_λ form an effective series g_n having no fixed points. We associate with g_n the rational transformation,

$$(4.1) \qquad\qquad y_j = G_j(x).$$

We first prove that *the transform C' of C is a curve in S_R, if and only if $n > 0$.*

The condition for C' to be a curve (§V-6.1) is that at least one of the elements $G_i(\xi)/G_j(\xi)$ of Σ is not a constant. Suppose $G_1(\xi)/G_0(\xi) \nsubseteq K$, and let $G_0(x)$ and $G_1(x)$ intersect C in $A_0 + B$ and $A_1 + B$ respectively. Then $G_1(\xi)/G_0(\xi)$ intersects C in $A_1 - A_0 \neq 0$, from which it follows that A_0 and A_1 are not both zero. Since the zero cycle is the only effective cycle of order 0, we must have $n > 0$. Conversely, if $n > 0$ there exist two polynomials $\Sigma \lambda_j G_j$, say G_0 and G_1, which do not intersect C in the same cycle. Then $G_1(\xi)/G_0(\xi)$ does not intersect C in the zero cycle and so is not an element of K. It follows that C' is a curve.

We shall in the future limit ourselves to the case in which $n > 0$.

Let the g_n above be of dimension r. Combining the results of §1.3 and §2.2, we see that the basic elements G_j of the system G_λ can be chosen in such a way that if $\phi_j = G_j(\xi)/G_0(\xi)$, we have $\phi_0, \cdots, \phi_r$ independent over K and $\phi_{r+1} = \cdots = \phi_R = 0$. It follows that every point and every parametrization of C' will have its last $R - r$ coordinates equal to zero. We can therefore consider the curve C' as lying in the S_r defined by $y_{r+1} = \cdots = y_R = 0$, and so limit ourselves to the case in which $R = r$.

C' is not determined directly by the g_n^r but by the polynomials G_λ that cut out g_n^r. We shall now show that the same C' is obtained if we consider a different system of polynomials cutting out g_n^r. Let $H_\mu = \Sigma_0^r \mu_i H_i$, intersect C in $A_\mu + B'$, where the A_μ are the cycles of g_n^r. Letting $\psi_j = H_j(\xi)/H_0(\xi)$, we have, as in §2.2, that $\psi_j = \Sigma_k a_j^k \theta \phi_k$, where $|a_j^k| \neq 0$ and $\theta \in \Sigma$. By properly choosing the basic polynomials of the system G_λ (this corresponds to a change of coordinates in S_r) we can reduce these equations to the form $\psi_j = \theta \phi_j$. Since $\psi_0 = \phi_0 = 1$ these reduce finally to $\psi_j = \phi_j$, and the required conclusion follows at once.

If we start with an arbitrary rational transformation (4.1) of a curve C, then $\Sigma \lambda_j G_j$ intersects C in $A_\lambda + B$, where the A_λ form an effective g_n^r with no fixed points. Two sets of polynomials determining the same rational transformation of C determine the same set of rational functions ϕ_i, defined as above. Also, the ϕ_i determine the linear series uniquely, for if the intersection of ϕ_λ with C could be expressed in the form $B_\lambda - B_0$ we would have $A_\lambda - A_0 = B_\lambda - B_0$, or $A_\lambda + B_0 = B_\lambda + A_0$. Since by assumption there are no places common to all the A_λ nor to all the B_λ this implies that $A_0 = B_0$, $A_\lambda = B_\lambda$.

These conclusions are summarized in

THEOREM 4.1. *There is a one-to-one correspondence between the rational transformations of C into curves and the effective series of positive order without fixed points on C.*

4.2. Structure of linear series. Our knowledge of the properties of rational transformations can now be used to yield information about the structure of a linear series. We first consider the case in which the transformation (4.1) is birational.

If $B = \Sigma n_P P$, then $\min O_P(G_j) = n_P$. Hence if $(\bar{x})$ is a parametrization of P, the transform of P is $P' = (\bar{y})$, where $\bar{y}_j = G_j(\bar{x})t^{-n_P}$. It is then evident that $y_\lambda = \Sigma \lambda_j y_j$ intersects C' in the cycle which is precisely the transform of the cycle A_λ on C. That is, the transforms onto C' of the cycles of g_n^r on C constitute the series on C' cut out by the hyperplanes of S_r. Since this series is of order n it follows that C' is a curve of order n.

Now let (4.1) be an arbitrary rational transformation of C into C'. As before, let $B = \Sigma n_P P$, and let $(\bar{x})$ be a parametrization of P. If $P' = (\bar{y})$ is the transform of P, then there is an $r_P \geqslant 1$ such that

$$\bar{y}_j(t^{r_P}) = G_j(\bar{x})t^{-n_P}.$$

Now

$$A_\lambda = [\Sigma_P O_P(G_\lambda)P] - B$$

$$= \Sigma_P O(G_\lambda(\bar{x})t^{-n_P})P$$

$$= \Sigma_P r_P O_{P'}(y_\lambda)P$$

$$= \Sigma_{P'}[\Sigma_\alpha r_{P_\alpha} O_{P'}(y_\lambda)P_\alpha],$$

where P_α are the places of C which transform into the place P' of C'. Let us designate the cycle $\Sigma_\alpha r_{P_\alpha}P_\alpha$ by $A_{P'}$. Then we have

$$A_\lambda = \Sigma_{P'} O_{P'}(y_\lambda)A_{P'}.$$

Thus each cycle of the series g_n^r is expressible as a sum of the cycles $A_{P'}$. By Theorem V-6.2 all but a finite number of the $A_{P'}$ are of the same order ν. Hence all but a finite set of the cycles $\Sigma_{P'} O_{P'}(y_\lambda)P'$ are of order n/ν. As these are the cycles in which the hyperplanes $y_\lambda = 0$ intersect C' we see that C' is a curve of order $n' = n/\nu$.

The set of cycles $A_{P'}$ is called an *involution* of order ν, and is designated by γ_ν. g_n^r is said to be *compounded* of γ_ν. Every curve carries a γ_1, namely the set of all its places, and every series on the curve is compounded of this. A series compounded of a γ_ν with $\nu > 1$ is said to be *composite*—otherwise it is *simple*. We can now make the following complete statement of our results.

THEOREM 4.2. *A rational transformation T is birational if and only if the associated series g is simple. If g is of order n and is compounded of an involution of maximum order $\nu \geqslant 1$, then the transform of C by T is of order n/ν.*

Examples. 1. A g_n^1 with no fixed points is a γ_n. For the g_n^1 on C defines a rational transformation of C into a line L, and each cycle of g_n^1 consists of the places of C which transform into a place of L. Hence any g_n^1 with $n > 1$ is composite, being compounded of itself. A g_n^1 is often called a *rational* involution.

2. Let $\lambda_0 G_0 + \lambda_1 G_1$ intersect C in $A_\lambda + B$, where the A_λ constitute a g_n^1 with no fixed points. Then $\lambda_0 G_0^r + \lambda_1 G_0^{r-1} G_1 + \cdots + \lambda_r G_1^r$ intersects C in $A_\lambda' + rB$, where the A_λ' constitute a g_{nr}^r with no fixed points compounded of the involution g_n^1.

3. On the non-singular cubic C (see §III-2.5, Exercise 4),

$$x_0(x_1^2 + x_2^2) + x_1(x_2^2 + x_0^2) + x_2(x_0^2 + x_1^2) - 2x_0 x_1 x_2 = 0,$$

the system

$$G_\lambda = \lambda_0 x_0(x_1^2 + x_2^2) + \lambda_1 x_1(x_2^2 + x_0^2) + \lambda_2 x_2(x_0^2 + x_1^2) = 0$$

cuts out a g_6^2 with no fixed points. Since C and each G_λ are invariant under the quadratic transformation

$$x_0' = x_1 x_2, \quad x_1' = x_2 x_0, \quad x_2' = x_0 x_1,$$

the g_6^2 is compounded of an involution γ_2 whose elements are the pairs of places with centers at the points (x_0, x_1, x_2) and $(x_1 x_2, x_2 x_0, x_0 x_1)$ of C. Hence the transform of C by

$$y_0 = x_0(x_1^2 + x_2^2), \; y_1 = x_1(x_0^2 + x_2^2), \; y_2 = x_2(x_0^2 + x_1^2),$$

is a cubic C'. Since C is unchanged by any permutation of the x_i, and since a permutation of the x_i causes a corresponding permutation of the y_i, C' must be unchanged by any permutation of the y_i. Hence C' has one of the forms

$$C_1' : x_0 x_1^2 + x_1 x_2^2 + x_2 x_0^2 - x_0 x_2^2 - x_1 x_0^2 - x_2 x_1^2 = 0,$$

$$C_2' : h(x_0 x_1^2 + x_0 x_2^2 + x_1 x_0^2 + x_1 x_2^2 + x_2 x_0^2 + x_2 x_1^2) + k x_0 x_1 x_2 +$$
$$l(x_0^3 + x_1^3 + x_2^3) = 0.$$

The point $(1,1,i)$ on C transforms into $(0,0,1)$ on C'; hence if $C' = C_2'$ we must have $l = 0$. The place

$$(1,t, -t(1 + 4t + 16t^2 + 84t^3 + \cdots))$$

of C transforms into the place

$$(2t + 8t^2 + 48t^3 + \cdots, 1 + t^2 + 8t^3 + \cdots,$$

$$- 1 - 4t - 17t^2 - 88t^3 + \cdots)$$

of C'; this eliminates C_1' and specifies $C' = C_2'$ with $k = 4h$. C' is then seen to be non-singular (§III-2.5, Exercise 4). It will appear later (§5.3) that a non-singular plane cubic is not a rational curve. It follows from Exercise 3 below that γ_ν is not a rational involution.

4.3. Normal curves. Some interesting results are obtained by applying Theorem 4.2 to the rational transformation obtained from a projection. In S_R let the curve C, of order n, be projected from the subspace S_s into the curve C' of the subspace S_r, where $r + s = R - 1$ (see §II-5.1). Let the hyperplanes of S_R which contain S_s cut out on C a $g_{n'}^{r'}$, $1 \leqslant r' \leqslant r, 1 \leqslant n' \leqslant n$, with no fixed points. Then C' is the transform of C determined by $g_{n'}^{r'}$, and on applying Theorem 4.2 we see that the order of C' is n'/ν, if ν is the order of the involution of which $g_{n'}^{r'}$ is compounded.

An immediate consequence of this result is

THEOREM 4.3. *The order of a curve is not decreased by projection if and only if the projection is a birational transformation and the center of projection does not intersect the curve.*

PROOF. $n'/\nu = n$ if and only if $\nu = 1$ and $n' = n$, and these conditions are equivalent to the two stated in the theorem.

A curve C, spanning a space of dimension r, is said to be *normal* if it is not the projection of a curve of the same order spanning a space of more than r dimensions.

THEOREM 4.4. *A curve C in S_R is normal if and only if the hyperplanes of S_R intersect C in a complete series.*

PROOF. Let C span S_r, $r \leqslant R$. Then the hyperplanes of S_r intersect C in the same series g_n^r as the hyperplanes of S_R, n being the order of C. Hence we can ignore S_R and consider C as lying in S_r.

Let C be the projection of a curve C', of order n, spanning $S_{r'}$ where $r' > r$. We may assume that the equations of the projection are

$$x_j = x_j', \quad j = 0, \cdots, r.$$

The hyperplanes $\Sigma_0^{r'} \lambda_i x_i' = 0$ of $S_{r'}$ intersect C' in a $g_n'^{r'}$ which contains the series $g_n'^r$ cut out by the hyperplanes $\Sigma_0^r \lambda_j x_j' = 0$. By Theorem 4.3

the projection is birational, and since g_n^r on C is cut out by $\Sigma_0^r \lambda_j x_j = 0$, g_n^r is the transform of $g_n^{\prime r}$. Hence $g_n^{\prime r'}$ is transformed into a $g_n^{r'}$ which contains g_n^r, and so g_n^r is not complete.

Conversely, if g_n^r is not complete there is a $g_n^{r'}$, $r' > r$, which contains it. If $g_n^{r'}$ is cut out on C by $\Sigma_0^{r'} \lambda_i G_i(x)$, we can assume the G's so chosen that $\Sigma_0^r \lambda_j G_j$ cuts out the same cycle of g_n^r as $\Sigma_0^r \lambda_j x_j$. This implies that $G_j(\xi)/G_0(\xi) = \xi_j/\xi_0$. The birational transformation T, $x_i' = G_i(x)$, then has the inverse $x_j = x_j'$, which is a projection from $S_{r'}$ into S_r. If C' is the transform of C by T, then C is the projection of C', and since C and C' have the same order n the theorem is proved.

As a corollary of Theorem 4.4 we have

THEOREM 4.5. *A simple series with no fixed points is complete if and only if the corresponding transformed curve is normal.*

4.4. Complete reduction of singularities. In §V-5.3 we defined a singular point of a space curve C as one which is the center of a place of order greater than one or of two or more places. It is useful to interpret singular points in terms of properties of linear series. Let g_n^r be a simple series with no fixed points on C, and let C' be the corresponding birational transform of C. Then to g_n^r will correspond the $g_n^{\prime r}$ on C' cut out by the hyperplanes of the space S_r in which C' lies. For any place P' of C', the series $g_n^{\prime r} - P'$ is evidently the $g_{n-1}^{\prime r-1}$ cut out on C' by the hyperplanes through the center p' of P'. It is then evident that p' *is singular if and only if* $g_n^{\prime r} - P'$ *has a fixed point*. Since the properties of series are preserved under birational transformations we can state the result that *the transform of C corresponding to g_n^r is non-singular if and only if $g_n^r - P$ has no fixed points for any P*. Such a g_n^r is sometimes called *totally simple*. A totally simple series is obviously simple.

By using this criterion we can prove the following important theorem.

THEOREM 4.6. *Every irreducible curve has a non-singular birational transform.*

PROOF. Our problem is to prove the existence of a totally simple g_n^r. We may assume that the curve we are dealing with is a plane curve F, for any curve is birationally equivalent to some plane curve. Let m be the order of F, and consider the $g_{n_0}^{r_0}$ cut out on F by the system of all curves of order $m - 1$. Since none of these can contain F, and since there are obviously no fixed points, we have

$$r_0 = (m - 1)(m + 2)/2, \quad n_0 = m(m - 1).$$

If $g_{n_0}^{r_0}$ is totally simple we are through. If not, let P be a place such that $g_{n_0}^{r_0} - P$ has a fixed point. Removing all the fixed points we obtain a $g_{n_1}^{r_1}$ with

$$r_1 = r_0 - 1, \quad n_1 \leqslant n_0 - 2.$$

The process can now be continued. If $g_{n_i}^{r_i}$ is not totally simple we can construct a $g_{n_{i+1}}^{r_{i+1}}$ with

$$r_{i+1} = r_i - 1, \quad n_{i+1} \leqslant n_i - 2.$$

Hence for each such i we have

$$r_i = r_0 - i, \quad n_i \leqslant n_0 - 2i.$$

Now $r_i \leqslant n_i$. Hence

$$r_0 - i \leqslant n_0 - 2i,$$

or

$$(m - 1)(m + 2)/2 \leqslant m(m - 1) - i,$$

which reduces to

$$i \leqslant (m - 1)(m - 2)/2.$$

Hence for some $j \leqslant (m - 1)(m - 2)/2 + 1$, $g_{n_j}^{r_j}$ must be totally simple. For such a j we have

$$r_j = r_0 - j \geqslant (m - 1)(m + 2)/2 - (m - 1)(m - 2)/2 - 1 = 2m - 3.$$

Ignoring the trivial case $m = 1$ we have $r_j \geqslant 1$, and so also $n_j \geqslant 1$. The transform of F corresponding to $g_{n_j}^{r_j}$ will then be a curve with no singularities.

4.5. Exercises. 1. A g_n^r with no fixed points is simple if n is prime and $r > 1$.

2. Every g_n^r compounded of a g_ν^1 is a subseries of a g_n^R constructed as in §4.2, Example 2.

3. If g_n^r is compounded of a g_ν^1, the transform of C corresponding to g_n^r is a rational curve.

4. It will be shown later that every g_2^1 on a non-singular cubic is cut out by a pencil of lines. Use this property to show directly that the γ_2 of §4.2, Example 3 is not rational.

5. If g_n^r has no fixed points, but $g_n^r - P$ has a fixed point for an infinite set of places P, then g_n^r is composite.

6. Any plane curve is the projection of a non-singular space curve.

7. Show that every cycle of a γ_ν is of order ν.

§5. THE CANONICAL SERIES

5.1. Jacobian cycles and differentials. Let g_n^1, $n > 0$, be an effective series with no fixed points. From Theorem V-6.2 and the considerations of §4.2 it follows that there are only a finite number of cycles of the involution g_n^1 which do not consist of n distinct places. Let P enter with coefficient m_P into a cycle of g_n^1. (Since each place is contained in a unique cycle of g_n^1 there is no ambiguity about m_P.) Then $\Sigma_P(m_P - 1)P$ is a cycle, called the *Jacobian* cycle J of g_n^1.

To investigate the structure of J let g_n^1 be cut out on C by the system $\lambda_0 G_0 + \lambda_1 G_1$. Let $\theta = -G_1(\xi)/G_0(\xi) \in \Sigma$. If A_∞ is the cycle of g_n^1 cut out by G_0, and if $\theta - \lambda$, $\lambda \in K$, intersects C in $A_\lambda - A_\infty$, then the A_λ; together with A_∞, constitute the cycles of g_n^1.

For any place P, m_P is the coefficient of P in the cycle A_{λ_P} of g_n^1 which contains P. Considering first the case $\lambda_P \neq \infty$, we have $O_P(\theta - \lambda_P) = m_P > 0$. Now if $(\bar{x})$ is a parametrization of P, then $\theta(\bar{x}) = \lambda_P + at^{m_P} + \cdots, a \neq 0$. Differentiating with respect to t, we have $\theta(\bar{x})' = am_P t^{m_P - 1} + \cdots$, and so

$$(5.1) \qquad O(\theta(\bar{x})') = m_P - 1.$$

That is, P appears in J with the coefficient $O(\theta(\bar{x})')$. On the other hand, if $\lambda_P = \infty$, then

$$O_P(\theta) = -m_P, \quad \theta(\bar{x}) = at^{-m_P}\cdots, \quad a \neq 0,$$

and

$$(5.2) \qquad O(\theta(\bar{x})') = -m_P - 1 = (m_P - 1) - 2m_P.$$

We thus see that J is intimately connected with the order of $\theta(\bar{x})'$ for the various places $(\bar{x})$. To capitalize on this relation we find it convenient to introduce a new symbol, $d\theta$, called the *differential* of θ. By $d\theta(\bar{x})$ we shall mean $\theta(\bar{x})'$, and by $O_P(d\theta)$ we shall mean $O(d\theta(\bar{x}))$ for a parametrization $(\bar{x})$ of P. It is readily seen that $O_P(d\theta)$ depends only on P and not on the particular parametrization used.

We can now combine equations (5.1) and (5.2) into

$$O_P(d\theta) = \begin{cases} m_P - 1 & \text{if } P \notin A_\infty, \\ m_P - 1 - 2m_P & \text{if } P \in A_\infty. \end{cases}$$

Hence

$$(5.3) \qquad \Sigma_P O_P(d\theta)P = \Sigma_P(m_P - 1)P - 2A_\infty.$$

$$= J - 2A_\infty.$$

The further investigation of J requires an investigation of the cycle $\Sigma_P O_P(d\theta)P$, which we shall say is the intersection of $d\theta$ with C. Let ϕ be any non-constant element of Σ. Then by Theorem V-3.1 there is an irreducible polynomial $g(x,y)$ such that $g(\phi,\theta) = 0$. Hence $g(\phi(\bar{x}), \theta(\bar{x})) = 0$ for any place $(\bar{x})$ of C, and so by differentiating we obtain

$$g_x(\phi(\bar{x}),\theta(\bar{x}))\phi(\bar{x})' + g_y(\phi(\bar{x}),\theta(\bar{x}))\theta(\bar{x})' = 0,$$

or

$$\frac{g(\bar{x})'}{\phi(\bar{x})''} = \frac{d\theta(\bar{x})}{d\phi(\bar{x})} = -\frac{g_x(\phi(\bar{x}),\theta(\bar{x}))}{g_y(\phi(\bar{x}),\theta(\bar{x}))} = \psi(\bar{x}),$$

where $\psi = -g_x(\phi,\theta)/g_y(\phi,\theta) \in \Sigma$. Hence we are led to define $d\theta/d\phi = \psi$.

It now follows from Theorem 2.4 that the intersections with C of $d\theta$ and $d\phi$ are equivalent cycles, and so there is a unique complete series which contains all the effective cycles of this type. This series is called the *canonical series* of C and is conventionally designated by the symbol K. Since there is little chance of confusing this series with the ground field we shall continue to use K for the canonical series.

If C is birationally transformed into C' the canonical series on C will be transformed into the canonical series on C', since each of these series is cut out by the differentials of Σ. Hence the order and the dimension of K are *birational invariants of C*. We shall see later (§6.4) that the order of K is always twice its dimension, so that we actually obtain only one numerical invariant instead of the two that might be expected.

5.2. Order of canonical series. The order of K can be computed from a conveniently simple birational transform of C. We have seen in §V-4.2 that every irreducible curve is birationally equivalent to a plane curve with ordinary singularities. Consider such a curve f and choose the point $(0,0,1)$ so that it is not on f nor on any tangent to f at a singular point. Let g_n^1 be cut out by $x - \lambda = 0$. Then J contains only those places with tangents parallel to the y-axis, and at ·the centers of these places we have $f_y = 0$. We therefore investigate the intersections of f_y with f.

(i) Consider first a singular point of f, which we may assume to have coordinates $(0,0)$. If this point has multiplicity $r \geqslant 2$ we have $f = F(x,y) + g(x,y)$, where F consists of the terms of f of degree r. Since all singularities of f are ordinary, F has distinct factors; and by the choice of the coordinate system, F has a term ay^r, $a \neq 0$. Hence $f_y = F_y + g_y$ has $(0,0)$ as a point of multiplicity $r - 1$, and its tangents are distinct from those of f. From Theorem IV-5.10 it follows that f_y has $r(r - 1)$ intersections with f at $(0,0)$.

(ii) If f_y intersects f at a place P with non-singular center, then $f_x \neq 0$ at this point and so P has a parametrization

$$\bar{y} = a + t, \quad \bar{x} = b + ct^r + \cdots, \quad c \neq 0.$$

By differentiating $f(\bar{x},\bar{y}) = 0$ with respect to t we get

$$f_x(\bar{x},\bar{y})(crt^{r-1} + \cdots) + f_y(\bar{x},\bar{y}) = 0.$$

Hence f_y is of order $r - 1$ on P. Now P appears with coefficient r in the cycle of g_n^1 cut out by $x - b = 0$ and so P appears in J with coefficient $r - 1$. Since no line $x - \lambda = 0$ is tangent to f at any singular point, it follows that $J = \Sigma(r - 1)P$, the summation being over all nonsingular intersections of f_y with f.

Since the total number of intersections of f and f_y is $n(n - 1)$ we therefore see that the order of J is

$$n(n - 1) - \Sigma r_i(r_i - 1),$$

the summation being over all the singular points, of multiplicities r_i. Since $K = | J - 2A |$ the order of K is

(5.4) $n(n - 1) - \Sigma r_i(r_i - 1) - 2n = n(n - 3) - \Sigma r_i(r_i - 1).$

In our earlier discussion of singular points we encountered the non-negative integer (Theorem III-7.5)

(5.5) $$p = \frac{(n - 1)(n - 2)}{2} - \Sigma \frac{r_i(r_i - 1)}{2}.$$

Comparing (5.4) and (5.5) we see that the order of K is $2p - 2$.

The following theorem summarizes our results concerning Jacobians.

THEOREM 5.1. *If J is the Jacobian cycle of an effective g_n^1 with no fixed points on a curve C, and A a cycle of g_n^1, then the cycle $J - 2A$ is the intersection of C with a differential, and is independent, to within equivalence, of the g_n^1 in terms of which it is defined. If C is a plane curve with ordinary singularities of multiplicities $r_1, r_2, \cdots$, the order of $J - 2A$ is $2p - 2$, where*

$$p = \frac{(n - 1)(n - 2)}{2} - \Sigma \frac{r_i(r_i - 1)}{2}.$$

5.3. Genus of a curve. The *genus p* of an irreducible curve C is defined to be zero if the canonical series of C is empty, otherwise to be one more than half the order of the canonical series. For a plane curve with ordinary singularities the genus is given by (5.5).

As mentioned above, the genus is a birational invariant; that is, birationally equivalent curves have the same genus, or, in other words, two curves with different genera are not birationally equivalent. This is the first time in the course of our study of curves that such a statement could be made; as far as our previous work had shown, all irreducible curves might have been birationally equivalent. We can see now that there are an infinite number of birationally non-equivalent curves. In particular two non-singular irreducible plane curves are not equivalent if their orders are different, unless one is a line and the other a conic.

We shall see later (§7.3) that even if two curves have the same genus they need not be birationally equivalent.

5.4. Exercises. 1. Let C be an irreducible plane curve of order n, class m, and genus p, and let $\gamma(P)$ designate the order of the place P of C. Then

$$m = 2p - 2 + 2n - \Sigma_P(\gamma(P) - 1).$$

This reduces to the standard Plücker formula (IV-6.2) for a curve with double points and cusps.

2. A curve is rational if and only if it is of genus 0.

3. Show that the Jacobian cycles of all the g_n^1's contained in a g_n^r are equivalent. They determine a complete series called the *Jacobian series* of the g_n^r.

§6. DIMENSION OF A COMPLETE SERIES

6.1. Adjoints. To make a more complete study of linear series—in particular, to determine the dimension of the canonical series—we utilize Nöther's Theorem. We have given a proof (Theorem IV-7.2) in a form that can be utilized whenever the curve F has no singularities but ordinary multiple points. Since every irreducible curve is birationally equivalent to a plane curve of this type, the properties of linear series which we prove for such curves will be true for all curves.

We assume then that F is an irreducible plane curve with only ordinary singularities. For any place P_i of F let r_i be the multiplicity of the center of P_i as a point of F. We designate by D the cycle $\Sigma(r_i - 1)P_i$. Any polynomial G cutting out D will be called an *adjoint* of F, and we shall also speak of the curve $G = 0$ as an adjoint of F. In using this terminology it will be convenient to regard the equation $G = 0$ as the equation of a curve even when G is a non-zero constant. From Theorem IV-5.11 it follows that G is an adjoint of F if and only if it has each r_i — fold point of F as a point of multiplicity at least $r_i - 1$. Adjoints of F will be designated by capital Greek letters.

The following theorem, known as the Residue Theorem, contains the basic application of Nöther's Theorem to linear series.

THEOREM 6.1. *If*

$$\Phi_m \text{ intersects } F \text{ in } A + B + D,$$

$$\Psi_m \text{ intersects } F \text{ in } A' + B + D,$$

$$\Theta_l \text{ intersects } F \text{ in } A + B' + D,$$

then there is a Ξ_l intersecting F in $A' + B' + D$.

(The subscripts indicate the degrees of the polynomials.)

PROOF. Applying Theorem IV-7.2 we find that

$$\Theta_l \Psi_m = M\Phi_m + NF.$$

M must be of degree l. Since $\Theta\Psi$ intersects F in $A + B + A' + B' + 2D$, so does $M\Phi$, and hence M intersects F in $A' + B' + D$. M is therefore the required adjoint Ξ_l.

The following consequence of Theorem 6.1 is sometimes also called the Residue Theorem.

THEOREM 6.2. *If $A \equiv A'$ and if there is an adjoint intersecting F in $A + B + D$, then there is an adjoint of the same order intersecting F in $A' + B + D$.*

PROOF. Let Φ_l intersect F in $A + B + D$, and let θ be a rational function intersecting F in $A' - A$. We may write $\theta = \Psi'_m/\Psi_m$, where Ψ and Ψ' are adjoints intersecting F in $A + B' + D$ and $A' + B' + D$ respectively. Applying Theorem 6.1 we have the desired result.

As an immediate corollary we have the following important result.

THEOREM 6.3. *If A is any effective cycle and if an adjoint of degree l intersects F in $A + B + D$, then $|A|$ is the residue with respect to $B + D$ of the series cut out by all curves of degree l.*

This theorem gives us a specific way of cutting out complete series. The following examples illustrate how this is done.

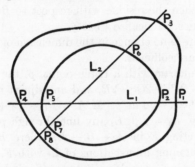

Figure 6.1

Examples. 1. Let F be a non-singular quartic (Figure 6.1). Then $D = 0$ and every polynomial is an adjoint. Let $A = P_1 + P_2 + P_3$, where the three places have non-collinear centers p_1, p_2, p_3. Let the line $L_1 = p_1 p_2$ intersect F in the additional points p_4, p_5, and let a line L_2 through p_3 intersect F in p_6, p_7, p_8. (For simplicity we shall assume that the eight points are distinct.) Then $L_1 L_2$ is an adjoint intersecting F in $A + B$, where $B = \Sigma_4^8 P_i$. Hence $|A|$ is the residue with respect to B of the g_8^5 cut out on F by all conics. But since no four of $p_4, \cdots, p_8$ are collinear there is only one conic containing them, and so $|A|$ is a g_3^0.

However, if the centers of the places of A are collinear, say $A = P_1 + P_2 + P_4$, then the adjoint L_1 intersects F in $A + B$, with $B = P_5$. $| A |$ is then the residue with respect to P_5 of the g_4^1 cut out by all lines on p_5, and so in this case $| A |$ is a g_3^1.

2. Let F be a quartic with one double point p. (Figure 6.2.) If P and Q are the places at p, then $D = P + Q$. As in Example 1, let $L_1 = p_1p_2$ cut F in p_4 and p_5. Supposing that L_1 does not pass through

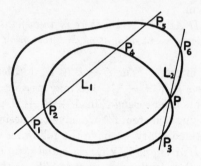

Figure 6.2

p, to obtain an adjoint we must take $L_2 = p_3p$. L_2 has just one residual intersection p_6. Then L_1L_2 intersects F in $A + B + D$, with $B = P_4 + P_5 + P_6$. $| A |$ is then the residue with respect to $B + D$ of the series cut out by the conics. Hence $| A |$ is a g_3^1.

In this case there is no change in the dimension of $| A |$ if the centers of its three places are collinear.

3. Let F be a quartic with a triple point, p, the places here being P,Q,R. Then $D = 2P + 2Q + 2R$, and an adjoint must have a point of multiplicity at least two at p. If $A = P_1 + P_2 + P_3$ as before, we may take $L_1 = p_1p$, $L_2 = p_2p$, L_3 any line through p_3. Then $L_1L_2L_3$ is an adjoint intersecting F in $A + B + D$, where $B = P_4 + P_5 + P_6$ consists of the remaining intersections of L_3 with F. $| A |$ is therefore cut out by cubics having a double point at p and passing through p_4,p_5,p_6. This is not a particularly good way of cutting out $| A |$ for it is difficult to tell much about the remaining intersections. We can simplify the situation by taking L_3 also through p, so that $B = P + Q + R$. Then the cubics must have a *triple* point at p, and so consist of any three lines on p. $| A |$ is thus seen to contain all effective cycles of order 3 on F.

We leave to the reader the investigation of the complete series of orders 2 and 3 on a quartic with two or three double points.

6.2. Lower bound on dimension. The preceding examples seem to indicate that an increase in the order of D causes an increase in the dimension of a complete series of given order. The precise connection will now be established. We shall designate the order of D by 2δ; hence $\delta = \Sigma r_i(r_i - 1)/2$. The genus p of the curve is given by $p = (m - 1)(m - 2)/2 - \delta$, m being the order of F.

THEOREM 6.4. *If g_n^r is complete then $r \geqslant n - p$.*

PROOF. Consider first the g_n^r which is the residue with respect to D of the series cut out by all adjoints of degree $l \geqslant m$. The dimension of this system of curves is

$$R \geqslant \frac{l(l + 3)}{2} - \delta.$$

Hence, by Theorem 1.1, $r = R - q$, where q is the number of Φ_l containing F as a factor. But $H_{l-m}F$ is an adjoint for any H, and so q is the number of independent polynomials of degree $l - m$; that is, $q = (l - m + 1)(l - m + 2)/2$. Hence

$$r \geqslant l(l + 3)/2 - \delta - (l - m + 1)(l - m + 2)/2$$
$$= lm - \delta - (m - 1)(m - 2)/2$$
$$= lm - \delta - p - \delta$$
$$= n - p,$$

since $n = lm - 2\delta$. Now any $g_{n'}^{r'}$ is a residue of such a g_n^r with respect to some cycle B. If the order of B is k we have

$$n' = n - k, \quad r' \geqslant r - k.$$

Hence $r' \geqslant n' - p$, which proves the theorem.

6.3. Dimension of canonical series. The adjoints of order $m - 3$ (if there are any) are of special interest because of the following theorem.

THEOREM 6.5. *If $p \geqslant 1$ the residue with respect to D of the series cut out by all adjoints of order $m - 3$ is the canonical series K.*

PROOF. The dimension of the system of all Φ_{m-3} is (§III-4.1) at least

$$\frac{(m - 3)m}{2} - \Sigma \frac{(r_i - 1)r_i}{2} = p - 1.$$

Hence there is at least one such adjoint. Let a Φ_{m-3} intersect F in the cycle $Q \cdot + D$, and let a line L intersect F in the cycle A. Then $L^2\Phi_{m-3}$ is an adjoint of order $m - 1$ intersecting F in $Q + D + 2A$. Now referring to the situation in §5.2, f_y' is an adjoint of order $m - 1$ intersecting F in $J + D$. Hence $J + D \equiv Q + D + 2A$, and so

$$| Q | = | J - 2A | = K.$$

That the Φ_{m-3} cut out the complete series $| Q |$ follows from Theorem 6.3.

As a corollary we have

THEOREM 6.6. *The dimension of the canonical series is at least $p - 1$.*

The exceptional case $p = 0$ in Theorem 6.5 can be removed by a suitable interpretation. When $p = 0$ the canonical series is empty, since the differentials cut out only virtual cycles, of order -2. Also, there are no Φ_{m-3}, since the order of D, $2\delta = (m - 1)(m - 2) = m^2 - 3m + 2$, is greater than the number of intersections, $m(m - 3)$, of F with a curve of order $m - 3$. With the understanding, then, that both K and the set of Φ_{m-3} are vacuous for $p = 0$, Theorem 6.5 can be considered to hold in all cases. Theorem 6.6 is obviously true for $p = 0$.

It is evident that the canonical series could have been defined as the residue with respect to D of the series cut out by the adjoints of order $m - 3$. Based on this definition the theorems next to be proved establish the birational invariance of this series and of the related concept of the genus, independent of the developments of §5.

6.4. Special cycles. The number i of independent cycles of K which contain a given effective cycle A is called the *index of specialty* (or, for short, the *index*) of A. In other words, $i - 1$ is the dimension of $K - A$. A is said to be *special* if its index is greater than zero. If $A \equiv A'$ then $K - A \equiv K - A'$, and so the index of A equals the index of A'. Hence we can speak of the index of a linear series, meaning thereby the index of any of its cycles. In particular, the index of K is 1.

It is convenient to call an adjoint of order $m - 3$ a special adjoint. Every special series can be cut out by special adjoints.

The basic property of the index is expressed in the following theorem, often called the Reduction Theorem.

THEOREM 6.7. *For any effective cycle A and any place P at least one of the following equations holds:*

$$\dim |A + P| = \dim |A|,$$

$$\operatorname{index} |A + P| = \operatorname{index} |A|.$$

PROOF. By applying a quadratic transformation, if necessary, to our curve F, we may assume that the center of P is non-singular. Suppose that index $|A + P| \neq$ index $|A|$. Then there is a special adjoint Φ intersecting F in $A + B + D$, where $P \not\subseteq B$. Let L be a line intersecting F in $P + C$, where C is the sum of $m - 1$ places with distinct centers (Theorem III-2.6). Then $L\Phi$ is an adjoint of degree $m - 2$ intersecting F in $A + B + D + C + P$, and so $|A + P|$ is the residue with respect to $B + C + D$ of the series cut out by all adjoints of degree $m - 2$. But C consists of $m - 1$ collinear places, and so a Φ_{m-2} cutting out C must contain L as a factor, and so must contain P. That is, P is common to all cycles of $|A + P|$, and so $|A| = |A + P| - P$ has the same dimension as $|A + P|$.

6.5. Theorem of Riemann-Roch. We are now ready to prove the central theorem concerning linear series. We shall state it in two parts.

THEOREM 6.8. (Theorem of Riemann.) *If a complete g_n^r is not special, then $r = n - p$.*

PROOF. Suppose $r > n - p$. We proceed by induction on r. If $r = 0$, then $n \leqslant p - 1$. Since the dimension of K is $\geqslant p - 1 \geqslant n$, a cycle of K may be found containing any cycle of g_n^r, and so g_n^r is special. Now suppose the theorem true for all series of dimension $r - 1$. Let P be a place of F which is not a fixed place of g_n^r. Then $g_n^r - P = |A|$ is a g_{n-1}^{r-1}. Since by assumption $r > n - p$, we have $r - 1 > n - 1 - p$, and so by the assumption of the induction A is special. Since dim $|A + P| = r$ and dim $|A| = r - 1$, it follows from Theorem 6.7 that index $|A + P| = $ index $|A| > 0$. That is, $g_n^r = |A + P|$ is special.

By combining this theorem with Theorem 6.4 we obtain an alternate definition of the genus of a curve. For a complete g_n^r with $n > 2p - 2$ is certainly not special, and so $r = n - p$, or $p = n - r$. Since (Theorem 6.4) $p \geqslant n - r$ for any complete g_n^r, p can be defined as the minimum of $n - r$ for all complete series g_n^r.

THEOREM 6.9. (Theorem of Riemann-Roch.) *If i is the index of a complete g_n^r, then $r = n - p + i$.*

PROOF. Theorem 6.8 is the special case of this theorem for $i = 0$. We proceed by induction, assuming the theorem true for any $g_{n'}^{r'}$ of index $i - 1$. Let A be a cycle of g_n^r and P a place not a fixed place of $K - A$. Then index $|A + P| = i - 1$, and so by Theorem 6.7, $|A + P|$ is a g_{n+1}^r. Hence $r = n + 1 - p + i - 1 = n - p + i$.

The following corollaries of Theorem 6.9 indicate its importance.

THEOREM 6.10. *K is a g_{2p-2}^{p-1} and it is the only such series on F.*

PROOF. We have seen that the order of K is $2p - 2$ and its index is 1. Hence its dimension is $2p - 2 - p + 1 = p - 1$. Any g_{2p-2}^{p-1}, complete or not, has $p - 1 \leqslant 2p - 2 - p + i$, so that $i \geqslant 1$ and the series is special. Being therefore contained in K and having the same order and dimension it must coincide with K.

Since p is birationally invariant the invariance of K follows from this theorem independently of the considerations of §5.

THEOREM 6.11. *If $|A| = g_n^r$ is special, then A imposes exactly $n - r$ independent conditions on the cycles of K which contain it.*

PROOF. Since there are p independent cycles of K and i of them contain A, the number of independent conditions imposed is $p - i = n - r$.

The following theorem is in a sense the converse of the Reduction Theorem.

THEOREM 6.12. *For any effective cycle A and any place P at most one of the following equations holds.*

$$\dim |A + P| = \dim |A|,$$

$$\mathrm{index}\, |A + P| = \mathrm{index}\, |A|.$$

PROOF. Let $|A|$ be a g_n^r of index i, and $|A + P|$ a $g_{n+1}^{r'}$ of index i'. Then

$$r = n - p + i, \quad r' = n + 1 - p + i'.$$

These equations cannot both hold if $r = r'$ and $i = i'$.

THEOREM 6.13: (Reciprocity Theorem of Brill and Nöther.) *If the complete series g_n^r and $g_{n'}^{r'}$ are residual with respect to K (that is, $|g_n^r + g_{n'}^{r'}| = K$), then $n - 2r = n' - 2r'$.*

PROOF. We have $i = r' + 1$, $i' = r + 1$. Hence $r = n - p + i = n - p + r' + 1$, and similarly $r' = n' - p + r + 1$. The desired relation is obtained by subtracting the two equations.

THEOREM 6.14. (Clifford's Theorem.) *For a special g_n^r, $n \geqslant 2r$.*

PROOF. We may assume that g_n^r is complete, for if the inequality holds for a complete series it obviously holds for every sub-series. Let $g_n^r = |A|$ and let $|A + B| = K$. Let i and i' be the indices of $|A|$ and $|B|$. Since i independent cycles of K contain A and only one contains $A + B$, B must impose at least $i - 1$ independent conditions on the cycles of K containing it. That is, $p - i' \geqslant i - 1$. On substituting $i = r - n + p$ and $i' = r + 1$ in this inequality we obtain the desired result.

THEOREM 6.15. *K has no fixed places.*

PROOF. Suppose P is a fixed place of K and $A + P$ a cycle of K. Then $|A| = g_{2p-3}^{p-1}$, contradicting Theorem 6.14.

6.6. Exercises. 1. A normal curve of order n in a space of dimension r has genus at least $n - r$.

2. The conditions imposed on the curves of order $\geqslant m - 3$ by requiring that they be adjoints of a curve of order m are independent.

§7. CLASSIFICATION OF CURVES

7.1. Composite canonical series. We shall now proceed to investigate curves from the birational point of view. We shall classify them according to the behavior of the canonical series, find a normal form for each class, and discuss some of their properties.

The following lemma will be useful.

THEOREM 7.1. *If a curve carries a g_2^1 every special series with no fixed points is compounded of this g_2^1. Conversely, if K is composite the curve carries a g_2^1.*

PROOF. We need consider only the case $p > 2$. Then g_2^1 is complete and special, and so its cycles impose on the special adjoints containing them exactly $2 - 1 = 1$ condition (Theorem 6.11). That is, any special cycle containing a place P necessarily contains P', where $P + P' \in g_2^1$. This proves the first part of the theorem. Conversely, if K is composite, every special cycle containing P must contain some other point P'. Hence the cycle $P + P'$ imposes one condition on the adjoints containing it, and as above $| P + P' |$ is a g_2^1.

7.2. Classification. We consider first the case $p = 0$. Then K is empty, and so every cycle is non-special. Hence $r = n$ for every complete series. Conversely, if a curve carries a g_n^n for some $n > 0$ then the index of this series is p. But this is impossible for a series of positive order unless $p = 0$.

By Theorem III-3.2 (or §2.4, Exercise 4) every curve of genus zero is rational. Conversely, any rational curve is birationally equivalent to a line, and is of genus zero. Thus the three properties, rationality, genus zero, and existence of a g_n^n with $n > 0$, are all equivalent.

Now let $p = 1$. K is then g_0^0, and every cycle of positive order is non-special. Such a curve is called *elliptic**; its most important property is stated in

THEOREM 7.2. *An elliptic curve C carries an infinite number of non-equivalent g_2^1's. These can be put into one-to-one correspondence with the places of C.*

PROOF. Let P be a fixed place of C. If Q is any place of C, $| P + Q |$ is a g_2^1. If $Q' \neq Q$ then $| P + Q | \neq | P + Q' |$, for $Q \equiv Q'$ would imply the existence of a g_1^1, which is impossible. Since any g_2^1 of C must have a cycle containing P, the set of g_2^1's obtained by making all choices of Q is exhaustive. This proves the theorem.

The curves with $p > 1$ are divided into two classes, those with a composite canonical series being called *hyperelliptic*. From Theorem 7.1 we see that a hyperelliptic curve contains a unique g_2^1 of which its canonical series is compounded; a non-hyperelliptic curve does not contain any g_2^1.

7.3. Canonical forms. We have made considerable use of the fact that any irreducible curve is birationally equivalent to a curve of some special type, in particular to a plane curve with ordinary singularities. The following theorem gives us more specific information of this kind.

---

* An unfortunate term, since an ellipse is not elliptic! The elliptic curve gets its name from its connection with elliptic functions.

THEOREM 7.3. (i) *A curve of genus zero is birationally equivalent to a line.*

(ii) *An elliptic curve is birationally equivalent to a non-singular plane cubic.*

(iii) *A hyperelliptic curve of genus p is birationally equivalent to a plane curve of order $p + 2$ having just one singular point, of multiplicity p.*

(iv) *A non-hyperelliptic curve of genus $p > 2$ is birationally equivalent to a projectively unique, normal, non-singular curve of order $2p - 2$ in S_{p-1}.*

PROOF. (i) This has already been shown.

(ii) A complete g_3 on an elliptic curve is of dimension 2, and is simple since its order is a prime. The corresponding rational transformation is therefore birational and transforms the curve into a plane cubic. A plane cubic of genus 1 is necessarily non-singular.

(iii) Let A be a cycle of order $p + 2$, no two places of A forming a cycle of g_2^1. Then A is not special, and so $| A | = g_{p+2}^2$. Suppose that g_{p+2}^2 is composite. Then if P is a place of A, $| A - P |$ has a fixed cycle Q of positive order, and so $| A - P - Q |$ is a g_k^1 with $k \leqslant p$. Such a g_k^1 is necessarily special, and so by Theorem 7.1, $A - P - Q$, and hence A, must contain a cycle of g_2^1, contrary to assumption. Hence g_{p+2}^2 is simple. In the same way we can prove that g_{p+2}^2 has no fixed places. The corresponding birational transformation therefore takes our curve into a plane curve F of order $p + 2$. Since $p < (p + 1)p/2$ for $p \geqslant 2$ this curve necessarily has singularities. Consider the g_{p+2-r}^1 cut out by the lines on a point a of multiplicity $r > 1$. This series is complete, for it is the residue of g_{p+2}^2 with respect to the cycle $\Sigma n_\alpha P_\alpha$, where P_α is a place of order n_α with center a. Furthermore g_{p+2-r}^1 is special and has no fixed points, and so is compounded of g_2^1. The index of g_{p+2-r}^1 is therefore $p - (p + 2 - r)/2$, for each cycle of g_2^1 imposes just one condition on the cycles of K containing it, and the conditions are independent for any set of at most p cycles of g_2^1. Hence $1 = p + 2 - r - p + p - (p + 2 - r)/2$, which gives $r = p$. Finally $p = (p + 1) \cdot p/2 - p(p - 1)/2$, and so a can have no singularities in its neighborhood (Theorem III-7.5), nor can there be any singularities distinct from a.

(iv) Since $K = g_{2p-2}^{p-1}$ is complete and simple and has no fixed points it determines a birational transformation of the curve into a normal curve C of order $2p - 2$ in S_{p-1}. To show that C is non-singular we need to prove that $| K - P |$ has no fixed place for any P. If $| K - P |$ had a fixed place Q the argument used in Theorem 7.1 would show that $| P + Q | = g_2^1$, and the curve would be hyperelliptic. Since K is the only g_{2p-2}^{p-1}, the curve C is projectively unique. C is called a *canonical curve*.

The following theorem complements parts (iii) and (iv) of Theorem 7.3.

THEOREM 7.4. *For any $p \geqslant 3$ there exist both hyperelliptic and non-hyperelliptic curves of genus p. There exist curves, necessarily hyperelliptic, of genus 2.*

PROOF. For the hyperelliptic case we need merely show the existence of a plane curve of order $p + 2$ with one ordinary p-fold point. Such a curve is $f(x)y^2 + g(x) = 0$, where f and g are polynomials of degrees p and $p + 2$ and the roots of $fg = 0$ are all distinct. For the non-hyperelliptic curves we consider two cases. If p is odd, $p = 2k + 1 \geqslant 3$, the curve $fy^3 - g = 0$, where f and g are of orders k and $k + 3$ and $fg = 0$ has no double roots, has a single k-fold point a and is of genus p. (If $k = 1$ the curve is a non-singular quartic.) The special adjoints are curves of order k having a as a $(k - 1)$-fold point. Such curves include the curves consisting of $k - 1$ lines through a and another arbitrary line. Such a composite curve can obviously be chosen to contain a given point P and avoid any other given point P'. Hence K is not composite. If p is even, $p = 2k$, the curve $fy^3 - g = 0$, of order $k + 3$ as above but with $g = 0$ having one double root, the roots of $fg = 0$ being otherwise distinct, has a k-fold point and a double point, and is of genus p. The above argument can again be applied to show that this curve is not hyperelliptic.

7.4. Exercises. 1. If two non-singular plane quartics are birationally equivalent they are projectively equivalent.

2. A curve with a complete g_n^{n-1}, $n \geqslant 3$, is elliptic.

3. Each g_2^1 on an elliptic cubic is cut out by a pencil of lines whose base point is on the curve.

4. If the equality holds in Clifford's Theorem then either g_n^r is the canonical series or the curve is hyperelliptic.

5. Each cycle of a special g_n^r on a canonical curve lies on an S_{n-r-1}.

6. A hyperelliptic curve of genus p is birationally equivalent to a curve $y^2 = h(x)$, where h is a polynomial of degree $2p + 2$ with distinct roots.

§8. POLES OF RATIONAL FUNCTIONS

The close relationship existing between linear series and rational functions is indicated by the developments of §2. As a matter of fact, the properties of linear series can all be stated and proved directly in terms of properties of rational functions. Conversely, the theorems about linear series can be interpreted so as to give information about rational functions. We shall consider one particularly important theorem that is easily proved in this way.

If ϕ is a rational function intersecting the curve in $A - B$, where A and B are effective cycles having no common place, A is called the set of *zeros* of ϕ and B the set of *poles* of ϕ. We shall focus our attention on the set of poles.

Obviously every rational function (except zero) has a set of poles. Conversely, however, not every cycle can be the set of poles of some rational function. The following theorem gives us information regarding this situation.

THEOREM 8.1. *An effective cycle A is the set of poles of some rational function if and only if $| A |$ has no fixed places.*

PROOF. If A is the set of poles of ϕ then ϕ intersects the curve in $B - A$, where B, the set of zeros of ϕ, is effective and has no places in common with A. Since $B \equiv A$, $| A |$ contains both A and B, and hence has no fixed places. Conversely, let $| A |$ have no fixed places. We show first that there is $B \equiv A$ such that B and A have no common place. If $A = \Sigma n_\alpha P_\alpha$, then by assumption there is an $A_\alpha \equiv A$ such that A_α does not contain P_α. If G_α cuts out A_α, then $G' = \Sigma \lambda_\alpha G_\alpha$ cuts out a cycle B containing P_α only if the λ_α satisfy a certain linear condition. Choosing λ_α which satisfy none of these conditions, we obtain B of the desired type. The argument in the first part of the proof can now be reversed.

As a corollary we have

THEOREM 8.2. *The only curves on which every effective cycle is the set of poles of a rational function are the rational curves. In particular, these are the only curves on which a single place can be a set of poles.*

The following theorem is an application of Theorems 6.12 and 8.1.

THEOREM 8.3. *Let $A_N = P_1 + \cdots + P_N$ be a non-special cycle, the P_i being places not necessarily distinct, and define $A_0 = 0$, $A_n = P_1 + \cdots + P_n$. Then there exist $k \geqslant p$ values of n for which A_n is not the set of poles of a rational function, and the P_i can be so numbered that $k = p$.*

PROOF. Let the index of $| A_n |$ be i_n; then $i_0 = p$, $i_N = 0$. By Theorems 6.7 and 6.12

$$i_n = i_{n-1} \quad \text{if dim } | A_{n-1} | < \text{dim } | A_n |,$$

$$i_n = i_{n-1} - 1 \text{ if dim } | A_{n-1} | = \text{dim } | A_n |.$$

Hence there exist precisely p values of n for which dim $| A_{n-1} | = $ dim $| A_n |$; that is, for which P_n is fixed in $| A_n |$. From Theorem 8.1 it follows that $k \geqslant p$. To prove the last part of the theorem we merely renumber the P_i as follows. Let n_1 be the largest value of n for which $| A_n |$ has a fixed place. Renumber the places of A_{n_1} so that P_{n_1} is such a fixed place. Proceeding according to the new numbering, let n_2 be the largest value of n less than n_1 for which A_n has a fixed place, and renumber the places of A_{n_2} so that P_{n_2} is fixed. By continuing this process we eventually obtain an arrangement of the P's such that whenever $|A_n|$ has a fixed place P_n is fixed. From the preceding argument it then follows that $k = p$.

The following special case of Theorem 8.3 is known as the Weierstrass Gap Theorem:

THEOREM 8.4. *For any given place P of a curve of genus p there exist precisely p values of n, all $\leqslant 2p - 2$, for which nP is not the set of poles of a rational function.*

§9. GEOMETRY ON A NON-SINGULAR CUBIC

9.1. Addition of points on a cubic. Let F be a non-singular plane cubic. F is of class six and genus one, and has nine flexes. The canonical series is a g_0^0, and every complete series is a g_n^{n-1}; in particular there is a g_2^1 and no g_1^1. Since each point is the center of precisely one place, we shall use the words "point" and "place" more or less interchangeably.

To facilitate our considerations we shall define an addition of points of F. Let O be a flex of F. If A and B are points of F let the line AB (the tangent at A if $B = A$) intersect F in the residual point C_1, and let the line C_1O intersect F in the residual point C. We define $A + B = C$. The manipulation of this operation of addition will be simplified by expressing it in terms of equivalence of cycles. We have $A + B + C_1 \equiv C + O + C_1$. Hence $C \equiv A + B - O$. This equivalence defines C uniquely, for if $C' \equiv A + B - O$, then $C' \equiv C$ and so $C' = C$, since otherwise we would have a g_1^1 on F.

THEOREM 9.1. *With respect to addition the points of F form a commutative group with O as the zero element.*

PROOF. That $A + B = C$ implies $B + A = C$ follows immediately from the definition. To prove the associative law, let $A + B = X$, $X + C = Z$, $B + C = Y$, $A + Y = Z'$. These are equivalent to,

$$X \equiv A + B - O, \quad Z \equiv X + C - O \equiv A + B + C - 2O,$$

$$Y \equiv B + C - O, \quad Z' \equiv A + Y - O \equiv A + B + C - 2O.$$

Hence $Z' \equiv Z$, and so, as above, $Z' = Z$. Hence $(A + B) + C$ is the same point as $A + (B + C)$. If $A + O = B$, then $B \equiv A + O - O \equiv A$, and so $B = A$; that is, O is the zero element. Finally, if A' is the residual intersection of the line AO with F we readily verify that $A + A' = O$, and so A' is the negative of A. We write, as usual, $-A$ for A'.

$C = A_1 + A_2 + \cdots + A_n$ is now uniquely defined. As above, we see that this relation is the same as $A_1 + A_2 + \cdots + A_n \equiv C + (n - 1)O$.

THEOREM 9.2. *A cycle* $A_1 + \cdots + A_{3n}$ *is the intersection of F with a curve of order n if and only if $A_1 + \cdots + A_{3n} = O$.*

PROOF. $A_1 + \cdots + A_{3n} = O$ if and only if $A_1 + \cdots + A_{3n} \equiv 3nO$. Now $3nO$ is the intersection of F with a curve of order n, namely the nth power of the tangent at O. Since the system of all curves of order n intersects F in a complete series, the required conclusion follows.

9.2. Tangents. Since F is of class six, and the tangent at O accounts for three of the tangents through this point, there are three other tangents to F passing through O. These are obviously distinct, and so touch F at distinct points O_1, O_2, O_3. From Theorem 9.2 it follows that $2O_i = O$, or $O_i = -O_i$; also that the O_i and O are the only points having

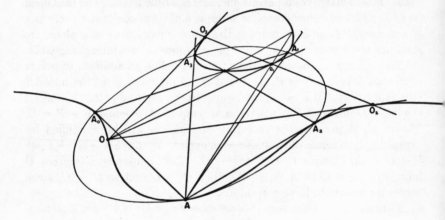

Figure 9.1

this property. However, $O' = O_1 + O_2$ has this property, and since $O_1 + O_2 \neq O$, we must have $O_1 + O_2 = O_3$, or $O_1 + O_2 + O_3 = O$. The three points are therefore collinear.

If A is any point of F there are four distinct tangents to F passing through A other than the tangent at A (if A is a flex the tangent at A is counted as one of the four). Let their points of tangency be A_0, A_1, A_2, A_3. Then $2A_i = -A$, and the A_i are the only points with this property. Now $A_0 + O_i, i = 1, 2, 3$, have this property, and so by proper numbering we have $A_i = A_0 + O_i, i = 1, 2, 3$. Then

$$A_0 + A_1 + A_2 + A_3 = 4A_0 + O_1 + O_2 + O_3 = -2A,$$

or

$$A_0 + A_1 + A_2 + A_3 + 2A = O.$$

Hence we have

THEOREM 9.3. *The points of contact of the four tangents to F from any of its points A lie on a conic tangent to F at A.* (Figure 9.1.)

Other properties of the points A_i follow readily from their relation to the O_i. We have, for example,

THEOREM 9.4. *The lines A_iA_j and A_kA_l, i,j,k,l all different, meet on F.*

PROOF.

$$A_0 + A_1 = 2A_0 + O_1, \quad A_2 + A_3 = 2A_0 + O_2 + O_3 = 2A_0 + O_1.$$

Hence A_0A_1 and A_2A_3 meet at the point $-(2A_0 + O_1) = A + O_1$. (Figure 9.1.) Similarly, A_0A_i and A_jA_k meet at $A + O_i$.

The flexes of F are solutions of the equation $3X = O$. If A and B are solutions of this, so is $-(A + B)$; hence we again have our familiar theorem that the line joining two flexes passes through a third. Let $U \neq O$ be a solution of the equation, and V a solution neither O, U, nor $-U$. Then the nine solutions are

$$\begin{array}{ccc}
O & U & -U \\
V & V + U & V - U \\
-V & -V + U & -V - U
\end{array}$$

The sextatic points of F are the centers of places at which a non-singular conic can have order 6. They are therefore the roots of $6Y = O$. Now if X satisfies $3X = O$, then the Y's defined by $2Y = -X$ satisfy $6Y = O$. Hence *the sextatic points of F are the contacts of the tangents from the flexes of F.* There are therefore 27 sextatic points.

9.3. The cross-ratio. The set of four tangents from any point of F has an important property which serves to characterize the curve. To discover this property we first consider the pencils of lines on two points A and B of F. (Figure 9.2.) Let C be one of the four points determined by $2C = A + B$, and for any point A_i define B_i by $B_i = -A_i - C$. Now if a line a through A cuts F in $A_1 + A_2$, we have $A_1 + A_2 + A = O$. Then

$$\begin{aligned}
B_1 + B_2 + B &= -A_1 - C - A_2 - C + B \\
&= -A_1 - A_2 + B - A - B \\
&= -A_1 - A_2 - A = O.
\end{aligned}$$

Hence $B_1 + B_2$ are on a line b through B. We thus obtain a one-to-one correspondence between the lines on A and on B. Since $A_1 = A_2$ obviously implies $B_1 = B_2$, and conversely, the tangents from A correspond to the tangents from B.

We next show that this one-to-one correspondence is a projectivity.

Let the corresponding lines a' and b' on A and B cut F in $A_1' + A_2'$ and $B_1' + B_2'$ respectively, and designate the lines CA_1B_1, CA_2B_2, $CA_1'B_1'$, CA_iB_i by c_1, c_2, c_1', c_2'. Then $abc_1'c_2'$ and $a'b'c_1c_2$ are quartics intersecting F in the same cycle

$$A_1 + A_2 + A_1' + A_2' + B_1 + B_2 + B_1' + B_2' + 2C.$$

Hence by Theorem 1.1 there is a linear combination of these quartics containing F as a factor. Since each of the quartics has C as a double point and contains the points X, Y of intersection of a and b', a' and b,

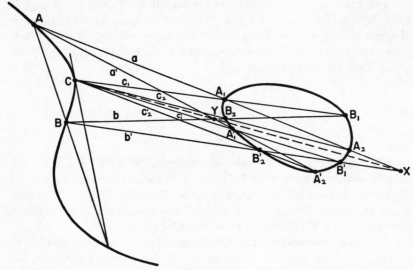

Figure 9.2

the composite curve must also have these properties. This requires that X, Y, C be collinear, and therefore the pencils of lines on A and B are projective, C being the center of homology. (See Veblen and Young, *Projective Geometry*, Vol. I, p. 104.)

We therefore have the following important result:

THEOREM 9.5. *The four tangents to a non-singular cubic from any of its points have a cross-ratio (or, more precisely, a set of six cross-ratios) which is independent of the point.*

This cross ratio is therefore associated with the cubic itself. Its importance is indicated by the following theorem.

THEOREM 9.6. (Salmon's Theorem.) *Two non-singular cubics have the same cross-ratio if and only if they are birationally equivalent.*

PROOF. To see that the cross-ratio is birationally invariant consider the g_2^1 cut out by the pencil of lines on a point A of the cubic. There is a projective correspondence between the lines of the pencil and the cycles of g_2^1, and the tangents from A correspond to the double points of g_2^1, that is, to the cycles of g_2^1 of the form $2P$. Hence the cross-ratio of the cubic is the cross-ratio of the four double points of any of its g_2^1's, and hence is birationally invariant. To prove the sufficiency of the condition we make use of the fact that any non-singular cubic is reducible to the form $y^2 = f(x)$ by a suitable choice of coordinates (Theorem III-6.1). Here the infinite point on the y-axis is a flex, and the four tangents from this point are the flex tangent, which is the line at infinity, and the lines $x = a_i$, where a_1, a_2, a_3 are the roots of $f(x) = 0$. Hence the cross-ratio of the cubic is the cross-ratio $(\infty, a_1; a_2, a_3)$. Now if $y = g(x)$ has the same cross-ratio $(\infty, b_1; b_2, b_3)$ there is a projective transformation taking ∞, b_1, b_2, b_3 into ∞, a_1, a_2, a_3. The two curves then have identical equations, and so the original cubics are actually projectively equivalent, hence also birationally equivalent.

Since every elliptic curve is birationally equivalent to a plane cubic, we see that the cross-ratio is defined for every elliptic curve and serves as means of separating these curves into their birationally equivalent classes.

9.4. Transformations into itself. With any point A of our cubic F we associate the transformation T_A which takes any point P into $A + P$. This transformation is rational, for the algebra involved in passing from P to $A + P$ consists in finding the third root of a cubic equation when the other two roots are known, and this is a rational operation. Since the inverse transformation is T_{-A}, which is also rational, T_A is a birational transformation of F into itself. The set of all such transformations obviously forms a commutative group, for

$$T_A T_B = T_{A+B} = T_B T_A, \quad (T_A T_B) T_C = T_{A+B+C} = T_A(T_B T_C),$$

$$T_O T_A = T_A, \quad T_A T_{-A} = T_O.$$

Similarly, the transformation S_A taking P into $A - P$ is birational. These do not form a group, but the set of all T_A and S_A do, for

$$S_A S_B = T_{A-B}, \quad S_A T_B = S_{A-B}, \quad T_A S_B = S_{A+B},$$

and the group properties are easily checked. This group G is not commutative, for $S_A T_B \neq T_B S_A$ unless $B = O$ or O_i.

The transformation S_A has a very simple geometric interpretation. For if $P' = A - P$ then $P' + P - A = O$, and so $P' + P$ is a cycle of the g_2^1 cut out by lines on $-A$. S_A merely interchanges the points of each cycle of g_2^1.

We shall now show that with two exceptional classes a non-singular cubic has no birational transformations into itself other than the T_A and the S_A. We first prove a similar theorem for rational curves.

THEOREM 9.7. *The only birational transformations of a rational curve into itself are those determined by a linear fractional transformation on a basic element of the field Σ.*

PROOF. If $\Sigma = K(\lambda)$, a rational transformation associates with λ an element $\mu = \phi(\lambda)$ of Σ. If the transformation is birational we must also have $\lambda = \psi(\mu)$. Let

$$\phi(\lambda) = \frac{a_0 + a_1\lambda + \cdots + a_r\lambda^r}{b_0 + b_1\lambda + \cdots + b_r\lambda^r}$$

be an expression for $\phi(\lambda)$ with the least possible value of r. Then

$$(a_0 + b_0\mu) + (a_1 + b_1\mu)\lambda + \cdots + (a_r + b_r\mu)\lambda^r = 0,$$

is irreducible, and so λ is of index r over $K(\mu)$. But $\lambda \in K(\mu)$, and so $r = 1$, which proves the theorem.

As a particular case of this theorem we have that every birational transformation of a line into itself is a projective transformation.

We now return to our cubic curve F. Let T be any birational transformation of F into itself, and consider first the case in which T has O for a fixed point. Let g_2^1 be cut out by the lines on the point O. Then O is a double point of g_2^1. Now T, being birational, transforms g_2^1 into a $g_2'^1$, and hence the double points of g_2^1 go into the double points of $g_2'^1$. But the double points of distinct g_2^1's are distinct, being contacts of tangents from different points of F. Hence $g_2'^1 = g_2^1$, that is, T transforms a cycle of g_2^1 into a cycle of g_2^1.

Let L be a line not on O and let λ be the coordinate of a point P_λ of L. The line $P_\lambda O$ cuts out a cycle C of g_2^1, the transform of C by T is a cycle C' of g_2^1, and C' lies on a line through O intersecting L in a point P_μ. Thus we have a single-valued transformation $\lambda \to \mu$ on L. This transformation is algebraic (§V-6.4), since the passage from the points of C to P_λ is a rational transformation T', and the passage from the points of C to P_μ is the rational transformation $T'T$. Hence by Theorem V-6.5 the transformation $\lambda \to \mu$ is rational. Since the inverse transformation can be treated in the same manner, the transformation is birational, and so by Theorem 9.7 it is a projectivity. But this projectivity π has a fixed point Q, the transform of O by T'; and the points Q_1, Q_2, Q_3, which are the transforms by T' of O_1, O_2, O_3, the other double points of g_2^1, are permuted among themselves by π. If π takes Q_i into $Q_{i'}$ then the cross-ratios $(Q, Q_1; Q_2, Q_3)$ and $(Q, Q_{1'}; Q_{2'}, Q_{3'})$ are equal. There are then three cases.

(i) The six cross-ratios of the four points are distinct. Then $(Q,Q_1; Q_2,Q_3) = Q,Q_{1'}; Q_{2'},Q_{3'})$ implies $Q_{i'} = Q_i$, and π is the identity. It follows that T transforms each cycle of g_2^1 into itself. For any given one of these cycles, T must therefore either interchange the two points or leave them both fixed. If for some cycle, not a double point of course, it leaves the points fixed, then these fixed points determine another $g_2'^1$ with the same properties as g_2^1. But this obviously cannot be the case unless every point of F is fixed, in which case T is the identity transformation T_O. Hence the only other possibility is for T to interchange the points of each cycle of g_2^1, in which case we have $T = S_O$.

(ii) There are only three distinct cross-ratios, $-1, 2, \frac{1}{2}$. The cubic is then said to be *harmonic*. We have $(Q,Q_1; Q_2,Q_3) = (Q,Q_1; Q_3,Q_2)$, and this is the only possible permutation of the Q's. That such a transformation can exist is seen by taking the equation of the curve in the form $y^2 = x(x^2 - 1)$ with O as the infinite point on the y-axis. Then $x' = -x, y' = iy$, where i satisfies $i^2 + 1 = 0$, is such a transformation. Call this transformation U. We see at once that $U^2 = S_O$. Now if T is any transformation interchanging Q_2 and Q_3 then UT leaves them fixed, and so $UT = T_O$ or S_O; that is, $T = S_OU$ or $T = U$.

(iii) There are only two distinct cross-ratios, $-\omega$, $-\omega^2$, where $\omega^2 + \omega + 1 = 0$. The cubic is called *equianharmonic*. In this case Q_1,Q_2,Q_3 can be permuted cyclically. Taking the curve in the form $y^2 = x^3 - 1$ we have the transformation V defined by $x' = \omega x, y' = y$, with $V^3 = T_O$, and $S_OV = VS_O$. Arguing as in (ii) we see that any transformation T giving a cyclic permutation to the Q's has one of the forms V, V^2, S_OV, S_OV^2.

Now let T be any birational transformation whatever of F into itself. Let T transform O into A. Then S_AT has O as a fixed point, and so is of one of the forms determined above. We can therefore state our complete results in the following form:

THEOREM 9.8. (i) *The birational transformations of an elliptic curve, which is not harmonic or equianharmonic, into itself form the group G with elements S_A, T_A.*

(ii) *The birational transformations of a harmonic elliptic curve into itself are of the form T or TU, where T is an element of G, and $U^2 = S_O$.*

(iii) *The birational transformations of an equianharmonic elliptic curve into itself are of the form T, TV, TV^2, where T is an element of G and $V^3 = T_O$.*

The further investigation of cases (ii) and (iii), in particular, the geometric properties of the transformations, we leave to the reader.

9.5. Exercises. 1. A *tritangent conic* to F is a conic intersecting F in a cycle of the form $2A + 2B + 2C$. Show that any pair of points of

F are two of the three contact points of each of four distinct tritangent conics, and give a construction for the four positions of the remaining contact points.

2. For any point A of F there are nine distinct points B such that there exists a conic intersecting F in the cycle $3A + 3B$.

3. Generalize Exercises 1 and 2 as much as you can.

4. The transformation $P \rightarrow 2P$ is a rational transformation of F into itself. The corresponding series is a g_{12}^2 compounded of an irrational γ_4. g_{12}^2 can be cut out by a system of quartics.

5. The g_2^1 of a hyperelliptic curve of genus p has $2p + 2$ double points, and two such curves are birationally equivalent if and only if the sets of double points of their g_2^1's are projectively equivalent.

6. In case (ii) of Theorem 9.8 we have

$$US_A = S_{UA}U, \quad UT_A = T_{UA}U,$$

$$(S_A U)^4 = (T_A U)^4 = T_O.$$

In case (iii) we have,

$$VS_A = S_{VA}V, \quad VT_A = T_{VA}V,$$

$$(S_A V)^6 = (S_A V^2)^6 = (T_A V)^3 = (T_A V^2)^3 = T_O.$$

7. Each transformation $S_A U$, $T_A U$ has two fixed points. $S_A V$ and $S_A V^2$ each have one fixed point, and $T_A V$ and $T_A V^2$ each have three.

Index

References are to pages. Definitions are indicated by italics.

CATALOG OF DOVER BOOKS

TEACH YOURSELF books. For adult self-study, for refresher and supplementary study.

The most effective series of home study mathematics books on the market! With absolutely no outside help, they will teach you as much as any similar college or high-school course, or will helpfully supplement any such course. Each step leads directly to the next, each question is anticipated. Numerous lucid examples and carefully-wrought practice problems illustrate meanings. Not skimpy outlines, not surveys, not usual classroom texts, these 204- to 380-page books are packed with the finest instruction you'll find anywhere for adult self-study.

TEACH YOURSELF ALGEBRA, P. Abbott. Formulas, coordinates, factors, graphs of quadratic functions, quadratic equations, logarithms, ratio, irrational numbers, arithmetical, geometrical series, much more. 1241 problems, solutions. Tables. 52 illus. 307pp. 6⅞ x 4¼.
Clothbound **$2.00**

TEACH YOURSELF GEOMETRY, P. Abbott. Solids, lines, points, surfaces, angle measurement, triangles, theorem of Pythagoras, polygons, loci, the circle, tangents, symmetry, solid geometry, prisms, pyramids, solids of revolution, etc. 343 problems, solutions. 268 illus. 334pp. 6⅞ x 4¼.
Clothbound **$2.00**

TEACH YOURSELF TRIGONOMETRY, P. Abbott. Geometrical foundations, indices, logarithms, trigonometrical ratios, relations between sides, angles of triangle, circular measure, trig. ratios of angles of any magnitude, much more. Requires elementary algebra, geometry. 465 problems, solutions. Tables. 102 illus. 204pp. 6⅞ x 4¼.
Clothbound **$2.00**

TEACH YOURSELF THE CALCULUS, P. Abbott. Variations in functions, differentiation, solids of revolution, series, elementary differential equations, areas by integral calculus, much more. Requires algebra, trigonometry. 970 problems, solutions. Tables. 89 illus. 380pp. 6⅞ x 4¼.
Clothbound **$2.00**

TEACH YOURSELF THE SLIDE RULE, B. Snodgrass. Fractions, decimals, A-D scales, log-log scales, trigonometrical scales, indices, logarithms. Commercial, precision, electrical, dualistic, Brighton rules. 80 problems, solutions. 10 illus. 207pp. 6⅞ x 4¼. Clothbound **$2.00**

See also: **TEACH YOURSELF ELECTRICITY, C. W. Wilman; TEACH YOURSELF HEAT ENGINES, E. De Ville; TEACH YOURSELF MECHANICS, P. Abbott.**

HOW DO YOU USE A SLIDE RULE? by A. A. Merrill. Not a manual for mathematicians and engineers, but a lucid step-by-step explanation that presents the fundamental rules clearly enough to be understood by anyone who could benefit by the use of a slide rule in his work or business. This work concentrates on the 2 most important operations: multiplication and division. 10 easy lessons, each with a clear drawing, will save you countless hours in your banking, business, statistical, and other work. First publication. Index. 2 Appendixes. 10 illustrations. 78 problems, all with answers. vi + 36pp. 6⅛ x 9¼. T62 Paperbound 60¢

THEORY OF OPERATION OF THE SLIDE RULE, J. P. Ellis. Not a skimpy "instruction manual", but an exhaustive treatment that will save you uncounted hours throughout your career. Supplies full understanding of every scale on the Log Log Duplex Decitrig type of slide rule. Shows the most time-saving methods, and provides practice useful in the widest variety of actual engineering situations. Each operation introduced in terms of underlying logarithmic theory. Summary of prerequisite math. First publication. Index. 198 figures. Over 450 problems with answers. Bibliography. 12 Appendices. ix + 289pp. 5⅜ x 8.
S727 Paperbound **$1.50**

ARITHMETICAL EXCURSIONS: AN ENRICHMENT OF ELEMENTARY MATHEMATICS, H. Bowers and J. Bowers. For students who want unusual methods of arithmetic never taught in school; for adults who want to increase their number sense. Little known facts about the most simple numbers, arithmetical entertainments and puzzles, figurate numbers, number chains, mysteries and folklore of numbers, the "Hin-dog-abic" number system, etc. First publication. Index. 529 numbered problems and diversions, all with answers. Bibliography. 50 figures. xiv + 320pp. 5⅜ x 8. T770 Paperbound **$1.65**

APPLIED MATHEMATICS FOR RADIO AND COMMUNICATIONS ENGINEERS, C. E. Smith. No extraneous material here!—only the theories, equations, and operations essential and immediately useful for radio work. Can be used as refresher, as handbook of applications and tables, or as full home-study course. Ranges from simplest arithmetic through calculus, series, and wave forms, hyperbolic trigonometry, simultaneous equations in mesh circuits, etc. Supplies applications right along with each math topic discussed. 22 useful tables of functions, formulas, logs, etc. Index. 166 exercises, 140 examples, all with answers. 95 diagrams. Bibliography. x + 336pp. 5⅜ x 8. S141 Paperbound **$1.75**

FAMOUS PROBLEMS OF ELEMENTARY GEOMETRY, Felix Klein. Expanded version of the 1894 Easter lectures at Göttingen. 3 problems of classical geometry, in an excellent mathematical treatment by a famous mathematician: squaring the circle, trisecting angle, doubling cube. Considered with full modern implications: transcendental numbers, pi, etc. Notes by R. Archibald. 16 figures. xi + 92pp. 5⅜ x 8.　　　　　　　　　　T348 Clothbound **$1.50**
　　　　　　　　　　　　　　　　　　　　　　　　　　　T298 Paperbound **$1.00**

✱　　　　　✱　　　　　✱

ELEMENTARY MATHEMATICS FROM AN ADVANCED STANDPOINT, Felix Klein.

This classic text is an outgrowth of Klein's famous integration and survey course at Göttingen. Using one field of mathematics to interpret, adjust, illuminate another, it covers basic topics in each area, illustrating its discussion with extensive analysis. It is especially valuable in considering areas of modern mathematics. "Makes the reader feel the inspiration of . . . a great mathematician, inspiring teacher . . . with deep insight into the foundations and interrelations," BULLETIN, AMERICAN MATHEMATICAL SOCIETY.

Vol. 1. ARITHMETIC, ALGEBRA, ANALYSIS. Introducing the concept of function immediately, it enlivens abstract discussion with graphical and geometrically perceptual methods. Partial contents: natural numbers, extension of the notion of number, special properties, complex numbers. Real equations with real unknowns, complex quantities. Logarithmic, exponential functions, goniometric functions, infinitesimal calculus. Transcendence of e and pi, theory of assemblages. Index. 125 figures. ix + 274pp . 5⅜ x 8.　　　S150 Paperbound **$1.75**

Vol. 2. GEOMETRY. A comprehensive view which accompanies the space perception inherent in geometry with analytic formulas which facilitate precise formulation. Partial contents: Simplest geometric manifolds: line segment, Grassmann determinant principles, classification of configurations of space, derivative manifolds. Geometric transformations: affine transformations, projective, higher point transformations, theory of the imaginary. Systematic discussion of geometry and its foundations. Indexes. 141 illustrations. ix + 214pp. 5⅜ x 8.
　　　　　　　　　　　　　　　　　　　　　　　　　　　S151 Paperbound **$1.75**

✱　　　　✱　　　　✱

COORDINATE GEOMETRY, L. P. Eisenhart. Thorough, unified introduction. Unusual for advancing in dimension within each topic (treats together circle, sphere; polar coordinates, 3-dimensional coordinate systems; conic sections, quadric surfaces), affording exceptional insight into subject. Extensive use made of determinants, though no previous knowledge of them is assumed. Algebraic equations of 1st degree, 2 and 3 unknowns, carried further than usual in algebra courses. Over 500 exercises. Introduction. Appendix. Index. Bibliography. 43 illustrations. 310pp. 5⅜ x 8.　　　　　　　　S600 Paperbound **$1.65**

MONOGRAPHS ON TOPICS OF MODERN MATHEMATICS, edited by **J. W. A. Young.** Advanced mathematics for persons who haven't gone beyond or have forgotten high school algebra. 9 monographs on foundation of geometry, modern pure geometry, non-Euclidean geometry, fundamental propositions of algebra, algebraic equations, functions, calculus, theory of numbers, etc. Each monograph gives proofs of important results, and descriptions of leading methods, to provide wide coverage. New introduction by Prof. M. Kline, N. Y. University. 100 diagrams. xvi + 416pp. 6⅛ x 9¼.　　　　　　　　S289 Paperbound **$2.00**

MATHEMATICS, INTERMEDIATE TO ADVANCED

Geometry

THE FOUNDATIONS OF EUCLIDEAN GEOMETRY, H. G. Forder. The first rigorous account of Euclidean geometry, establishing propositions without recourse to empiricism, and without multiplying hypotheses. Corrects many traditional weaknesses of Euclidean proofs, and investigates the problems imposed on the axiom system by the discoveries of Bolya and Lobatchefsky. Some topics discussed are Classes and Relations; Axioms for Magnitudes; Congruence and Similarity; Algebra of Points; Hessenberg's Theorem; Continuity; Existence of Parallels; Reflections; Rotations; Isometries; etc. Invaluable for the light it throws on foundations of math. Lists: Axioms employed, Symbols, Constructions. 295pp. 5⅜ x 8.
　　　　　　　　　　　　　　　　　　　　　　　　　　　S481 Paperbound **$2.00**

ADVANCED EUCLIDEAN GEOMETRY, R. A. Johnson. For years the standard textbook on advanced Euclidean geometry, requires only high school geometry and trigonometry. Explores in unusual detail and gives proofs of hundreds of relatively recent theorems and corollaries, many formerly available only in widely scattered journals. Covers tangent circles, the theorem of Miquel, symmedian point, pedal triangles and circles, the Brocard configuration, and much more. Formerly "Modern Geometry." Index. 107 diagrams. xiii + 319pp. 5⅜ x 8.
　　　　　　　　　　　　　　　　　　　　　　　　　　　S669 Paperbound **$1.65**

THE THIRTEEN BOOKS OF EUCLID'S ELEMENTS, edited by **Sir Thomas Heath.** Definitive edition of one of the very greatest classics of Western world. Complete English translation of Heiberg text, together with spurious Book XIV. Detailed 150-page introduction discussing aspects of Greek and Medieval mathematics. Euclid, texts, commentators, etc. Paralleling the text is an elaborate critical apparatus analyzing each definition, proposition, postulate, covering textual matters, mathematical analysis, commentators of all times, refutations, supports, extrapolations, etc. This is the FULL EUCLID. Unabridged reproduction of Cambridge U. 2nd edition. 3 volumes. Total of 995 figures, 1426pp. 5⅜ x 8.

S88,89,90, 3 volume set, paperbound **$6.00**

THE GEOMETRY OF RENE DESCARTES. With·this book Descartes founded analytical geometry. Excellent Smith-Latham translation, plus original French text with Déscartes' own diagrams. Contains Problems the Construction of Which Requires Only Straight Lines and Circles; On the Nature of Curved Lines; On the Construction of Solid or Supersolid Problems. Notes. Diagrams. 258pp. 5⅜ x 8.

S68 Paperbound **$1.50**

See also: **FOUNDATIONS OF GEOMETRY,** B. Russell; **THE PHILOSOPHY OF SPACE AND TIME,** H. Reichenbach; **FAMOUS PROBLEMS OF ELEMENTARY GEOMETRY,** F. Klein; **MONOGRAPHS ON TOPICS OF MODERN MATHEMATICS,** ed. by J. W. Young.

Calculus and function theory, Fourier theory, real and complex functions, determinants

A COLLECTION OF MODERN MATHEMATICAL CLASSICS, edited by **R. Bellman.** 13 classic papers, complete in their original languages, by Hermite, Hardy and Littlewood, Tchebychef, Fejér, Fredholm, Fuchs, Hurwitz, Weyl, van der Pol, Birkhoff, Kellogg, von Neumann, and Hilbert. Each of these papers, collected here for the first time, triggered a burst of mathematical activity, providing useful new generalizations or stimulating fresh investigations. Topics discussed include classical analysis, periodic and almost periodic functions, analysis and number theory, integral equations, theory of approximation, non-linear differential equations, and functional analysis. Brief introductions and bibliographies to each paper. xii + 292pp. 6 x 9.

S730 Paperbound **$2.00**

MATHEMATICS OF MODERN ENGINEERING, E. G. Keller and R. E. Doherty. Written for the Advanced Course in Engineering of the General Electric Corporation, deals with the engineering use of determinants, tensors, the Heaviside operational calculus, dyadics, the calculus of variations, etc. Presents underlying principles fully, but purpose is to teach engineers to deal with modern engineering problems, and emphasis is on the perennial engineering attack of set-up and solve. Indexes. Over 185 figures and tables. Hundreds of exercises, problems, and worked-out examples. References. Two volume set. Total of xxxiii + 623pp. 5⅜ x 8.

S734 Vol I Paperbound **$1.65**
S735 Vol II Paperbound **$1.65**
The set **$3.30**

MATHEMATICAL METHODS FOR SCIENTISTS AND ENGINEERS, L. P. Smith. For scientists and engineers, as well as advanced math students. Full investigation of methods and practical description of conditions under which each should be used. Elements of real functions, differential and integral calculus, space geometry, theory of residues, vector and tensor analysis, series of Bessel functions, etc. Each method illustrated by completely-worked-out examples, mostly from scientific literature. 368 graded unsolved problems. 100 diagrams. x + 453pp. 5⅝ x 8⅜.

S220 Paperbound **$2.00**

THEORY OF FUNCTIONS AS APPLIED TO ENGINEERING PROBLEMS, edited by **R. Rothe, F. Ollendorff, and K. Pohlhausen.** A series of lectures given at the Berlin Institute of Technology that shows the specific applications of function theory in electrical and allied fields of engineering. Six lectures provide the elements of function theory in a simple and practical form, covering complex quantities and variables, integration in the complex plane, residue theorems, etc. Then 5 lectures show the exact uses of this powerful mathematical tool, with full discussions of problem methods. Index. Bibliography. 108 figures. x + 189pp. 5⅜ x 8.

S733 Paperbound **$1.35**

ADVANCED CALCULUS, E. B. Wilson. An unabridged reprinting of the work which continues to be recognized as one of the most comprehensive and useful texts in the field. It contains an immense amount of well-presented, fundamental material, including chapters on vector functions, ordinary differential equations, special functions, calculus of variations, etc., which are excellent introductions to these areas. For students with only one year of calculus, more than 1300 exercises cover both pure math and applications to engineering and physical problems. For engineers, physicists, etc., this work, with its 54 page introductory review, is the ideal reference and refresher. Index. ix + 566pp. 5⅜ x 8.

S504 Paperbound **$2.45**

CALCULUS OF VARIATIONS, A. R. Forsyth. Methods, solutions, rather than determination of weakest valid hypotheses. Over 150 examples completely worked-out show use of Euler, Legendre, Jacoby, Weierstrass tests for maxima, minima. Integrals with one original dependent variable; with derivatives of 2nd order; two dependent variables, one independent variable; double integrals involving 1 dependent variable, 2 first derivatives; double integrals involving partial derivatives of 2nd order; triple integrals; much more. 50 diagrams. 678pp. 5⅝ x 8⅜. **S622 Paperbound $2.95**

LECTURES ON THE CALCULUS OF VARIATIONS, O. Bolza. Analyzes in detail the fundamental concepts of the calculus of variations, as developed from Euler to Hilbert, with sharp formulations of the problems and rigorous demonstrations of their solutions. More than a score of solved examples; systematic references for each theorem. Covers the necessary and sufficient conditions; the contributions made by Euler, Du Bois Reymond, Hilbert, Weierstrass, Legendre, Jacobi, Erdmann, Kneser, and Gauss; and much more. Index. Bibliography. xi + 271pp. 5⅜ x 8. **S218 Paperbound $**

A TREATISE ON THE CALCULUS OF FINITE DIFFERENCES, G. Boole. A classic in the literature of the calculus. Thorough, clear discussion of basic principles, theorems, methods. Covers MacLaurin's and Herschel's theorems, mechanical quadrature, factorials, periodical constants, Bernoulli's numbers, difference-equations (linear, mixed, and partial), etc. Stresses analogies with differential calculus. 236 problems, answers to the numerical ones. viii + 336pp. 5⅜ x 8. **S695 Paperbound $1.85**

THE ANALYTICAL THEORY OF HEAT, Joseph Fourier. This book, which revolutionized mathematical physics, is listed in the Great Books program, and many other listings of great books. It has been used with profit by generations of mathematicians and physicists who are interested in either heat or in the application of the Fourier integral. Covers cause and reflection of rays of heat, radiant heating, heating of closed spaces, use of trigonometric series in the theory of heat, Fourier integral, etc. Translated by Alexander Freeman. 20 figures. xxii + 466pp. 5⅜ x 8. **S93 Paperbound $2.00**

AN INTRODUCTION TO FOURIER METHODS AND THE LAPLACE TRANSFORMATION, Philip Franklin. Concentrates upon essentials, enabling the reader with only a working knowledge of calculus to gain an understanding of Fourier methods in a broad sense, suitable for most applications. This work covers complex qualities with methods of computing elementary functions for complex values of the argument and finding approximations by the use of charts; Fourier series and integrals with half-range and complex Fourier series; harmonic analysis; Fourier and Laplace transformations, etc.; partial differential equations with applications to transmission of electricity; etc. The methods developed are related to physical problems of heat flow, vibrations, electrical transmission, electromagnetic radiation, etc. 828 problems with answers. Formerly entitled "Fourier Methods." Bibliography. Index. x + 289pp. 5⅜ x 8. **S452 Paperbound $1.75**

THE FOURIER INTEGRAL AND CERTAIN OF ITS APPLICATIONS, Norbert Wiener. The only book-length study of the Fourier integral as link between pure and applied math. An expansion of lectures given at Cambridge. Partial contents: Plancherel's theorem, general Tauberian theorem, special Tauberian theorems, generalized harmonic analysis. Bibliography. viii + 201pp. 5⅜ x 8. **S272 Paperbound $1.50**

INTRODUCTION TO THE THEORY OF FOURIER'S SERIES AND INTEGRALS, H. S. Carslaw. 3rd revised edition. This excellent introduction is an outgrowth of the author's courses at Cambridge. Historical introduction, rational and irrational numbers, infinite sequences and series, functions of a single variable, definite integral, Fourier series, Fourier integrals, and similar topics. Appendixes discuss practical harmonic analysis, periodogram analysis. Lebesgues theory. Indexes. 84 examples, bibliography. xiii + 368pp. 5⅜ x 8. **S48 Paperbound $2.00**

FOURIER'S SERIES AND SPHERICAL HARMONICS, W. E. Byerly. Continues to be recognized as one of most practical, useful expositions. Functions, series, and their differential equations are concretely explained in great detail; theory is applied constantly to practical problems, which are fully and lucidly worked out. Appendix includes 6 tables of surface zonal harmonics, hyperbolic functions, Bessel's functions. Bibliography. 190 problems, approximately half with answers. ix + 287pp. 5⅜ x 8. **S536 Paperbound $1.75**

ASYMPTOTIC EXPANSIONS, A. Erdélyi. The only modern work available in English, this is an unabridged reproduction of a monograph prepared for the Office of Naval Research. It discusses various procedures for asymptotic evaluation of integrals containing a large parameter and solutions of ordinary linear differential equations. Bibliography of 71 items. vi + 108pp. 5⅜ x 8. **S318 Paperbound $1.35**

LINEAR INTEGRAL EQUATIONS, W. V. Lovitt. Systematic survey of general theory, with some application to differential equations, calculus of variations, problems of math, physics. Partial contents: integral equation of 2nd kind by successive substitutions; Fredholm's equation as ratio of 2 integral series in lambda, applications of the Fredholm theory, Hilbert-Schmidt theory of symmetric kernels, application, etc. Neumann, Dirichlet, vibratory problems. Index. ix + 253pp. 5⅜ x 8. **S175 Clothbound $3.50**
S176 Paperbound $1.60

ELLIPTIC INTEGRALS, H. Hancock. Invaluable in work involving differential equations containing cubics or quartics under the root sign, where elementary calculus methods are inadequate. Practical solutions to problems that occur in mathematics, engineering, physics: differential equations requiring integration of Lamé's, Briot's, or Bouquet's equations; determination of arc of ellipse, hyperbola, lemiscate; solutions of problems in elastica; motion of a projectile under resistance varying as the cube of the velocity; pendulums; many others. Exposition is in accordance with Legendre-Jacobi theory and includes rigorous discussion of Legendre transformations. 20 figures. 5 place table. Index. 104pp. 5⅛ x 8.
S484 Paperbound **$1.25**

FIVE VOLUME "THEORY OF FUNCTIONS' SET BY KONRAD KNOPP

This five-volume set, prepared by Konrad Knopp, provides a complete and readily followed account of theory of functions. Proofs are given concisely, yet without sacrifice of completeness or rigor. These volumes are used as texts by such universities as M.I.T., University of Chicago, N. Y. City College, and many others. "Excellent introduction . . . remarkably readable, concise, clear, rigorous," JOURNAL OF THE AMERICAN STATISTICAL ASSOCIATION.

ELEMENTS OF THE THEORY OF FUNCTIONS, Konrad Knopp. This book provides the student with background for further volumes in this set, or texts on a similar level. Partial contents: foundations, system of complex numbers and the Gaussian plane of numbers, Riemann sphere of numbers, mapping by linear functions, normal forms, the logarithm, the cyclometric functions and binomial series. "Not only for the young student, but also for the student who knows all about what is in it," MATHEMATICAL JOURNAL. Bibliography. Index. 140pp. 5⅜ x 8.
S154 Paperbound **$1.35**

THEORY OF FUNCTIONS, PART I, Konrad Knopp. With volume II, this book provides coverage of basic concepts and theorems. Partial contents: numbers and points, functions of a complex variable, integral of a continuous function, Cauchy's integral theorem, Cauchy's integral formulae, series with variable terms, expansion of analytic functions in power series, analytic continuation and complete definition of analytic functions, entire transcendental functions, Laurent expansion, types of singularities. Bibliography. Index. vii + 146pp. 5⅜ x 8.
S156 Paperbound **$1.35**

THEORY OF FUNCTIONS, PART II, Konrad Knopp. Application and further development of general theory, special topics. Single valued functions, entire, Weierstrass, Meromorphic functions. Riemann surfaces. Algebraic functions. Analytical configuration, Riemann surface. Bibliography. Index. x + 150pp. 5⅜ x 8.
S157 Paperbound **$1.35**

PROBLEM BOOK IN THE THEORY OF FUNCTIONS, VOLUME 1, Konrad Knopp. Problems in elementary theory, for use with Knopp's THEORY OF FUNCTIONS, or any other text, arranged according to increasing difficulty. Fundamental concepts, sequences of numbers and infinite series, complex variable, integral theorems, development in series, conformal mapping. 182 problems. Answers. viii + 126pp. 5⅜ x 8.
S158 Paperbound **$1.35**

PROBLEM BOOK IN THE THEORY OF FUNCTIONS, VOLUME 2, Konrad Knopp. Advanced theory of functions, to be used either with Knopp's THEORY OF FUNCTIONS, or any other comparable text. Singularities, entire & meromorphic functions, periodic, analytic, continuation, multiple-valued functions, Riemann surfaces, conformal mapping. Includes a section of additional elementary problems. "The difficult task of selecting from the immense material of the modern theory of functions the problems just within the reach of the beginner is here masterfully accomplished," AM. MATH. SOC. Answers. 138pp. 5⅜ x 8. S159 Paperbound **$1.35**

*   *   *

LECTURES ON THE THEORY OF ELLIPTIC FUNCTIONS, H. Hancock. Reissue of the only book in English with so extensive a coverage, especially of Abel, Jacobi, Legendre, Weierstrasse, Hermite, Liouville, and Riemann. Unusual fullness of treatment, plus applications as well as theory, in discussing elliptic function (the universe of elliptic integrals originating in works of Abel and Jacobi), their existence, and ultimate meaning. Use is made of Riemann to provide the most general theory. 40 page table of formulas. 76 figures. xxiii + 498pp.
S483 Paperbound **$2.55**

THE THEORY AND FUNCTIONS OF A REAL VARIABLE AND THE THEORY OF FOURIER'S SERIES, E. W. Hobson. One of the best introductions to set theory and various aspects of functions and Fourier's series. Requires only a good background in calculus. Provides an exhaustive coverage of: metric and descriptive properties of sets of points; transfinite numbers and order types; functions of a real variable; the Riemann and Lebesgue integrals; sequences and series of numbers; power-series; functions representable by series sequences of continuous functions; trigonometrical series; representation of functions by Fourier's series; complete exposition (200pp.) on set theory; and much more. "The best possible guide," Nature. Vol. I: 88 detailed examples, 10 figures. Index. xv + 736pp. Vol. II: 117 detailed examples, 13 figures. Index. x + 780pp. 6⅛ x 9¼.
Vol. I: S387 Paperbound **$3.00**
Vol. II: S388 Paperbound **$3.00**

ALMOST PERIODIC FUNCTIONS, A. S. Besicovitch. This unique and important summary by a well-known mathematician covers in detail the two stages of development in Bohr's theory of almost periodic functions: (1) as a generalization of pure periodicity, with results and proofs; (2) the work done by Stepanoff, Wiener, Weyl, and Bohr in generalizing the theory. Bibliography. xi + 180pp. 5⅜ x 8.
S18 Paperbound **$1.75**

THEORY OF FUNCTIONALS AND OF INTEGRAL AND INTEGRO-DIFFERENTIAL EQUATIONS, Vito Volterra. Unabridged republication of the only English translation. An exposition of the general theory of the functions depending on a continuous set of values of another function, based on the author's fundamental notion of the transition from a finite number of variables to a continually infinite number. Though dealing primarily with integral equations, much material on calculus of variations is included. The work makes no assumption of previous knowledge on the part of the reader. It begins with fundamental material and proceeds to Generalization of Analytic Functions, Integro-Differential Equations, Functional Derivative Equations, Applications, Other Directions of Theory of Functionals, etc. New introduction by G. C. Evans. Bibliography and criticism of Volterra's work by E. Whittaker. Bibliography. Index of authors cited. Index of subjects. xxxx + 226pp. 5⅜ x 8.　　S502 Paperbound **$1.75**

AN ELEMENTARY TREATISE ON ELLIPTIC FUNCTIONS, A. Cayley. Still the fullest and clearest text on the theories of Jacobi and Legendre for the advanced student (and an excellent supplement for the beginner). A masterpiece of exposition by the great 19th century British mathematician (creator of the theory of matrices and abstract geometry), it covers the addition-theory, Landen's theorem, the 3 kinds of elliptic integrals, transformations, the q-functions, reduction of a differential expression, and much more. Index. xii + 386pp. 5⅜ x 8.
S728 Paperbound **$2.00**

THE APPLICATIONS OF ELLIPTIC FUNCTIONS, A. G. Greenhill. Modern books forgo detail for sake of brevity—this book offers complete exposition necessary for proper understanding, use of elliptic integrals. Formulas developed from definite physical, geometric problems; examples representative enough to offer basic information in widely useable form. Elliptic integrals, addition theorem, algebraical form of addition theorem, elliptic integrals of 2nd, 3rd kind, double periodicity, resolution into factors, series, transformation, etc. Introduction. Index. 25 illus. xi + 357pp. 5⅜ x 8.　　S603 Paperbound **$1.75**

THE THEORY OF FUNCTIONS OF REAL VARIABLES, James Pierpont. A 2-volume authoritative exposition, by one of the foremost mathematicians of his time. Each theorem stated with all conditions, then followed by proof. No need to go through complicated reasoning to discover conditions added without specific mention. Includes a particularly complete, rigorous presentation of theory of measure; and Pierpont's own work on a theory of Lebesgue integrals, and treatment of area of a curved surface. Partial contents, Vol. 1: rational numbers, exponentials, logarithms, point aggregates, maxima, minima, proper integrals, improper integrals, multiple proper integrals, continuity, discontinuity, indeterminate forms. Vol. 2: point sets, proper integrals, series, power series, aggregates, ordinal numbers, discontinuous functions, sub-, infra-uniform convergence, much more. Index. 95 illustrations. 1229pp. 5⅜ x 8.　　S558-9, 2 volume set, paperbound **$4.90**

FUNCTIONS OF A COMPLEX VARIABLE, James Pierpont. Long one of best in the field. A thorough treatment of fundamental elements, concepts, theorems. A complete study, rigorous, detailed, with carefully selected problems worked out to illustrate each topic. Partial contents: arithmetical operations, real term series, positive term series, exponential functions, integration, analytic functions, asymptotic expansions, functions of Weierstrass, Legendre, etc. Index. List of symbols. 122 illus. 597pp. 5⅜ x 8.　　S560 Paperbound **$2.45**

ELEMENTS OF THE THEORY OF REAL FUNCTIONS, J. E. Littlewood. Based on lectures given at Trinity College, Cambridge, this book has proved to be extremely successful in introducing graduate students to the modern theory of functions. It offers a full and concise coverage of classes and cardinal numbers, well-ordered series, other types of series, and elements of the theory of sets of points. 3rd revised edition. vii + 71pp. 5⅜ x 8.
S171 Clothbound **$2.85**
S172 Paperbound **$1.25**

TRANSCENDENTAL AND ALGEBRAIC NUMBERS, A. O. Gelfond. First English translation of work by leading Soviet mathematician. Thue-Siegel theorem, its p-adic analogue, on approximation of algebraic numbers by numbers in fixed algebraic field; Hermite-Lindemann theorem on transcendency of Bessel functions, solutions of other differential equations; Gelfond-Schneider theorem on transcendency of alpha to power beta; Schneider's work on elliptic functions, with method developed by Gelfond. Translated by L. F. Boron. Index. Bibliography. 200pp. 5⅜ x 8.　　S615 Paperbound **$1.75**

THEORY OF MAXIMA AND MINIMA, H. Hancock. Fullest treatment ever written; only work in English with extended discussion of maxima and minima for functions of 1, 2, or n variables, problems with subsidiary constraints, and relevant quadratic forms. Detailed proof of each important theorem. Covers the Scheeffer and von Dantscher theories, homogeneous quadratic forms, reversion of series, fallacious establishment of maxima and minima, etc. Unsurpassed treatise for advanced students of calculus, mathematicians, economists, statisticians. Index. 24 diagrams. 39 problems, many examples. 193pp. 5⅜ x 8.　　S665 Paperbound **$1.50**

DICTIONARY OF CONFORMAL REPRESENTATIONS, H. Kober. Laplace's equation in 2 dimensions solved in this unique book developed by the British Admiralty. Scores of geometrical forms & their transformations for electrical engineers, Joukowski aerofoil for aerodynamists. Schwartz-Christoffel transformations for hydrodynamics, transcendental functions. Contents classified according to analytical functions describing transformation. Twin diagrams show curves of most transformations with corresponding regions. Glossary. Topological index. 447 diagrams. 244pp. 6⅛ x 9¼.　　S160 Paperbound **$2.00**

THE TAYLOR SERIES, AN INTRODUCTION TO THE THEORY OF FUNCTIONS OF A COMPLEX VARIABLE, P. Dienes. This book investigates the entire realm of analytic functions. Only ordinary calculus is needed, except in the last two chapters. Starting with an introduction to real variables and complex algebra, the properties of infinite series, elementary functions, complex differentiation and integration are carefully derived. Also biuniform mapping, a thorough two part discussion of representation and singularities of analytic functions, overconvergence and gap theorems, divergent series, Taylor series on its circle of convergence, divergence and singularities, etc. Unabridged, corrected reissue of first edition. Preface and index. 186 examples, many fully worked out. 67 figures. xii + 555pp. 5⅜ x 8.
S391 Paperbound $2.75

INTRODUCTION TO BESSEL FUNCTIONS, Frank Bowman. A rigorous self-contained exposition providing all necessary material during the development, which requires only some knowledge of calculus and acquaintance with differential equations. A balanced presentation including applications and practical use. Discusses Bessel Functions of Zero Order, of Any Real Order; Modified Bessel Functions of Zero Order; Definite Integrals; Asymptotic Expansions; Bessel's Solution to Kepler's Problem; Circular Membranes; much more. "Clear and straightforward . . . useful not only to students of physics and engineering, but to mathematical students in general," Nature. 226 problems. Short tables of Bessel functions. 27 figures. Index. x + 135pp. 5⅜ x 8.
S462 Paperbound $1.35

MODERN THEORIES OF INTEGRATION, H. Kestelman. Connected and concrete coverage, with fully-worked-out proofs for every step. Ranges from elementary definitions through theory of aggregates, sets of points, Riemann and Lebesgue integration, and much more. This new revised and enlarged edition contains a new chapter on Riemann-Stieltjes integration, as well as a supplementary section of 186 exercises. Ideal for the mathematician, student, teacher, or self-studier. Index of Definitions and Symbols. General Index. Bibliography. x + 310pp. 5⅝ x 8⅜.
S572 Paperbound $2.00

A TREATISE ON THE THEORY OF DETERMINANTS, T. Muir. Unequalled as an exhaustive compilation of nearly all the known facts about determinants up to the early 1930's. Covers notation and general properties, row and column transformation, symmetry, compound determinants, adjugates, rectangular arrays and matrices, linear dependence, gradients, Jacobians, Hessians, Wronskians, and much more. Invaluable for libraries of industrial and research organizations as well as for student, teacher, and mathematician; very useful in the field of computing machines. Revised and enlarged by W. H. Metzler. Index. 485 problems and scores of numerical examples. iv + 766pp. 5⅜ x 8.
S670 Paperbound $2.95

THEORY OF DETERMINANTS IN THE HISTORICAL ORDER OF DEVELOPMENT, Sir Thomas Muir. Unabridged reprinting of this complete study of 1,859 papers on determinant theory written between 1693 and 1900. Most important and original sections reproduced, valuable commentary on each. No other work is necessary for determinant research: all types are covered—each subdivision of the theory treated separately; all papers dealing with each type are covered; you are told exactly what each paper is about and how important its contribution is. Each result, theory, extension, or modification is assigned its own identifying numeral so that the full history may be more easily followed. Includes papers on determinants in general, determinants and linear equations, symmetric determinants, alternants, recurrents, determinants having invariant factors, and all other major types. "A model of what such histories ought to be," NATURE. "Mathematicians must ever be grateful to Sir Thomas for his monumental work," AMERICAN MATH MONTHLY. Four volumes bound as two. Indices. Bibliographies. Total of lxxxiv + 1977pp. 5⅜ x 8.
S672-3 The set, Clothbound $10.00

A COURSE IN MATHEMATICAL ANALYSIS, Edouard Goursat. Trans. by E. R. Hedrick, O. Dunkel. Classic study of fundamental material thoroughly treated. Exceptionally lucid exposition of wide range of subject matter for student with 1 year of calculus. Vol. 1: Derivatives and Differentials, Definite Integrals, Expansion in Series, Applications to Geometry. Problems. Index. 52 illus. 556pp. Vol. 2, Part I: Functions of a Complex Variable, Conformal Representations, Doubly Periodic Functions, Natural Boundaries, etc. Problems. Index. 38 illus. 269pp. Vol. 2, Part 2: Differential Equations, Cauchy-Lipschitz Method, Non-linear Differential Equations, Simultaneous Equations, etc. Problems. Index. 308pp. 5⅜ x 8.
Vol. 1 S554 Paperbound $2.25
Vol. 2 part 1 S555 Paperbound $1.65
Vol. 2 part 2 S556 Paperbound $1.65
3 vol. set $5.00

INFINITE SEQUENCES AND SERIES, Konrad Knopp. First publication in any language! Excellent introduction to 2 topics of modern mathematics, designed to give the student background to penetrate farther by himself. Sequences & sets, real & complex numbers, etc. Functions of a real & complex variable. Sequences & series. Infinite series. Convergent power series. Expansion of elementary functions. Numerical evaluation of series. Bibliography. v + 186pp. 5⅜ x 8.
S152 Clothbound $3.50
S153 Paperbound $1.75

TRIGONOMETRICAL SERIES, Antoni Zygmund. Unique in any language on modern advanced level. Contains carefully organized analyses of trigonometric, orthogonal, Fourier systems of functions, with clear adequate descriptions of summability of Fourier series, proximation theory, conjugate series, convergence, divergence of Fourier series. Especially valuable for Russian, Eastern European coverage. Bibliography. 329pp. 5⅜ x 8.
S290 Paperbound $1.50

COLLECTED WORKS OF BERNHARD RIEMANN. This important source book is the first to contain the complete text of both 1892 Werke and the 1902 supplement, unabridged. It contains 31 monographs, 3 complete lecture courses, 15 miscellaneous papers, which have been of enormous importance in relativity, topology, theory of complex variables, and other areas of mathematics. Edited by R. Dedekind, H. Weber, M. Noether, W. Wirtinger. German text. English introduction by Hans Lewy. 690pp. 5⅜ x 8.   S226 Paperbound **$2.85**

See also: A HISTORY OF THE CALCULUS. C. B. Boyer; CALCULUS REFRESHER FOR TECHNICAL MEN, A. A. Klaf; MONOGRAPHS ON TOPICS OF MODERN MATHEMATICS, ed. by J. W. A. Young; THE CONTINUUM AND OTHER TYPES OF SERIAL ORDER, E. V. Huntington.

Symbolic logic

AN INTRODUCTION TO SYMBOLIC LOGIC, Susanne K. Langer. Probably the clearest book ever written on symbolic logic for the philosopher, general scientist and layman. It will be particularly appreciated by those who have been rebuffed by other introductory works because of insufficient mathematical training. No special knowledge of mathematics is required. Starting with the simplest symbols and conventions, you are led to a remarkable grasp of the Boole-Schroeder and Russell-Whitehead systems clearly and quickly. PARTIAL CONTENTS: Study of forms, Essentials of logical structure, Generalization, Classes, The deductive system of classes, The algebra of logic, Abstraction of interpretation, Calculus of propositions, Assumptions of PRINCIPIA MATHEMATICA, Logistics, Logic of the syllogism, Proofs of theorems. "One of the clearest and simplest introductions to a subject which is very much alive. The style is easy, symbolism is introduced gradually, and the intelligent non-mathematician should have no difficulty in following the argument," MATHEMATICS GAZETTE. Revised, expanded second edition. Truth-value tables. 368pp. 5⅜ x 8.
S164 Paperbound **$1.75**

THE ELEMENTS OF MATHEMATICAL LOGIC, Paul Rosenbloom. First publication in any language. This book is intended for readers who are mature mathematically, but have no previous training in symbolic logic. It does not limit itself to a single system, but covers the field as a whole. It is a development of lectures given at Lund University, Sweden, in 1948. Partial contents: Logic of classes, fundamental theorems, Boolean algebra, logic of propositions, logic of propositional functions, expressive languages, combinatory logics, development of mathematics within an object language, paradoxes, theorems of Post and Goedel, Church's theorem, and similar topics. iv + 214pp. 5⅜ x 8.   S227 Paperbound **$1.45**

A SURVEY OF SYMBOLIC LOGIC: THE CLASSIC ALGEBRA OF LOGIC, C. I. Lewis. Classic survey of the field, comprehensive and thorough. Indicates content of major systems, alternative methods of procedure, and relation of these to the Boole-Schroeder algebra and to one another. Contains historical summary, as well as full proofs and applications of the classic, or Boole-Schroeder, algebra of logic. Discusses diagrams for the logical relations of classes, the two-valued algebra, propositional functions of two or more variables, etc. Chapters 5 and 6 of the original edition, which contained material not directly pertinent, have been omitted in this edition at the author's request. Appendix. Bibliography. Index. viii + 352pp. 5⅝ x 8⅜.
S643 Paperbound **$2.00**

INTRODUCTION TO SYMBOLIC LOGIC AND ITS APPLICATIONS, R. Carnap. One of the clearest, most comprehensive, and rigorous introductions to modern symbolic logic by perhaps its greatest living master. Symbolic languages are analyzed and one constructed. Applications to math (symbolic representation of axiom systems for set theory, natural numbers, real numbers, topology, Dedekind and Cantor explanations of continuity), physics (the general analysis of concepts of determination, causality, space-time-topology, based on Einstein), biology (symbolic representation of an axiom system for basic concepts). "A masterpiece," Zentralblatt für Mathematik und ihre Grenzgebiete. Over 300 exercises. 5 figures. Bibliography. Index. xvi + 241pp. 5⅜ x 8.   S453 Paperbound **$1.85**
Clothbound **$4.00**

SYMBOLIC LOGIC, C. I. Lewis, C. H. Langford. Probably the most cited book in symbolic logic, this is one of the fullest treatments of paradoxes. A wide coverage of the entire field of symbolic logic, plus considerable material that has not appeared elsewhere. Basic to the entire volume is the distinction between the logic of extensions and of intensions. Considerable emphasis is placed on converse substitution, while the matrix system presents the supposition of a variety of non-Aristotelian logics. It has especially valuable sections on strict limitations, existence of terms, 2-valued algebra and its extension to propositional functions, truth value systems, the matrix method, implication and deductibility, general theory of propositions, propositions of ordinary discourse, and similar topics. "Authoritative, most valuable," TIMES, London. Bibliography. 506pp. 5⅜ x 8.   S170 Paperbound **$2.00**

THE LAWS OF THOUGHT, George Boole. This book founded symbolic logic some hundred years ago. It is the 1st significant attempt to apply logic to all aspects of human endeavour. Partial contents: derivation of laws, signs & laws, interpretations, eliminations, conditions of a perfect method, analysis, Aristotelian logic, probability, and similar topics. xviii + 424pp. 5⅜ x 8.   S28 Paperbound **$2.00**

THE PRINCIPLES OF SCIENCE, A TREATISE ON LOGIC AND THE SCIENTIFIC METHOD, W. S. Jevons. Treating such topics as Inductive and Deductive Logic, the Theory of Number, Probability, and the Limits of Scientific Method, this milestone in the development of symbolic logic remains a stimulating contribution to the investigation of inferential validity in the natural and social sciences. It significantly advances Boole's logic, and contains a detailed introduction to the nature and methods of probability in physics, astronomy, everyday affairs, etc. In his introduction, Ernest Nagel of Columbia University says, "[Jevons] continues to be of interest as an attempt to articulate the logic of scientific inquiry." Index. liii + 786pp. 5⅜ x 8.   S446 Paperbound **$2.98**

Group theory, algebra, sets

LECTURES ON THE ICOSAHEDRON AND THE SOLUTION OF EQUATIONS OF THE FIFTH DEGREE, Felix Klein. The solution of quintics in terms of rotation of a regular icosahedron around its axes of symmetry. A classic & indispensable source for those interested in higher algebra, geometry, crystallography. Considerable explanatory material included. 230 footnotes, mostly bibliographic. 2nd edition, xvi + 289pp. 5⅜ x 8.   S314 Paperbound **$1.85**

LINEAR GROUPS, WITH AN EXPOSITION OF THE GALOIS FIELD THEORY, L. E. Dickson. The classic exposition of the theory of groups, well within the range of the graduate student. Part I contains the most extensive and thorough presentation of the theory of Galois Fields available, with a wealth of examples and theorems. Part II is a full discussion of linear groups of finite order. Much material in this work is based on Dickson's own contributions. Also includes expositions of Jordan, Lie, Abel, Betti-Mathieu, Hermite, etc. "A milestone in the development of modern algebra," W. Magnus, in his historical introduction to this edition. Index. xv + 312pp. 5⅜ x 8.   S482 Paperbound **$1.95**

INTRODUCTION TO THE THEORY OF GROUPS OF FINITE ORDER, R. Carmichael. Examines fundamental theorems and their application. Beginning with sets, systems, permutations, etc., it progresses in easy stages through important types of groups: Abelian, prime power, permutation, etc. Except 1 chapter where matrices are desirable, no higher math needed. 783 exercises, problems. Index. xvi + 447pp. 5⅜ x 8.   S299 Clothbound **$3.95**
S300 Paperbound **$2.00**

THEORY OF GROUPS OF FINITE ORDER, W. Burnside. First published some 40 years ago, this is still one of the clearest introductory texts. Partial contents: permutations, groups independent of representation, composition series of a group, isomorphism of a group with itself, Abelian groups, prime power groups, permutation groups, invariants of groups of linear substitution graphical representation, etc. 45pp. of notes. Indexes. xxiv + 512pp. 5⅜ x 8.
S38 Paperbound **$2.45**

THEORY AND APPLICATIONS OF FINITE GROUPS, G. A. Miller, H. F. Blichfeldt, L. E. Dickson. Unusually accurate and authoritative work, each section prepared by a leading specialist: Miller on substitution and abstract groups, Blichfeldt on finite groups of linear homogeneous transformations, Dickson on applications of finite groups. Unlike more modern works, this gives the concrete basis from which abstract group theory arose. Includes Abelian groups, primepower groups, isomorphisms, matrix forms of linear transformations, Sylow groups, Galois' theory of algebraic equations, duplication of a cube, trisection of an angle, etc. 2 Indexes. 267 problems. xvii + 390pp. 5⅜ x 8.   S216 Paperbound **$2.00**

CONTINUOUS GROUPS OF TRANSFORMATIONS, L. P. Eisenhart. Intensive study of the theory and geometrical applications of continuous groups of transformations; a standard work on the subject, called forth by the revolution in physics in the 1920's. Covers tensor analysis, Riemannian geometry, canonical parameters, transitivity, imprimitivity, differential invariants, the algebra of constants of structure, differential geometry, contact transformations, etc. "Likely to remain one of the standard works on the subject for many years . . . principal theorems are proved clearly and concisely, and the arrangement of the whole is coherent," MATHEMATICAL GAZETTE. Index. 72-item bibliography. 185 exercises. ix + 301pp. 5⅜ x 8.
S781 Paperbound **$1.85**

THE THEORY OF GROUPS AND QUANTUM MECHANICS, H. Weyl. Discussions of Schroedinger's wave equation, de Broglie's waves of a particle, Jordan-Hoelder theorem, Lie's continuous groups of transformations, Pauli exclusion principle, quantization of Maxwell-Dirac field equations, etc. Unitary geometry, quantum theory, groups, application of groups to quantum mechanics, symmetry permutation group, algebra of symmetric transformation, etc. 2nd revised edition. Bibliography. Index. xxii + 422pp. 5⅜ x 8.   S268 Clothbound **$4.50**
S269 Paperbound **$1.95**

ALGEBRAIC THEORIES, L. E. Dickson. Best·thorough introduction to classical topics in higher algebra develops theories centering around matrices, invariants, groups. Higher algebra, Galois theory, finite linear groups, Klein's icosahedron, algebraic invariants, linear transformations, elementary divisors, invariant factors; quadratic, bi-linear, Hermitian forms, singly and in pairs. Proofs rigorous, detailed; topics developed lucidly, in close connection with their most frequent mathematical applications. Formerly "Modern Algebraic Theories." 155 problems. Bibliography. 2 indexes. 285pp. 5⅜ x 8.   S547 Paperbound **$1.50**

ALGEBRAS AND THEIR ARITHMETICS, L. E. Dickson. Provides the foundation and background necessary to any advanced undergraduate or graduate student studying abstract algebra. Begins with elementary introduction to linear transformations, matrices, field of complex numbers; proceeds to order, basal units, modulus, quaternions, etc.; develops calculus of linear sets, describes various examples of algebras including invariant, difference, nilpotent, semi-simple. "Makes the reader marvel at his genius for clear and profound analysis," Amer. Mathematical Monthly. Index. xii + 241pp. 5⅜ x 8.   S616 Paperbound **$1.35**

THE THEORY OF EQUATIONS WITH AN INTRODUCTION TO THE THEORY OF BINARY ALGEBRAIC FORMS, W. S. Burnside and A. W. Panton. Extremely thorough and concrete discussion of the theory of equations, with extensive detailed treatment of many topics curtailed in later texts. Covers theory of algebraic equations, properties of polynomials, symmetric functions, derived functions, Horner's process, complex numbers and the complex variable, determinants and methods of elimination, invariant theory (nearly 100 pages), transformations, introduction to Galois theory, Abelian equations, and much more. Invaluable supplementary work for modern students and teachers. 759 examples and exercises. Index in each volume. Two volume set. Total of xxiv + 604pp. 5⅜ x 8.   S714 Vol I Paperbound **$1.85**
                    S715 Vol II Paperbound **$1.85**
                    The set **$3.70**

COMPUTATIONAL METHODS OF LINEAR ALGEBRA, V. N. Faddeeva, translated by **C. D. Benster.** First English translation of a unique and valuable work, the only work in English presenting a systematic exposition of the most important methods of linear algebra—classical and contemporary. Shows in detail how to derive numerical solutions of problems in mathematical physics which are frequently connected with those of linear algebra. Theory as well as individual practice. Part I surveys the mathematical background that is indispensable to what follows. Parts II and III, the conclusion, set forth the most important methods of solution, for both exact and iterative groups. One of the most outstanding and valuable features, of this work is the 23 tables, double and triple checked for accuracy. These tables will not be found elsewhere. Author's preface. Translator's note. New bibliography and index. x + 252pp. 5⅜ x 8.   S424 Paperbound **$1.95**

ALGEBRAIC EQUATIONS, E. Dehn. Careful and complete presentation of Galois' theory of algebraic equations; theories of Lagrange and Galois developed in logical rather than historical form, with a more thorough exposition than in most modern books. Many concrete applications and fully-worked-out examples. Discusses basic theory (very clear exposition of the symmetric group); isomorphic, transitive, and Abelian groups; applications of Lagrange's and Galois' theories; and much more. Newly revised by the author. Index. List of Theorems. xi + 208pp. 5⅜ x 8.   S697 Paperbound **$1.45**

THEORY OF SETS, E. Kamke. Clearest, amplest introduction in English, well suited for independent study. Subdivision of main theory, such as theory of sets of points, are discussed, but emphasis is on general theory. Partial contents: rudiments of set theory, arbitrary sets and their cardinal numbers, ordered sets and their order types, well-ordered sets and their cardinal numbers. Bibliography. Key to symbols. Index. vii + 144pp. 5⅜ x 8.
                    S141 Paperbound **$1.35**

Number theory

INTRODUCTION TO THE THEORY OF NUMBERS, L. E. Dickson. Thorough, comprehensive approach with adequate coverage of classical literature, an introductory volume beginners can follow. Chapters on divisibility, congruences, quadratic residues & reciprocity, Diophantine equations, etc. Full treatment of binary quadratic forms without usual restriction to integral coefficients. Covers infinitude of primes, least residues, Fermat's theorem, Euler's phi function, Legendre's symbol, Gauss's lemma, automorphs, reduced forms, recent theorems of Thue & Siegel, many more. Much material not readily available elsewhere. 239 problems. Index. I figure. viii + 183pp. 5⅜ x 8.   S342 Paperbound **$1.65**

ELEMENTS OF NUMBER THEORY, I. M. Vinogradov. Detailed 1st course for persons without advanced mathematics; 95% of this book can be understood by readers who have gone no farther than high school algebra. Partial contents: divisibility theory, important number theoretical functions, congruences, primitive roots and indices, etc. Solutions to both problems and exercises. Tables of primes, indices, etc. Covers almost every essential formula in elementary number theory! Translated from Russian. 233 problems, 104 exercises. viii + 227pp. 5⅜ x 8.   S259 Paperbound **$1.60**